VISCOUS DRAG
REDUCTION

VISCOUS DRAG REDUCTION

Proceedings of the Symposium on Viscous Drag Reduction
held at the LTV Research Center, Dallas, Texas
September 24 and 25, 1968

Edited by C. Sinclair Wells

LTV Research Center, Dallas, Texas

Sponsored by Office of Naval Research
Naval Ship Research and Development Center
National Aeronautics and Space Administration

ℚ PLENUM PRESS · NEW YORK · 1969

Library of Congress Catalog Card Number 77-76496

FOREWORD

The Symposium on Viscous Drag Reduction was held at the LTV
Research Center in Dallas, Texas on September 24 and 25, 1968.
Attendance at the symposium was by invitation, in order to assure
participation in the discussions by interested workers. Invitation
lists were assembled through discussions with the sponsors. The
formal paper presentations were divided into four sessions: Boundary
Layer Transition, Prediction and Control; Drag Reduction with Polymer Additives; Applications of Polymer Drag Reduction; and Wall
Turbulence. Each session was introduced by an invited paper, which
generally summarized the state of knowledge for that subject.

Topics covered in the contributed papers include: effects of
hypersonic speeds, wing sweep, and distributed suction on boundary
layer transition; general characterization of drag reduction due to
additives in pipe flows and boundary layer flows; instrumentation
for flow measurements in additive solutions; applications of drag
reduction to various vehicles; effects of compliant walls on turbulent skin friction; rheology of additive solutions; effects of
additives on wall pressure fluctuations and radiated noise; and
general theories of wall turbulence as applied to drag reduction.

The Symposium was held under the sponsorship of the Office of
Naval Research (Fluid Dynamics Branch), the Office of Advanced
Research and Technology, NASA (Fluid Mechanics Branch), and the
Naval Ship Research and Development Center. The LTV Research
Center, Ling-Temco-Vought, Inc., acted as host. Without the support
and cooperation of these various organizations, such a meeting
could not have taken place. I am particularly grateful to the
following members of these organizations for their personal encour-
agement: Ralph D. Cooper and Stanley W. Doroff of ONR; John T.
Howe of NASA; Paul S. Granville and David A. Jewell of NSRDC; the
management of the LTV Research Center, including Henry B. Gibbons,
Felix W. Fenter and John Harkness; and Mr. Raymond C. Blaylock,
Vice President-Technical Director, Ling-Temco-Vought, Inc. The
good efforts of Jack G. Spangler, Program Chairman, Chan P. Wood,
Arrangements Chairman, and Mrs. Sherry Dunaway, who efficiently han-
dled a myriad of details, are acknowledged gratefully.

C.S.W.

ATTENDANCE LIST

J. A. Almo	University of Minnesota
J. J. Bertin	University of Texas at Austin
R. A. Biggs	Union Carbide Corp.
E. Bilgen	Canadian General Electric Company
T. J. Black	Mechanical Technology Inc.
R. C. Blaylock	Ling-Temco-Vought, Inc.
E. F. Blick	University of Oklahoma
H. A. Blum	Southern Methodist University
F. W. Boggs	Pennsylvania State University
J. F. Brady	Naval Underwater Weapons Research & Engineering Station
H. Brandt	University of California, Davis
E. A. Bukzin	Naval Ship Systems Command
R. F. Burdyn	Mobil Research & Development Corp.
B. Cagle	Office of Naval Research
R. D. Cooper	Office of Naval Research
W. B. Coley	LTV Aerospace Corp.
J. P. Craven	Strategic Systems Project Office, Department of the Navy
H. R. Crawford	The Western Company
A. E. Cronk	Texas A&M University
S. W. Doroff	Office of Naval Research
A. T. Ellis	University of California at San Diego
A. G. Fabula	Naval Undersea Warfare Center
J. E. Fairchild	University of Texas at Arlington
J. H. Faull, Jr.	Office of Naval Research
I. M. Felsen	Naval Ship Research & Development Center
F. W. Fenter	LTV Research Center
C. A. Friehe	Johns Hopkins University
J. L. Gaddis	University of Texas at Austin
H. B. Gibbons	LTV Research Center
C. G. Gilbert	Naval Ship Engineering Center
W. B. Giles	General Electric Company
J. H. Green	Naval Undersea Warfare Center
L. W. Gross	Northrop Corporate Laboratories
W. B. Goarty	Marathon Oil
A. Haji-Sheikh	University of Texas at Arlington
J. Harkness	LTV Research Center
H. C. Hershey	Ohio State University
W. J. Hesse	LTV Aerospace Corp.
W. R. Hoover	Naval Ship Research & Development Center
R. G. Howard	Naval Ship Research & Development Center

J. W. Hoyt	Naval Undersea Warfare Center
M. Inouye	NASA Ames Research Center
D. A. Jewell	Naval Ship Research & Development Center
B. Johnson	U. S. Naval Academy
J. M. Killen	University of Minnesota
K. W. Koeritz	Ling-Temco-Vought, Inc.
T. Kowalski	University of Waterloo
J. P. Lamb	University of Texas at Austin
T. G. Lang	Naval Undersea Warfare Center
B. Latto	McMaster University
T. J. Lawley	LTV Aerospace Corp.
E. R. Lindgren	University of Florida
R. C. Little	Naval Research Laboratory
L. Lopez	IBM Houston Scientific Center
L. F. Marcous	Naval Ship Research & Development Center
A. T. McDonald	Purdue University
J. F. McMahon	Pennsylvania State University
R. C. McWherter	LTV Aerospace Corp.
W. A. Meyer	LTV Research Center
J. B. Middlebrook	LTV Research Center
M. V. Morkovin	Illinois Institute of Technology
E. L. Morrisette	NASA Langley Research Center
R. H. Nadolink	Naval Underwater Weapons Research & Engineering Station
L. D. Nichols	Moleculon Research Corp.
B. Noonan	Naval Ordnance Laboratory
G. K. Patterson	University of Missouri at Rolla
T. E. Peirce	Naval Ordnance Systems Command
W. Pfenninger	The Boeing Company
J. K. Quermann	LTV Aerospace Corp.
I. Radin	University of Missouri at Rolla
G. S. Raetz	Northrop-Norair
J. F. Ripken	University of Minnesota
R. S. Rothblum	Naval Ship Research & Development Center
J. G. Spangler	LTV Research Center
T. Sarpkaya	Naval Postgraduate School
J. G. Savins	Mobil Research & Development Corp.
H. H. Shuster	Johns Hopkins University
W. C. Schwemer	LTV Research Center
D. D. Seath	University of Texas at Arlington
O. Seidman	Naval Ordnance Systems Command
P. N. Shankar	General Electric Company
N. W. Sheetz, Jr.	Naval Ordnance Laboratory
M. Spindler	LTV Aerospace Corp.
C. J. Stalmach	LTV Aerospace Corp.
R. J. Stenson	Naval Ship Research & Development Center
F. W. Stone	Union Carbide Corp.
R. I. Tanner	Brown University
K. L. Treiber	U. S. Army Engineer Research & Development Laboratories

M. P. Tulin	Hydronautics Inc.
J. P. Tullis	Colorado State University
W. P. van de Watering	Hydronautics Inc.
P. S. Virk	Massachusetts Institute of Technology
R. R. Walters	LTV Research Center
C. S. Wells	LTV Research Center
J. M. Wetzel	University of Minnesota
A. White	Hendon College of Technology, London
D. A. White	University College, London
W. D. White	Naval Undersea Warfare Center
N. F. Whitsitt	The Western Company
D. C. Wiggert	Hydronautics Inc.
N. Witbeck	Columbia Research Corp.
J. H. Wolff	Naval Ship Research & Development Center
J. Wu	Hydronautics Inc.
S. J. Zaroodny	U. S. Army Ballistic Research Laboratory

CONTENTS

Session III - Applications of Polymer Drag Reduction

Chairman: W. A. Meyer

Invited Lecture:

Papers:

CONTENTS

ON THE MANY FACES OF TRANSITION

Mark V. Morkovin

Illinois Institute of Technology

ABSTRACT

For a given shear-layer geometry the high-Reynolds-numbers turbulent flows possess strong, stable in-the-large, nearly universal features associated with the large number of degrees of freedom in the flows. These features include a range of scales of dominant energetic motion, a range of operating intensity levels, and average three-dimensional phase relations which, together, somehow insure the maintenance of a self-regenerative process. In seeking a rational approach to the bewildering variety of transitional behavior (Ref. 1), the author conjectures that many instability paths to turbulence are admissible and that their effectiveness hinges on whether the given mechanism supplies the proper scales, intensity level, and 3D phase relations needed for self-regeneration.

Conceptual lessons are drawn from a recently completed critical survey of the literature on transition to turbulence, and a number of unifying conjectures are advanced for subsonic speeds. In particular, the roles of linear amplification, non-linear limiting, and secondary instability inducted by unsteady nonlinear effects are discussed. These mechanisms are illustrated for a number of transitional flows, including those in presence of roughness and streamwise vorticity. A clarification is advanced for the question of fast versus slow transition raised at the recent Institute on Transition. (Ref. 2) Finally, an overall model of the linear and nonlinear processes leading to transition is proposed.

CONTRAST BETWEEN TRANSITION[1] AND SUBSEQUENT TURBULENT EVOLUTION OF A SHEAR LAYER

Recently, the author documented (Refs. 1, 4) some of the great variety of combinations of primary and secondary instabilities that can lead to transition of a shear layer from laminar to turbulent behavior. For a given such combination, i.e., for a specific road to turbulence, the location of the transition region depends strongly on the unsteady disturbance input (Refs. 3, 4, 5) and on the equally elusive steady departures (especially three-dimensional) from the presumed laminar velocity distribution (Refs. 6, 7, 8, 48). The multiplicity of possible paths to turbulence and the unavailability of information concerning the amplitudes and nature of the disturbance input into the runaway instabilities combine to make the prediction of transition a peculiarly nondeterministic problem. Even if we succeed in delineating the regimes of parameters[2], under which various unexplained phenomena (Refs. 1, 4) such as the transition reversal with cooling and the early-blunt-body transition, etc., are likely to occur, transition prediction will remain a matter of probability[3] projections, often based on inadequate parametric samples.

In contrast, the development of a turbulent shear layer, following the completion of transition, appears to be a quasideterministic process (Refs. 12, 13). At sufficiently high Reynolds numbers, the large number of degrees of freedom apparently lead to stochastically well defined laws and structural features which are nearly universal for a given shear layer geometry. For instance, for incompressible boundary layers with mild pressure gradients and for pipe flows, these features (Refs. 14-18) include

---

[1] For an up-to-date, orderly and factual exposition of transition, the reader is referred to Tani (Ref. 40). Here we propose to focus on concepts which might help to interpret more general transitional and turbulent pheonmena.

[2] These parameters include those characterizing the unsteady and steady disturbances, roughness, non-uniformities in wall distribution of suction or transpiration, etc.

[3] Transition probabilities for design purposes (such as needed in Refs. 9-11) should be matched by corresponding evaluation of risks and probabilities of performance deterioration.

a range of scales of dominant energetic motions, roughly $1/3\delta$-3δ (δ = local boundary layer thickness or pipe radius), a range of operating intensity levels with $(u'/U_e)_{max}$ on the order of 10-14%, and average three-dimensional phase relations, in particular -R_{uv} is nearly 0.5. For jets and wakes, the turbulent velocity correlations are of comparable magnitude and the maximal intensities $(u'/\Delta U_{max})$ tend to be relatively larger, 20-30%. The ratio of the corresponding scales of the dominant energetic motion to the half width of these symmetric free shear layers is believed to be of the same order as for the cited wall shear layers. Somehow, a combination of these features of motion insures <u>turbulent self-regeneration</u> as contrasted with laminar unsteadiness which may ultimately decay as for Figure 1 (borrowed from G. R. Hall (Ref. 19)).

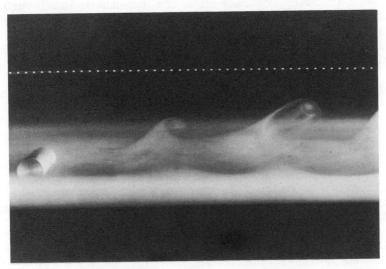

Figure 1.   Instability of Inflected Laminar Profile Below Critical Re of "Roughness."

On the basis of studies leading to References 1 and 4, we <u>propose</u> that often enough several instability paths can lead to turbulence and that their effectiveness depends upon whether the corresponding instability mechanisms provide the proper scales, intensity levels, and <u>three-dimensional</u> phase relations needed for turbulent self-regeneration. <u>We conjecture</u> further that, at times, the nature, amplitudes, and scale distribution of the unsteady and steady input disturbances will govern which set of instability mechanisms first produces self-regenerative turbulence.

VORTICITY AMPLIFICATION AND NONLINEAR INHIBITING

It is fruitful to view shear layers and their instabilities in terms of total vorticity, $\vec{\omega}$, which for compressible flows with constant viscosity obeys the equation

$$\frac{D\,(\vec{\omega}/\rho)}{Dt} \;=\; (\frac{\vec{\omega}}{\rho})\cdot\text{grad}\ \vec{u} \;+\; \nu\nabla^2\vec{\omega} \tag{1}$$

Rate of change, following "particles"	$\approx$	Production of vorticity	$+$	Diffusion of vorticity

For two-dimensional instability mechanisms such as the Tollmien-Schlichting waves (henceforth denoted TS waves) the production term is zero in sharp contrast with the two-dimensional turbulent shear layers which are dominated by this term. This contrast is basic to the understanding of the relation between instability theories and actual onset of turbulence: somewhere in the transition process the production must be activated.

When we think of mean flow and fluctuations around the mean (either laminar or turbulent), i.e.,

$$\vec{\omega} = \vec{\Omega} + \vec{\omega}' \; ; \qquad \vec{u} = \vec{V} + \vec{u}'$$

and we linearize Equation (1), we obtain the Orr-Sommerfeld equation. This equation contains on the left-hand side among others the term $u_2\,\partial(\rho\Omega_3)/\partial y$ (usually written $v[\rho U']'$) and couples the fluctuating vorticity with the mean-flow vorticity reservoir. As is well known (Ref. 20), when $(\rho U')'$ is zero within the shear layer, i.e. when the profile has a "generalized inflection point," there exists a powerful inviscid amplification mechanism (Ref. 6) (which can also (Ref. 21) be visualized in terms of the Biot-Savart vorticity induction law and feed-back interaction). As long as the fluctuation levels are small enough to be governed by the linearized equation, the growth rate is exponential in time or space. Amplitudes of such laminar self-enhancing motions of proper scale and phase can grow by factors of hundreds in a few wavelengths, e.g. in the case of the three-dimensional inflected profile over a single roughness element in Figure 1 or the doubly inflected two-dimensional profile of a low-speed wake behind a flat plate in Figure 2 (courtesy of F. N. M. Brown).

Such growths, of course, lead to u' and $\vec{\omega}$' values for which
the nonlinear terms can no longer be neglected in Equation (1),
and we are pushed beyond the Orr-Sommerfeld equation. On the basis
of the analytical work of Stuart (Ref. 22) and others and
of numerous qualitative and quantitative observations, e.g. Sato
and Kuriki (Ref. 23), Freymuth (Ref. 24), Sato (Ref. 25), etc.,
we conjecture that the nonlinear effects in two-dimensional instabilities tend to be self-limiting as well as inhibiting of other
modes of unsteady motion[1]. Thus (Fig. 2), the velocity fluctuations first grow exponentially, then much more slowly, reaching
a maximum, and then start to decay--see discussion of Figures
7b and 8 in Reference 26. Similarly, by enhancing two-dimensionality through mild excitation via soundwaves (Refs. 23-25, 27),
experimenters apparently inhibited the effects of random free-
stream three-dimensionality. Berger (Ref. 28), in fact, managed
to postpone transition to turbulence in the wake of a two-
dimensional cylinder from Re of 170 or so to 350 by minutest
vibrations of the cylinder at the Strouhal frequency.

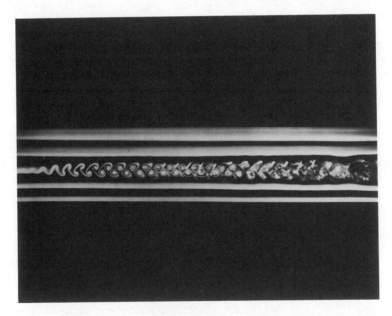

Figure 2.   Instability and Transition of Wake Behind a Flat Plate.

---

[1]   Similar effects appear to be present in convectional instabilities, even three-dimensional ones. It would be desirable
to identify systematically the possible exceptions. The insen-
sitivity of turbulence itself to Reynolds number is ascribed to
nonlinear inertial effects (Batchelor (Ref. 49), Chapter VI)
but there the additional factor of randomness may enter.

Thus it seems that two-dimensional and three-dimensional
linear mechanisms in presence of a mean vorticity reservoir provide us with the most powerful (exponential) initial amplification. This observation remains true even when there is no
generalized inflection point such as for boundary layers in zero
and favorable pressure gradients. Then Prandtl's viscous
mechanism (Ref. 29) induces phase differences in u_1' and u_2'
fluctuations near the wall which facilitate absorption of
energy from the mean flow and lead to growth when the so-called
linear critical Reynolds number is exceeded. Even though local
amplification rates are smaller than for inviscid instabilities,
total amplification ratios of 5000-10,000 can be reached
(Refs. 5, 30) before transition sets in for Blasius layers
carefully shielded from input disturbances.

CRITERIA[1] FOR ONSET OF SELF-SUSTAINING WALL TURBULENCE AND THE ROLE OF LINEAR AMPLIFICATION

Instead of shielding the Blasius layer, Elder (Ref. 31)
utilized strong, local disturbances from spark discharges to find
how intense a fluctuation velocity had to be in order to inoculate
a self-regenerative, growing turbulent spot in the layer. Though
interpretation of his measurements may differ, he concluded
that whenever u_1' exceeded 18 ± 2.5% of the free stream
velocity, a turbulent breakdown on the flat plate would ensue
in the range $2 \times 10^4 < Re_x < 10^6$ which he studied. Klebanoff
et al (Ref. 32) found a sharp peak of u_1' of 16% of U_e at
y/δ of 0.4 at the final breakdown[2] of a long Tollmien-Schlichting
amplification chain. The maximum u_1' values before the onset of
turbulence, inferrable from Kovasznay et al (Ref. 33), Tani and
Komoda (Ref. 34), and Tani et al (Ref. 7) range from 10 to 16%
of U_e.

A fluctuation intensity, integrated over the spectrum, can
hardly provide an adequate criterion for the onset of self-
sustaining turbulence. Nevertheless, the high intensity levels

---

[1]   A generation ago Liepmann (Ref. 38) suggested that turbulence
      sets in when the Reynolds stress of the laminar fluctuations
      approaches in magnitude the laminar shear stress at the wall.
      See Smith and Gamberoni (Ref. 39) for discussion and possible
      implementation of such a conjecture.

[2]   Over short periods, absolute fluctuation amplitudes as high
      as 40% of U_e were observed, presumably corresponding
      to the kinky motions in Figure 3.

should have significance. These results suggest that for a
Blasius layer, fluctuation levels on the order of those encountered
in the fully turbulent boundary layer or larger are needed for
the onset of self-regenerative turbulence. Such high fluctuation levels cannot generally be sustained in the free stream.
In fact, one seldom finds free-stream turbulence levels higher
than 1% of U_e, and generally much lower in flight. We
can therefore conjecture that for most non-separated boundary
layers some type of the powerful linear amplification should
contribute substantially to the intensity build-up before local
transition takes place. **Thus, for Bennett's hot-wire study (Ref. 44)**
of transition in presence of u_1'/U_e of 0.42% in the free
stream, one can estimate a total amplification of 400 or more
for the dominant Tollmien-Schlichting frequency before transition
(item C21 of Ref. 4).

The above linear amplification mechanism may be associated
with only a local departure of the mean profile from a more stable
shape such as in the case of Figure 1 where a fixed roughness
caused an inflectional distortion. Similarly, a temporary
distortion of the vorticity distribution can lead to a new or
more powerful linear amplification (Ref. 45). Hama and Nutant's
successive cine' shots (Ref. 48) of periodic hydrogen bubble
traces from a thin vertical wire, protruding from the wall to the
free stream through a disturbed near-Blasius layer, Figure 3,
illustrate such rapid linear (and ultimately nonlinear) growth
of secondary motions during the time when the layer has a temporar-
ily inflected velocity profile (40% of a Tollmien-Schlichting
period). It now appears that even in turbulent boundary layers,
instantaneous inflectional velocity profiles near the wall and
their instability probably contribute substantially to the high
level of fluctuations at the outer edge of the laminar sublayer
(Ref. 47 and Friday Morning Session of Ref. 12).

FINITE, NONLINEARIZABLE DISTURBANCES

We note that a finite local or instantaneous distortion into
an especially unstable vorticity distribution can be the result
of nonlinearizable disturbances. This observation suggests
caution in the interpretation of the principle of nonlinear
limiting. It may be valid for one scale of disturbance, which
however, by its finite distortion of the vorticity distribution
may prepare the rest for a rapid secondary linear instability
on a different, usually smaller scale. This is essentially the
view proposed by Klebanoff (Ref. 32) and Greenspan and Benney
(Ref. 46) for the secondary "spike-like" instability grafted onto
the finite Tollmien-Schlichting oscillations of a Blasius layer,
seen in Figure 3. For later purposes we note that Figure 3

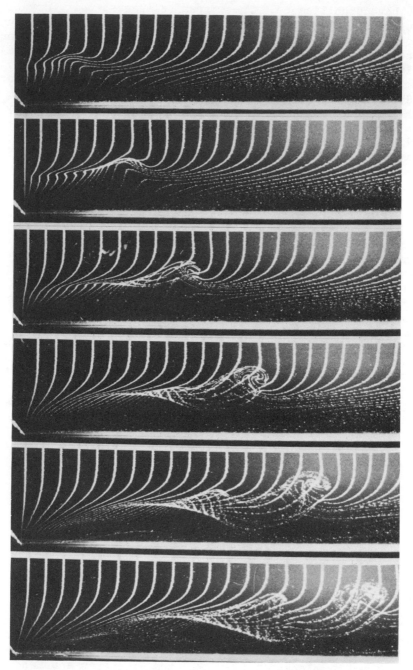

Figure 3. Secondary Instability of Blasius Layer.

shows only about 60% of the Tollmien-Schlichting wave-
length, λ_{TS}, so that in Figure 3 the streamwise scale of the
secondary instability is approximately seven times smaller than
λ_{TS}.

Distortion of the mean profile by finite disturbances as
a destabilizing effect has been proposed originally by Meksyn and
Stuart (Ref. 22). However, the time-mean velocity profile
corresponding to Figure 3 is only mildly more unstable (Refs. 32, 48)
than the original Blasius profile. The rapidity of the instability
corresponding to the instantaneous profile is a key feature
missing from most of the nonlinear theories.

Heretofore, the aforementioned unexplained transition
phenomena were usually ascribed to vague finite-disturbance
effects by exclusion arguments. We can now ask whether in the
given shear layer the disturbances are of the proper scale and
intensity as to create instantaneous or local vorticity distributions for which extra fast and powerful linear amplification
processes could be present (Figs. 1 and 3). For instance, we
could speculate that should free-stream turbulence be raised monotonically, beyond the 0.42% level of Bennett (Ref. 44),
a level would be reached where such instantaneously and locally
highly unstable distributions would arise frequently enough in
the Blasius layer to lead to breakdown and turbulent regeneration
more efficiently than the Tollmien-Schlichting primary and subsequent secondary instabilities. The reader will recognize that
this conjecture is a modern reformulation of G. I. Taylor's
criterion (Ref. 50) in which instantaneous local separation induced
by turbulent disturbances was postulated as the condition for
turbulent self-regeneration.

One apparently nonlinear transition mechanism, the transverse
(also called lateral) contamination, has remained unexplained
since its discovery by Charters (Ref. 35) despite the microscopic
experiments of Schubauer and Klebanoff (Ref. 51) from whom Figure 4
is borrowed. In particular, the near-constancy of the angle of
the resulting turbulent wedges at low speeds and its narrower
spreading at supersonic speeds provides challenging tests for theoretical models. We could speculate whether here too an instantaneously and locally highly unstable reorganization of the oncoming
laminar vorticity layer could take place, but this time in the
spanwise direction, induced through the dualistic vorticity-pressure
action at distance by the turbulent neighbor. Careful hydrogen-
bubble experiments a'la Hama and Nutant (Ref. 48), Kline et al

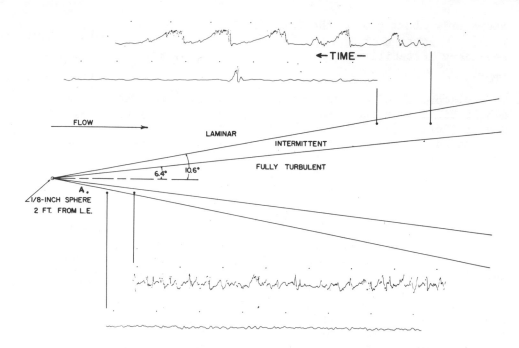

Figure 4.   Turbulence Wedge Produced by Roughness.

(Ref. 47), e.g. with vertical wire (as in Figure 3) located at point A of Figure 4, should throw much light on this omnipresent mechanism.

The sister mechanism of the _growth of turbulent spots_ (see Figure 5), (courtesy of J.W. Elder (Ref. 31)), once they are born, probably spreads in an analogous fashion in the transverse direction (Ref. 51). However, the surface advance of the downstream and upstream edges of the spot at the rate of 88% and 50% of the freestream velocity (Ref. 51), respectively, must reflect additional features of the induction process associated with advection and sustenance of the intense turbulent vorticity at different levels from the walls. In particular, the quenching of self-regeneration at the trailing edge should furnish us with quantitative information on the criteria for self-regeneration of wall turbulence. There the local mean velocity profiles are much more convex (Ref. 51) and stable than the Blasius profile but hardly more so than a normal turbulent profile. Somehow, the turbulent vorticity at some distance from the wall is con-

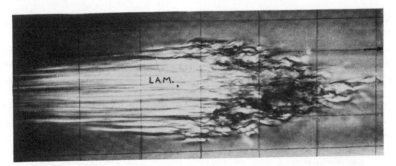

Figure 5.   Growing Turbulent Spot in Plan View.

vected away in such a manner that it lacks the ability to induce
self-regeneration in the lower strata as in fully turbulent
layers at comparably low Reynolds numbers (Ref. 47). We could
speculate on the implications of this phenomenon to fully developed turbulent wall layers and to their relaminarization in
sufficiently strong favorable pressure gradients. Clearly, the
wide implications of possible lessons from the flow field configurations near the upstream edge of the turbulent spot again
strongly suggest the usage of the quantitative hydrogen bubble
technique for detailed exploration in both horizontal and
vertical planes.

A practically important case of nonlinearizable road to
transition, combining the features of transverse and <u>advection
contamination</u>, often occurs on swept-back aircraft wings. Turbulence from the boundary layer on the fuselage tends to propagate
along the otherwise laminar swept-back leading edges of the wings
(which then experience increased drag) unless special turbulence
bypass designs are utilized (Refs. 36, 37).

EFFECTS OF THREE-DIMENSIONAL SINGLE ROUGHNESS ELEMENTS

The variety of behaviors, governed by Equation (1) and some
of the preceding concepts will now be illustrated in connection
with the multiplicity of effects caused by purely passive roughness
elements. In Figure 3, typical of single 3D roughnesses, we
observe the consequences of the powerful linear amplification
of the minutest disturbances (made possible by the locally 3D inflected velocity profile) and the development of nonlinear self-
limiting as the velocity amplitudes associated with the rolled-up
vortices cease growing past the right end of the photograph. Even
though the 3D production of Equation (1) is activated and the motion

is intense, the Reynolds number (essentially the ratio of the
production to the diffusion term in Equation (1)) is here
apparently low enough for the unsteady motion to subside. Tani
et al (Ref. 7) have documented that in such cases a spanwise
unevenness of the mean boundary layer develops, with two thicker
ridges, adjacent to a central depression, 15-20% thinner
than normal, and two additional outer depressions adjoining the
ridges, all with Blasius profiles within accuracy of measurements.
They have shown that such mean-flow three-dimensionality enhances
the rapidity of TS instability. In particular, there is some
evidence that it brings about unsteady energy transfer in the
spanwise direction in the nonlinear regime. There is little
question that intense fluctuations develop earlier than normally
in one or the other outer depressions, presumably culminating
in a secondary instability similar to that of Figure 3 and in
the birth of a turbulent spot. Thus, the 3D roughness element
plays a rather subtle but non-negligible role in bringing about
an earlier than normal transition in the lower Reynolds number
domain.

Hall (Ref. 19) explored visually the changes from the
preceding behavior with variations in Reynolds number for different
obstacle shapes and heights above the wall (his Figs. 5, 14, and
15). In proximity of thus documented critical Reynolds numbers,
Re_k, (characterized by the undisturbed-profile velocity at the
height k of the obstacle) a very small change in Reynolds number
per unit length will alter the regular, ultimately decaying flow
pattern of Figure 1 into patterns in which one of the early
vorticity formations becomes the apex[1] of a spreading turbulent
wedge, similar to Figure 4, (Hall's Figs. 3 and 11). Clearly,
at the head of this wedge, we may be able to characterize better[2]
the criteria for turbulence self-regeneration. For the preceding
relatively small changes in Reynolds number leading to the rapid
upstream motion of the turbulent wedge, there is very little
change in the 3D scales of the vortex formations such as in Figure 1.
We conjecture, therefore, that here the onset was primarily
intensity- and phase-limited. These scales of motion indeed appear
to be within the range of the ultimate energetic turbulent motion

---

[1]   Occasionally at lower Re_x values the wedge appears to start
        with spanwise induction of regular longitudinal vortices (Refs.
        41-43).

[2]   Experiments with an "active" roughness-tripper are now in
        progress at Illinois Institute of Technology.

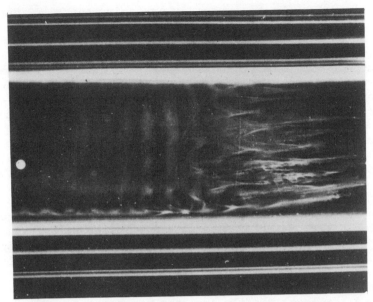

Figure 6.   Instability and Breakdown in Boundary Layer of Axisymmetric
             Ogive-cylinder Body.

as cited in the first section of this paper. Apparently, with the
affinity of scales assured, we can bypass the TS mechanism altogether
if we can replace it with another strongly amplifying mechanism--
here the local inflectional instability.

      It is instructive to compare this postcritical onset of tran-
sition with the precritical one when the scales of Figure 1 are
at first replaced with the scales of the Tollmien-Schlichting
mechanism, λ_{TS}. The TS waves which are sufficiently amplified to
possibly influence transition usually stretch over eight to ten
boundary layer thicknesses, i.e. lack the length-scale affinity
with their ultimate target, the turbulent motions. Furthermore,
their spanwise scales also tend to be too large for a direct development into normal turbulence. We should therefore anticipate a
scale shift and three-dimensionalization before TS motion evolves
into turbulence. Small degrees of three-dimensionality in the
mean flow or in the disturbances develop slowly during the "lineariz-
able stage" of the TS amplification and rapidly during the nonlinear
stages as Figure 6, borrowed from Knapp and Roache (Ref. 27),
dramatically illustrates. In Figure 6, equidistant smoke filaments
travel from far upstream on the left; the middle one impinges on
the nose of an ogive-shaped axisymmetric model, which is seen framed
between the two brightly-scattering smoke lines. Gradually,
toward the center of Figure 6, amplifying TS waves accentuate the

accumulation of smoke in vertically appearing bands, λ_{TS} apart; the regularity of these is then rapidly destroyed by the afore-mentioned three-dimensionalization during the nonlinear stages.

Study of many variations of Figure 6 and of their details has convinced Knapp and Roache (Ref. 27) that these smoke patterns represent motions at least qualitatively similar to those of the secondary instabilities in Figure 3 (Ref. 48) and in the hot-wire studies of References 8, 32, 33, and 34. Broadly speaking this stage brings about the three-dimensional activation of the production terms in Equation (1), raises the intensity of the fluctuations, and shifts the scale from λ_{TS} to sizes commensurate with turbulent motion.

The two modes in which a single 3D roughness influences transition are represented schematically in the upper two loops of Figure 7. It is interesting that Klebanoff used the upper direct 3D roughness path in Figure 7 as illustration of the likely geometry of the secondary instability in smooth-plate transition and displayed the match between the instantaneous inflectional profile of the latter and the local profile over the roughness in Figure 31 of Reference 32.

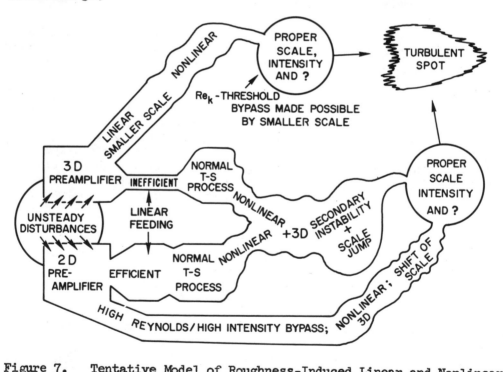

Figure 7.   Tentative Model of Roughness-Induced Linear and Nonlinear Processes Leading to Turbulence in a Boundary Layer.

EFFECTS OF TWO-DIMENSIONAL SINGLE ROUGHNESS ELEMENTS

In an as yet unpublished hot-wire study of the development of
fluctuations along a flat plate in presence of circular wires of
height $k < \delta$, attached to the wall, Klebanoff (Ref. 52) illuminated
the mechanisms governing the transition of these flows with nominally
two-dimensional locally inflected velocity profiles. Klebanoff
shows that free-stream disturbances at a given frequency partly
penetrate and "buffet" the boundary layer, without basic influence
on its instability, and partly evoke an amplifying TS response.
The latter process, not yet analyzed, the author called "internali-
zation or assimilation of free-stream disturbances" and "TS feeding
on disturbance spectra" in Section 5 of Reference 1. In such terms,
Klebanoff demonstrated that local introduction of the inflected
profiles in effect inserts a _wider_ _band_ preamplifier (feeding on
the internalized disturbance spectra) in series with the normal TS
amplification, which is again effective some distance after reattach-
ment.

In view of the two-dimensionality of the profiles, the comparison
between the theoretical amplification characteristics of an inflected
Falkner-Skan profile in a mildly adverse pressure gradient
(β = -0.05) and those of the Blasius layer can illustrate the
preamplifier concept. Figure 8 (compiled from Wazzan et al

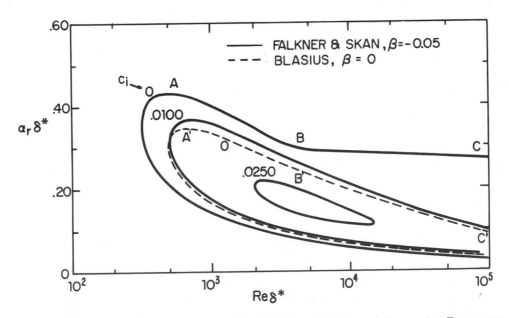

Figure 8.   Instability Map of Flat-Plate Boundary Layer in Zero and
              Mildly Adverse Pressure Gradient.

(Ref. 53)) displays the curves of constant dimensionless amplification rates c_i = 0, 0.01, and 0.025 in the wave-number α_r (equal
to $2\pi/\lambda_{TS}$) and Reynolds-number plane, $\delta*$ being the displacement
thickness. Clearly, the increased broadness of the neutral curve,
c_i = 0, of the inflected profile corresponds to a wider band of
amplified wave numbers (and therefore frequencies). Furthermore,
the waves experiencing zero amplification for the Blasius case
are amplified at the substantial dimensionless rate of about 0.01
by the inflected profile as judged by the near overlap of the two
curves. Finally, the critical Reynolds number of the inflected
profile is smaller by almost 40%; i.e. for approximately 300 <
$Re_{\delta}*$<500, there is amplification for the β = -0.05 profile while
the β = 0 profile damps all disturbances.

Thus at lower Reynolds numbers Klebanoff's roughness-inflected
profiles passed on to the Blasius layer downstream more energetic
and wider fluctuation spectra. For amplified fluctuation levels
below about 1% of U_e, these spectra were then further TS
amplified in the reattached layer, leading to the secondary instability, three-dimensionalization, a shift to smaller scales, and an
earlier than normal transition as already discussed in connection
with Figure 3. By increasing the Reynolds number per unit length,
Klebanoff could reach the nonlinear stage and transition before the
re-establishment of the Blasius layer. Clearly, one could induce
transition to occur directly in the region of inflected profiles by
increasing the disturbance level and U_e. The nature of the
secondary instabilities (if any) for these latter cases has not
been studied.

The possible sequences of processes for the two-dimensional
roughness are recorded schematically as the lower two loops in
Figure 7. At subsonic speeds the preamplification by the 2D roughness elements is more effective in bringing about early transition
than that by 3D elements--except possibly in strong favorable
pressure gradients. (At supersonic speeds the situation tends to
be reversed, for understandable reasons (Ref. 1)).

TWO-DIMENSIONAL WAKES AND JETS

If in the Falkner-Skan family of laminar profiles the measure
of the adverse pressure gradient, β, is made more and more negative,
the corresponding c_i = 0 curves in Figure 8 move to the left and
broaden, continuing the earlier trend from β = 0 to -0.05. The
nearly horizontal segments BC (where the inviscid amplification
character really takes over) move up and wipe out the maximum of
A. For the separating layer (β = -0.1988), BC reaches the level

$a_r \delta*$ of 1.3 and for the relevant Reynolds numbers $Re_\delta* < 200$, c_{imax} occurs for $a_r \delta*$ of approximately 0.7. In other words, as a layer becomes more and more free of the wall constraint, the ratio λ/δ decreases from the cited high values of the Blasius layer. The scales of the laminarly unstable motions become commensurate with those of the energetic turbulent mixing motions. For transition to the self-regenerating mode of vorticity, a secondary instability does no longer appear necessary, though it still could occur. Three-dimensionalization and activation of production in Equation (1), however, remains mandatory.

Thus, the wake in Figure 2 exhibits no change of λ as it grows to the nonlinear stage. Past the middle of Figure 2, three-dimensionalization occurs and turbulence gradually takes over from the laminar motions of commensurate scale. Similar gradual changes were observed in the hot-wire studies of Sato and Kuriki, who traced the three-dimensional disturbance to a "slight waviness about 0.2mm in height" of the trailing edge of the plate, which generated the wake (page 346, Ref. 23).

According to Sato (Ref. 25), similar scale relations and gradual transition to turbulence also prevailed for two-dimensional jets. Sato (Refs. 23, 25) and others (Ref. 2) remarked on the contrast between this slow transition and the fast transition, marked with sudden spikes and bursts, in the case of wall-constrained instabilities. It would seem desirable to characterize the otherwise subjective description "fast" for "slow" non-dimensionally, namely with respect to the only available time scale--the period of the primary laminar instability. Then, for Figure 3 and its equivalent hot-wire traces, the aforementioned downshift from λ_{ns} to a scale 6-15 shorter should correspond to 6-15 shorter time fluctuations. These could indeed appear as sudden to an observer psychologically conditioned to the relatively long primary period. Since the wall constraint postpones the final three-dimensional reorganization to much higher Reynolds numbers, finer-scale vorticity (Ref. 54) can readily develop alongside the spiky signals corresponding to Figure 3. For the wakes and jets, the shift from the primary scale need not occur and is generally not observed--hence the slow transition mode. Other significant differences exist between these free laminar layers and wall layers--the absence of the singular critical layer and the absence of the wall-anchored, high, mean-flow vorticity reservoir--which could be correlated with the fast-slow transition character. The requirement for self-regeneration of turbulence, however, cannot be bypassed and provides us with the preceding tentative useful correlation.

For singly inflected laminar mixing layers, the experimental and theoretical situation appears insufficiently defined. At least over a range of Reynolds numbers, a secondary instability, increasing the primary scale by a factor of two and almost simultaneously generating much finer scales, seems to take place (Refs. 24, 55). According to Wille (Ref. 56), Freymuth (Ref. 24), and others, the successive, nonlinearly limited, rolled-up vortices of the primary instability begin to dance around each other in pairs, then fuse into a single vortex in a probably turbulent fashion and thus lead to the first subharmonic. A single row of concentrated vortices is unstable. According to Kelly (Ref. 57), the happenstance that the propagation speed of the subharmonic matches that of the primary wave may contribute to this special behavior. In the field of the fusing pair of vortices, strong instantaneous local shear layers develop, possibly providing the stage for the breakdown to turbulence. According to Michalke (Ref. 2), turbulence onset here is "sudden", but there may be exceptions to the secondary instability described above.

MEAN FLOWS WITH STREAMWISE VORTICITY

Recently, Komoda (Ref. 58) subjected a flat-plate laminar layer to spanwise alternating pressure gradients which induced spanwise variations of thickness of $\pm 20\%$ and $\pm 40\%$, but kept the longitudinal velocity profiles "very close to Blasius". His multiple hot-wire arrays revealed an entirely different pattern on nonlinear vorticity interaction than observed by Klebanoff et al (Ref. 32), Kovasznay et al (Ref. 33), and Tani and Komoda (Ref. 34) in presence of milder three-dimensionality. In the new pattern a local intense vertical (Ref. 1) shear develops and turbulence evolves near it but without indication of the regular spike signals. The thickness of the high-vorticity layer is of order $\delta/2$ so that we could expect self-regenerative turbulent processes to take hold at the high intensity levels registered by Komoda. The richness of three-dimensional patterns associated with the nonlinear terms in Equation (1) has not yet been fully revealed. Study of Komoda's contour maps provides a conditioning exercise for our imagination.

In presence of mean streamwise vorticity Ω_1 a number of new terms in Equation (1) and in the linearized Orr-Sommerfeld instability equation appear. A glance at a three-dimensional boundary layer, Figure 9, makes us expect additional, more complicated modes of vorticity interaction and amplification even in the early linear stages. Such new, competing linear instability modes have been analyzed by J. T. Stuart (Ref. 60) and W. B. Brown (Ref. 59) and observed on sufficiently sweptback wings (Ref. 61), rotating disks (Ref. 60), spinning projectiles (Ref. 27), and

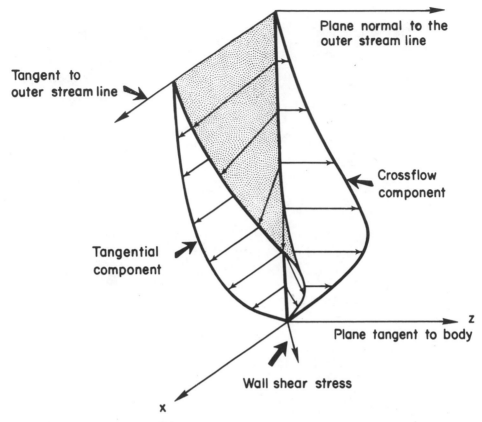

Figure 9.   Velocity Field in a Three-Dimensional Boundary Layer.

axisymmetric bodies at angles of attack. Normal two-dimensional
TS waves (with wave fronts parallel to the z axis in Figure 9) then
apparently amplify more slowly than special (Refs. 59, 60) skew
wave fronts, primarily sensitive to mean cross-flow profiles.

'These modes are generally nonlinearly self-limited, developing
into finite-amplitude skew vortical motions within the boundary
layer, such as seen in Figures 10 and 11 to be discussed later
(courtesy, Faller and Kaylor (Ref. 3)). For sweptback wings (Refs.
22, 61) these vortical formations orient themselves essentially in
the local streamwise direction and remain fixed in time with respect
to the surface. They have transverse scales (Ref. 61) on the
order of δ. They apparently grow streamwise rather slowly after
reaching the nonlinear stage so that the distance between their
first palpable appearance and their final breakdown into turbulence
is significant. Of special practical importance is the fact that
transition occurs much sooner than if only TS waves were present.

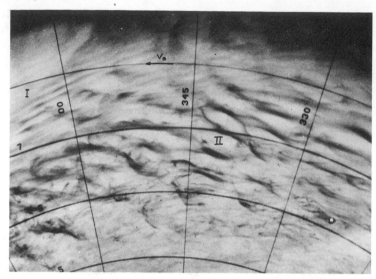

Figure 10. Instability Modes and Transition in Ekman Layer.

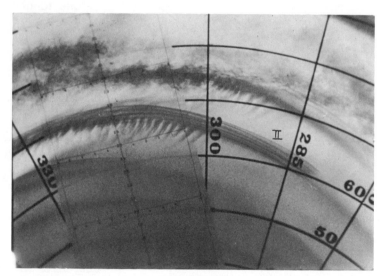

Figure 11. Type II and Gill Instabilities and Transition in Boundary
            Layer on Bottom of Rotating Tank.

F. N. M. Brown's remarkable smoke visualization of these vortices on
a spinning projectile (Fig. 1 of Reference 27) discloses that
transition to turbulence apparently occurs without a change of
scale of an additional laminar instability. While impressions
from isolated visualizations may be misleading, we may conjecture
again that the a priori three-dimensionalization of vorticity and

the affinity of the pre- and post-breakdown scales of motion combine
to make the path of turbulence more effective and thus lead to the
early transition on sweptback wings.

In the meteorologically important three-dimensional boundary
layers in rotating systems, the diversity of possible motions
increases in presence of Coriolis' effects. Experiments (Refs. 3, 62)
and theory (Refs. 3, 63) indicate the existence of two spiral-like
unequally unstable vortical formations inside the Ekman boundary
layer between a frictional surface and the rotating bulk of the
fluid: **type I** (**inflectional**; $\lambda \sim 3\delta$) **and type II** (**Coriolis - induced**:
$\lambda \sim 6$ to $9\ \delta$). Thus, in the rotating-tank arrangement of Faller
and Kaylor (Fig. 10), nearly stationary roll waves of type I are
seen inclined about 14° to the left of the anticlockwise circular
bulk velocity, $V_\theta \sim 1/r$, while somewhat disturbed waves of type II
move rapidly inward, slanted to the right. Faller (Ref. 3, p. 320)
speculates about the possibility of an interaction between the
two wave systems being essential for transition to turbulence, e.g.
at the higher Reynolds numbers of the inner circles in Figure 10.
If we assumed that the ratio of the scales of energetic turbulent
motions to the shear-layer thickness is not much affected by the
rotation, the waves of the dominant type-II instability would
appear too long for a direct development of turbulence without
such three-dimensional nonlinear interaction or without some other
secondary instability.

By accelerating the tank from rest, Faller and Kaylor also
simulate the rotating disk experiments, in which the boundary layer
moves outward underneath the (relative) circular free-stream motion
(Reynolds number increasing outward). Figure 11 not only reveals
that the fast moving type-II roll waves can exist over rotating
disks, but also exhibits a new kind of secondary instability,
(picturesquely called gill instability) shortly preceding "fast"
transition to turbulence. Here the primary scale is about 11δ
while the gill measure is 2δ or less. Apparently the gill instability
plays here a role similar to that of the "instantaneous" inflectional
instability in the breakdown of TS waves in Figure 3. Interestingly,
Faller's Figure 12, showing inferred streamlines, indicates a high
probability of a strong inflection in the instantaneous velocity
profile. Thus it would seem that the concepts we were groping
for in the first four sections may have relevance even to three-
dimensional boundary layers in rotating systems.

CONCLUDING REMARKS

Faller and Kaylor noted that one or the other type of instability could be enhanced by manipulation of flow disturbances.
Then, depending upon which type reached finite amplitudes first,
either the gill-preceded transition or the more gradual interaction
transition would follow. A number of similar non-unique paths to
turbulence, brought about by competing instability mechanisms,
were described in Reference 1, especially at supersonic speeds,
where there is a critical need (Refs. 9-11) for better understanding
of observed effects. For a more complete assessment of the transition probabilities, we would need a more complete specification of
the total environment, including disturbances, nonhomogeneity of
boundary conditions, etc.

A useful overall view (Ref. 1) is presented in Figure 12.
In particular, we should keep in mind that a given occurrence of
transition may be governed by a single strong factor in the environment or by the influences of several hard-to-measure factors which
cumulate in different and nonlinear ways when the Reynolds number
or another parameter such as the cooling ratio Tw/Tr is varied.
In Figure 12, the diagonal box referrring to dominant and multiple
responsibility for transition emphasizes the importance of the
concept. Rapid changes in transition Reynolds number are often
indicative that there is an underlying shift between controlling
factor or mechanisms.

However, the removal of a "locally dominant" factor does not
guarantee large improvement or even simplification of the problem.
Thus Pate and Schueler (Ref. 64) in a prolonged, painstaking
search for the explanation of the puzzling variation of transition
Reynolds number in supersonic wind tunnels with the dimensional
variable, Reynolds number per unit length, adduced strong evidence
that it was governed by the powerful, Reynolds-number sensitive
radiation of sound from the turbulent boundary layer on the side-
walls. Their colleague, Potter (Ref. 65), designed a ballistic-
range experiment in which there was no acoustic irradiation of the
boundary layer on his models and yet found essentially the same
unit-Reynolds-number effect! Somehow, in his vastly different
parametric environment, a different factor or a number of factors
brought about a similar final variation. In the author's opinion
there can be little rational progress in transition work at supersonic speeds without a clarification of the preceding paradox.

At any speeds, rational approach to prediction of transition
probabilities depends strongly on the relative roles of the linear
and nonlinear processes leading to transition. If, for a given
design, the linear box in Figure 12 should correspond to a major

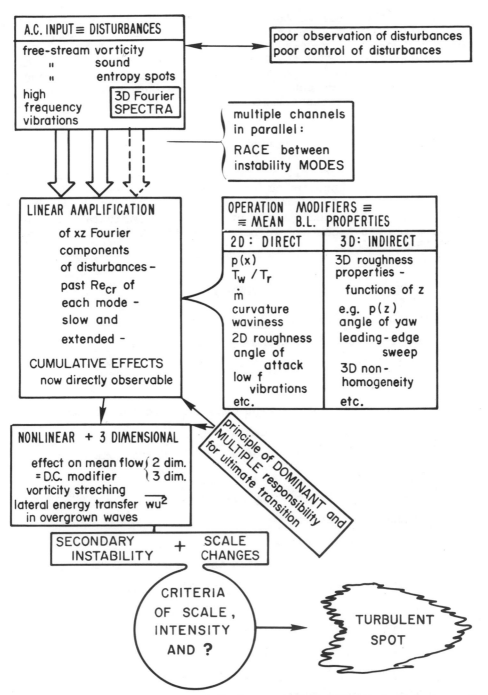

Figure 12.   Tentative Model of Systems of Instability Processes and
             Controlling Factors Leading to Turbulence in Viscous
             Wall Layers.

portion of the roads to turbulence, then stability theories would
provide us with an invaluable tool. Should there be some bypass
of the theoretical models (e.g. Fig. 7), these must be fully charted,
experimentally, before the linear tool can be used in it's, thus cir-
cumscribed, domain of applicability. The approach and conjectures
offered herein represent an attempt at finding a current best-bet view
of the interplay between linear and nonlinear processes in transition.

ACKNOWLEDGMENTS

    As a search for criteria of earliest onset of turbulence,
this effort was supported under contract USAF F 44620-69-0022.
Many of the concepts arose from earlier work at the Research
Institute for Advanced Studies of the Martin Marietta Corpora-
tion, which was sponsored in part under Air Force Contract No.
F 33615-67-C-1662.

NOMENCLATURE

k distance from wall to top of obstacle

$\dot{m}$ mass flux rate into boundary layer at wall

p static pressure

r radial distance

Re Reynolds number, subscript denoting reference length

Re_{cr} critical Re for amplification

R_{uv} correlation coefficient of u and v fluctuations

T_w wall temperature

T_r recovery (adiabatic) temperature

TS Tollmien-Schlichting

$\vec{u}$ total velocity vector

u_1' root-mean-square fluctuation in streamwise direction

U_e streamwise mean-flow velocity at edge of boundary layer

ΔU change of velocity across a shear layer

v velocity normal to wall

$\vec{V}$ mean velocity vector

x coordinate in free-stream direction; distance from leading edge

y distance normal to wall

z spanwise distance

α wave number,

β Falkner-Skan measure of pressure gradient

δ boundary-layer thickness

λ wavelength

ν kinematic viscosity

ω vorticity

Ω mean vorticity

FIGURE CAPTIONS

1.   Instability of inflected laminar profile below critical Re of
     "roughness." Courtesy G. R. Hall (Ref. 19). (Cylinder length/
     diameter 2.5; boundary-layer thickness $\delta \sim 2$ in. and $Re_x \sim 10^6$;
     top of cylinder $\sim 0.25\delta$>smoke layer thickness; small, blocked
     gap under cylinder).

2.   Instability and transition of wake behind a flat plate.
     Courtesy F. N. M. Brown; Univ. Notre Dame; (Plate chord 12 in;
     $Re_c = 230000$; thickness 0.25 in.)

3.   Secondary instability of Blasius layer. Courtesy
     F. R. Hama and J. Nutant (Ref. 48) (Hydrogen - bubble wire
     to left of view, pulse frequence 13.6 sec^{-1}; 0.33 sec.
     between cine' frames;   stimulated TS period 5 sec; $\lambda_{TS} \sim 9$ in.;
     $\delta \sim 1$ in.)

4.   Turbulence wedge produced by roughness.
     Courtesy G. B. Schubauer and P. S. Klebanoff, NACA T. R. 1289.
     Time traces as sensed by hot-wire anemometer.

5.   Growing turbulent spot in plan view. Courtesy
     J. W. Elder (Ref. 31) (Layer downstream of spot on left is
     laminar despite the wiggles in the dye.)

6.   Instability and breakdown in boundary layer of axisymmetric
     ogive-cylinder body. Courtesy
     F. N. M. Brown (Ref. 27) Univ. Notre Dame (Nose at left; flow
     left to right; central smoke streak-tube spreads over body sur-
     face)

7.   Tentative model of roughness-induced linear and nonlinear
     processes leading to turbulence in a boundary layer.

8. Instability map of flat-plate boundary layer in zero and
    mildly adverse pressure gradient.
    Compiled from Wazzan et al (Ref. 53) (δ^* displacement thickness;
    $\alpha_r = 2\pi/\lambda$ $_{TS}$; c_i dimensionless amplification rate)

9. Velocity field in a three-dimensional boundary layer.

10. Instability modes and transition in Ekman layer.
    Courtesy A. J. Faller and R. E. Kaylor (Ref. 3) (4 m.rotating tank;
    bulk velocity V_θ circular $\sim 1/r$ away from rim and center;
    small radial inflow confined to Ekman layer at bottom; δ_E
    based on reaching 0.99 $V_\theta \sim 0.86$ cm; water depth 8 cm.)

11. Type II and gill instabilities and transition in boundary
    layer on bottom of rotating tank.
    Courtesy A. J. Faller and R. E. Kaylor (Ref. 3) (angular rotation
    0.325 sec^{-1}; water depth 15 cm; $\lambda_{II} \sim 7.7$ cm.)

12. Tentative model of systems of instability processes and control-
    ling factors leading to turbulence in viscous wall layers.

REFERENCES

1. Morkovin, M. V., "Critical Evaluation of Transition from
    Laminar to Turbulent Shear Layers with Emphasis on Hypersonically
    Traveling Bodies", forthcoming AFFDL Tech. Rept., early 1969

2. NATO Advanced Study Institute on "Transition from Laminar to
    Turbulent Flow", M. J. Lighthill, Director, Imperial College,
    London, July 1968

3. Faller, A. J. and R. E. Kaylor, "Investigations of Stability
    and Transition in Rotating Boundary Layers", p. 309, Dynamics
    of Fluids and Plasmas: Academic Press, New York, 1966

4. Morkovin, M. V., "Notes on Instability and Transition to
    Turbulence", Von Karman Institute for Fluid Dynamics, Brussels,
    Belgium, 1968

5. Spangler, J. G. and C. S. Wells, Jr., "Effect of Freestream
    Disturbances on Boundary-layer Transition", AIAA Jour., 6,
    543, 1968

6. Gill, A. E., "A Mechanism for Instability of Plane Couette
    Flow and of Poiseuille Flow in a Pipe", Jour. Fluid Mech., 21,
    503, 1965

7. Tani, I., H. Komoda, Y. Komatsu and M. Iuchi, "Boundary-layer Transition by Isolated Roughness", Aero. Res. Inst. Tokyo, Rept. No. 375, 1962

8. Klebanoff, P. and K. D. Tidstrom, "Evolution of Amplified Wave Leading to Transition in a Boundary Layer with Zero Pressure Gradient", NASA Tech. Note D-195, 1959

9. Neumann, R. D., "Thermal Design of Hypersonic Cruise Vehicles-- Problem Areas for Consideration", AIAA Paper No. 68-1087, Oct 1968

10. Plank, P. P. and I. F. Sakata, "Wing Structure Requirements for a Typical Hypersonic Cruise Vehicle", AIAA Paper No. 68-1089, Oct 1968

11. Schadt, G. H., "Aerodynamic Heating Problems and Their Influence on Earth Orbit Lifting Entry Spacecraft", AIAA Paper No. 68-1126, Oct 1968

12. Kline, S. J., M. V. Morkovin, G. Sovran and D. J. Cockrell, Calculation of Turbulent Boundary Layers - 1968 AFOSR-IFP-Stanford Conference. Proceedings, available from Mech. Eng. Dept., Stanford University

13. Abramovich, G. N., The Theory of Turbulent Jets: M. I. T. Press, Cambridge, Mass. 1963

14. Inference from presentations of A. Townsend and L. S. G. Kovasznay in (Ref. 2)

15. Hinze, J. O., Turbulence: McGraw-Hill Co., New York, 1959

16. Townsend, A., The Structure of Turbulent Shear Flow: Cambridge Univ. Press, 1956

17. Grant, H. L., "The Large Eddies of Turbulent Motion", Jour. Fluid Mech., 4, 149, 1958

18. Favre, A. J., "Review on Space-time Correlations in Turbulent Fluids", Jour. Applied Mech., Series E of Transactions of the ASME, 35, 241, 1965

19. Hall, G. R., "Interaction of the Wake from Bluff Bodies with an Initially Laminar Boundary Layer", AIAA Jour., 5, 1386, 1967

20. Betchov, R. and Wm. O. Criminale, Jr., Stability of Parallel Flows: Chapter VIII, Academic Press, New York, 1967

21. Lighthill, M. J., "Aerodynamic Background", Chapter 2 (especially pp. 47-59, 67-72, and 86-102) of Laminar Boundary Layers, L. Rosenhead, Editor: Oxford University Press, 1963

22. Stuart J. T., "Hydrodynamic Stability", Chapter 9 of Laminar Boundary Layers, L. Rosenhead, Editor: Oxford University Press, 1963. Also presentation in (Ref. 2)

23. Sato, H. and K. Kuriki, "The Mechanism of Transition in the Wake of a Thin Flat Plate Placed Parallel to a Uniform Flow", Jour. Fluid Mech., 11, 321, 1961

24. Freymuth, P., "On Transition in a Separated Laminar Boundary Layer", Jour. Fluid Mech. 23, 683, 1965

25. Sato, H., "The Stability and Transition in a Two-Dimensional Jet", Jour. Fluid Mech., 7, 53, 1960. Also, presentation in (2)

26. Morkovin, M. V., "Flow Around Circular Cylinder--A Kaleidoscope of Challenging Fluid Phenomena", Symposium on Fully Separated Flows, p. 102 (ASME Publ., 1964)

27. Knapp, C. F. and P. J. Roache, "A Combined Visual and Hot-wire Anemometer Investigation of Boundary-layer Transition", AIAA Jour., 6, 29, 1968

28. Berger, E., "Suppression of Vortex Shedding and Turbulence behind Oscillating Cylinders", Physics of Fluids Supplement, p. S191, Nov 1967. Also p. 168 of Jahrbuch der Wissen. Gesell. fur Luft and Raumfahrt, 1964.

29. Lin, C. C., "On the Stability of Two-dimensional Parallel Flows", Proc. Nat. Acad. Sci. U. S., 30, 316, 1944

30. Schubauer, G. B. and H. K. Skramstad, "Laminar- Boundary-layer Oscillations and Transition on a Flat Plate", NACA Adv. Conf. Rept., April 1943, later Tech. Rept. No. 909

31. Elder, J. W., "An Experimental Investigation of Turbulent Spots and Breakdown to Turbulence", Jour. Fluid Mech., 9, 235, 1960

32. Klebanoff, P. S., K. D. Tidstrom and L. M. Sargent, "The Three-dimensional Nature of Boundary-layer Instability", Jour. Fluid Mech., 12, 1, 1962

33. Kovasznay, L. S. G. K., H. Komoda and B. R. Vasudeva, "Detailed Flow Field in Transition", Proc. 1962 Heat Transfer and Fluid Mech. Institute, Stanford Univ. Press, 1962

34. Tani, I. and H. Komoda, "Boundary-layer Transition in the Presence of Streamwise Vortices", Jour. Aerosp. Sci., 29, 440, 1962

35. Charters, A., "Transition Between Laminar and Turbulent Flow by Transverse Contamination", NACA T. N. 891, 1943

36. Gaster, M., "On the Flow along Swept Leading Edges", Aero Quart., 18, 165, 1967. Also Jour. Roy. Aero Soc. 69, 788, 1965

37. Pfenninger, W., "Some Results from the X-21 Program; Part I: Flow Phenomena at the Leading Edge of Swept Wings", L. R. Fowell, and P. P. Antonatos, "Part II: Laminar Flow Control Flight Test Results on the X-21A", AGARDograph 97, 1965

38. Liepmann, H. W., "Investigation of Boundary Layer Transition on Concave Walls", NACA W-87 Rept., 1945

39. Smith, A. M. O. and N. Gamberoni, "Transition, Pressure Gradient, and Stability Theory", Douglas Aircraft Co. (El Segundo) Rept. No. ES 26388, 1956

40. Tani, I., "Boundary-layer Transition", Annual Reviews of Fluid Mechanics, Vol. 1, Acad. Press, 1969

41. Gregory, N., and W. S. Walker, "The Effect on Transition of Isolated Surface Excrescences in the Boundary Layer", British ARC, Res. Memo. No. 2779, 1956

42. Mochizuki, M., "Hot-wire Investigations of Smoke Patterns Caused by Spherical Roughness Element", Natural Sci. Reports, Ochanomizu Univ., Tokyo, Japan, Vol. 12, No. 2, 1961

43. Mochizuki, M., "Smoke Observation on Boundary-layer Transition Caused by a Spherical Element", Jour. Phys. Soc., Japan, 16, 955, 1961

44. Bennett, H. W., "An Experimental Study of Boundary Layer Transition", Kimberley-Clark Corp. Report, Neenah, Wisconsin, 1953

45. Obremski, H. J. and M. V. Morkovin, "Application of a Quasi-steady Stability Model to Periodic Boundary Layers", submitted to AIAA Jour.

46. Greenspan, H. P. and D. J. Benney, "On Shear-layer Instability, Breakdown, and Transition", Jour. Fluid Mech., 15, 133, 1963

47. Kline, S. J., W. C. Reynolds, F. A. Schraub and P. W. Runstadler, "The Structure of Turbulent Boundary Layers", Jour. Fluid Mech., 30, 741, 1967

48. Hama, F. and J. Nutant, "Detailed Flow-field Observations in the Transition Process in a Thick Boundary Layer", Proc. 1963 Heat Transfer and Fluid Mech. Institute, Stanford Univ. Press

49. Batchelor, G. K., The Theory of Homogeneous Turbulence: Cambridge Univ. Press, 1953

50. Fage, A. and J. H. Preston, "On Transition from Laminar to Turbulent Flow", Proc. Roy. Soc. A. 178, 205, 1941

51. Schubauer, G. B. and P. S. Klebanoff, "Contribution on the Mechanics of Boundary-layer Transition", NACA Tech. Rept. No. 1289, 1956

52. Klebanoff, P., Paper presented partially at the 11th International Congress of Applied Mechanics, Munich, 1964; extra details by private communication.

53. Wazzan, A. R., T. T. Okamura and A. M. O. Smith, "Spatial and Temporal Stability Charts for the Falkner-Skan Boundary-layer Profiles", Douglas Aircraft Co., Report No. DAC-67086, 1968

54. Lin, C. C., "On the Stability of the Laminar Mixing Region between Two Parallel Streams in a Gas", NACA Tech. Note No. 2887, 1953

55. Browand, F. K., "An Experimental Investigation of an Incompressible, Separated Shear Layer", Jour. Fluid Mech., 26, 281, 1966

56. Wille, R., "Beitrage zur Phánomenologie der Freistrahlen", Z. Flugwiss. 11, 222, 1963

57. Kelly, R. E., "On the Resonant Interaction of Neutral Disturbances in Two Inviscid Shear Flows", Jour. Fluid Mech., 31, 789, 1968

58. Komoda H., "Nonlinear Development of Disturbance in a Laminar Boundary Layer", Physics of Fluids Supplement, p. S87, 1967

59. Brown, W. B., "A Stability Criterion for Three-dimensional Laminar Boundary Layers", P. 913 of Vol. II, Boundary Layer and Flow Control, Lachmann, G. V., Editor, Pergamon Press, 1961

60. Gregory, N., J. T. Stuart and W. S. Walker, "On the Stability of Three-dimensional Boundary Layers with Application to the Flow Due to a Rotating Disk", Phil. Trans. (A), 248, 155, 1955

61. Boltz, F. W., G. C. Kenyon and C. Q. Allen, "Effects of Sweep
     Angle on the Boundary Stability Characteristics of an Untapered
     Wing at Low Speeds", NASA TN D-338, 1960

62. Tatro, P. R. and E. L. Mollo-Christensen, "Experiments on
     Ekman Layer Instability", Jour. Fluid Mech., 28, 531, 1967

63. Lilly, D. K., "On the Instability of Ekman Boundary Flow",
     Jour. Atmospheric Sci., 23, 481, 1966

64. Pate. S. R. and C. J. Schueler, "An Investigation of Radiated
     Aerodynamic Noise Effects on Boundary-layer Transition in
     Supersonic and Hypersonic Wind Tunnels", AIAA Paper 68-375, 1968

65. Potter, J. L., "Observations on the Influence of Ambient
     Pressure on Boundary-layer Transition", AIAA Jour., 6, 1907, 1968

BOUNDARY-LAYER TRIPPING WITH EMPHASIS ON HYPERSONIC FLOWS

E. Leon Morrisette, David R. Stone, Allen H. Whitehead, Jr.

NASA Langley Research Center

ABSTRACT

Experiments on the effect of trip geometry, size, and location on the position of transition at local Mach numbers up to 8.5 are presented. The pressure drag of the trip is investigated at local Mach numbers of 4.7 and 5.5. Based on test results, a flow model was constructed which includes trip-produced multiple vortex filaments similar to those found at supersonic speeds that are assumed to be responsible for introducing the disturbances that lead to transition. The Reynolds number based on the distance from the leading edge to the roughness position as well as Mach number and wall-to-total temperature ratio should be considered in choosing the smallest effective trip size. The effect of trip shape on the position of transition at hypersonic speeds is small; however, certain shapes exhibit the advantageous characteristic of having drag coefficients which were relatively independent of roughness height over a restricted range of the variables tested.

INTRODUCTION

Turbulent flow will probably occur on many flight configurations at hypersonic speed. Because present wind-tunnel facilities cannot properly simulate these turbulent flow conditions, methods of artificially producing turbulent flow are being studied. The effect of trip size and location and its resultant effect on the transition position is well documented for subsonic and supersonic speeds. There is, however, a paucity of data at hypersonic speeds, especially data showing the effects on transition of varying the distance from the leading edge of the model to the trip.

33

The problem of tripping the boundary layer at hypersonic speeds becomes more severe for two reasons. In general, the models are smaller due to smaller facilities and the roughness size required for effective tripping increases. This results in the roughness drag being a substantial portion of the overall drag of the model.

The present paper is intended as a guide to the choice of trip size, spacing, and location for Mach numbers to 8.5, and to present the drag of several types of roughness elements at the higher Mach numbers. For configuration testing where drag measurement is a test output, a desirable trip is one which has a low and determinable pressure drag relative to the test vehicle. It will be shown that if the trips are properly sized, the heating-rate distribution agrees well with those obtained with a naturally turbulent boundary layer.

DISCUSSION

Flow Field about Roughness Elements

An understanding of the flow field around and downstream of a tripping element is desirable in determining the mechanism by which these elements promote transition and in assessing the drag of these elements. Based on oil pattern results obtained in the present investigation and from previously proposed flow models for cylindrical protuberances (e.g., Refs. 1 and 2), a proposed flow model for the spherical element is shown in Figure 1. The oil pattern indicates that the flow separates well ahead of the elements.

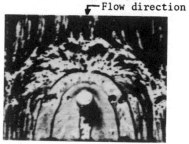

Flow direction

Oil accumulation from vortices

Separation boundary

Sphere

Dead-air region

Flow direction

Oil flow photograph and interpretation

Triple point

Separation shock

Separated region

Simplified flow field schematic
(chordwise cut at center line)

Oil accumulation

Figure 1.- Flow field about spherical element. M_e = 5.5; R_e/m = 6 x 10^6; k/δ =2.

The shock from the separation "wedge" is assumed to interact with a
bow shock wave produced ahead of the protuberance forming a triple
shock point. A group of vortices initiate ahead of the sphere and
pass around the element. (A number of vortices were noted ahead of
a cylindrical protuberance in Ref. 2.) The distinguishing traces
on the oil pattern suggest that three vortex filaments are present
near the surface ahead of the sphere, and physical reasoning suggests
the existence of a fourth vortex. Another filament apparently
initiates around 90° from the stagnation point of the sphere. It
appears that for roughness-induced transition the transition results
from a disturbance introduced by the vortices. The exact mechanism
is not known at this time; however, the vortices may break down and
introduce turbulence directly into the boundary layer as suggested
by Hall (Ref. 3) for incompressible flow. This is a mechanism
similar to that suggested by Van Driest (Ref. 4) for low supersonic
speeds, and indicates that a new mechanism or flow model as suggested
by Van Driest (Ref. 5) for hypersonic speeds is not necessary.

Required Trip Size

The guidelines for choosing an effective trip size are reasonably well established for subsonic flow where a constant value of
Reynolds number, based on roughness height and local conditions at
the top of the roughness in the undisturbed boundary layer, has been
found to be adequate to establish transition at the trip (Ref. 6).
The problem for supersonic and hypersonic flow is complicated by the
number of parameters to be considered in sizing the trip (Ref. 7).
For this flow regime the more important roughness transition parameters can be listed as follows: (1) Local Mach number, (2) roughness-
height Reynolds number, R_k, (3) roughness-position Reynolds number,
R_{xk}, (4) wall temperature, (5) model configuration, (6) pressure
gradient, (7) type of roughness, and (8) spacing of roughness.

Since the present discussion is limited to roughness-induced
boundary-layer transition on sharp cones and flat plates (or hollow
cylinders), the effect of pressure gradient is not included herein.

Definitions. The effect of roughness-induced transition for
both the sharp cone and the flat plate at different Mach numbers
is characterized in Figure 2. By placing the roughness elements
far forward of natural transition and increasing the unit Reynolds
number (Re) beyond some minimum value, transition moves rapidly
forward until, finally, further increase in unit Reynolds number
results in only slight movement of transition, as can be seen in
Figure 2(a) for roughness-induced transition on a cone (Ref. 4).
The value of R_k in the bend (or knee) of the transition curve is
taken to be the effective value and is designated $R_{k,eff}$. The value
of $R_{k,eff}$ for low supersonic Mach numbers is clearly defined as shown
by Figure 2; however, as Mach number increases, this movement of

transition becomes more gradual. For example, as shown in Figure 2(a) for the flat plate at Mach 6.0, it becomes increasingly more difficult to define $R_{k,eff}$. By holding unit Reynolds number constant and varying k, $R_{k,eff}$ can be more clearly defined (see Fig. 2(b)), than by holding k constant and varying the unit Reynolds number.

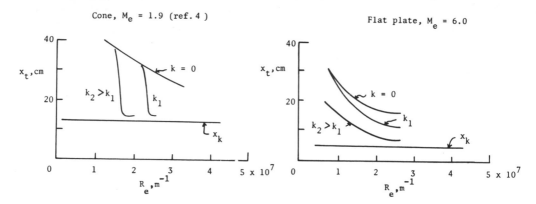

(a)   Transition position for various roughness heights.

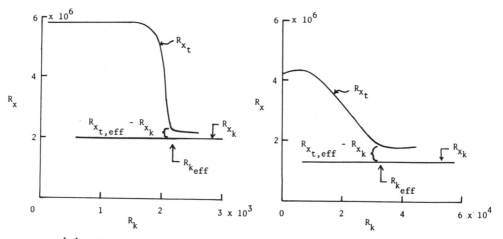

(b)   Transition Reynolds number as a function of trip Reynolds number - constant unit Reynolds number.

Figure 2.- Comparison of low supersonic trip-induced transition data with hypersonic data.

Minimum distance from trip to transition. Not only does the movement of transition become more gradual with increasing R_k at the higher Mach numbers, but the difference between the trip position Reynolds number and the transition Reynolds number ($R_{xt,eff} - R_{xk}$) increases. This increase is shown in Figure 3 for

the existing transition data on both cones and flat plates. Note
that the point of transition can be moved much closer to the trip
location for the flat plate than for a cone, especially at Mach
numbers above 4. The most recent data at Mach 8.5 indicate that this
difference Reynolds number increases as R_{x_k} decreases, at least,
at the higher Mach numbers.

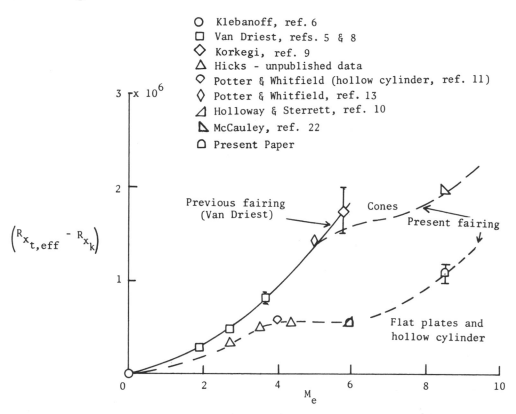

Figure 3.- Variation of Reynolds number based on distance
from trip to transition with Mach number. $R_{x_{to}} \gg R_{x_t}$.

        The results in Figure 3 are a further indication that the
mechanism of trip-induced transition is similar for supersonic and
hypersonic speeds. Van Driest's original suggestion (Ref. 5) that a
different mechanism was necessary was based on his observation that
the fairing shown on the figure through his data (originally presented in Ref. 8) and that of Korkegi (Ref. 9) at M = 5.8 was much
higher than the existing Mach 6 data (Ref. 10). It should be noted
that for the data of Korkegi, tripping of the boundary layer was
caused by disturbances introduced by tunnel sidewall contamination
and not by roughness. The existing data for cones at Mach numbers
up to 5 follow closely the fairing of Van Driest. It is apparent

that, in this form at least, flat plate and cone data cannot be combined since there are large quantitative variations between the results obtained on these two configurations.

Effect of spacing. Figure 4 shows the effect of spacing on the transition position immediately behind the elements at Mach 6.

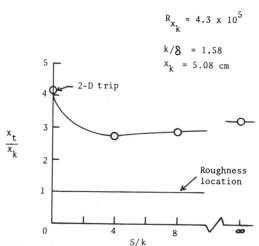

Figure 4.- Effect of roughness spacing on transition position directly behind the element.

A spacing of about four times the diameter of the elements moves transition closest to the trip for a given roughness size; however, transition location is insensitive to space over a large range of spacings, though the spanwise uniformity of the location of transition would be affected by too large a spacing. Note that transition for small trip spacing approaches that for the two-dimensional trip which is less efficient than three-dimensional trips at supersonic speeds (Ref. 11). Thus, a center-to-center element spacing of 4 diameters was chosen for the present investigation.

Effect of wall cooling. The effect of wall cooling has been investigated experimentally on sharp cones at M_e = 2.71 by Van Driest (Ref. 5). The value of $R_{k,eff}$ decreases with wall cooling and by using Van Driest's form for the effect of wall cooling on cones there is obtained (Fig. 5):

$$\frac{R_{k,eff}}{(R_{k,eff})_{aw}} = 1 - 0.81 \left(\frac{T_{aw}}{T_o} - \frac{T_w}{T_o} \right) \qquad (1)$$

Potter and Whitfield (Refs. 11-13) attempted to introduce a temperature parameter using theoretical considerations:

$$R_k' = R_k \, (T_k/T_w)^{\omega+0.5} \tag{2}$$

However, all of their data were taken at adiabatic wall conditions and no actual cool-wall data were used to substantiate their correlation. Their parameter is also shown in Figure 5 and indicates a much more pronounced effect of wall cooling than Van Driest's equation. Unpublished data of Aubrey M. Cary, Jr., at Langley Research Center on a flat plate at M_e = 6.0 are also shown in Figure 5. By first using a known value of $R_{k,eff}$ at Mach 6.0 and

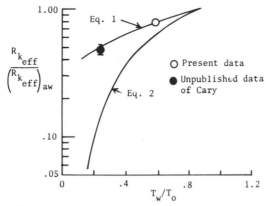

Figure 5.- Effect of wall-to-total temperature ratio on effective roughness size. M_e = 6.0.

T_w/T_o = 0.58, a value of $(Re_{k,eff})_{aw}$ could be determined using Van Driest's equation. Cary's data taken at a T_w/T_t = 0.24 were found to check the trend of Van Driest's equation (eq. (1)), indicating that the equation gives a good prediction of the effect of wall cooling, at least to a Mach number of 6.

Correlation. Figure 6 shows the effect of both Mach number and trip position Reynolds number (R_{x_k}) on the effective trip Reynolds number $(R_{k,eff})$ for both sharp cones and flat plates where all cool-wall data have been reduced to adiabatic wall conditions using Van Driest's equation (eq. (1)). Included in the figure are unpublished flat-plate data of Raymond M. Hicks of the Ames Research Center. $R_{k,eff}$ is found to increase slowly with increasing R_{x_k} and the increase is greater at high Mach numbers and trip position Reynolds numbers (Fig. 6(a)). Figure 6(b) compares values of

$(R_{k,eff})_{aw}$ for cones and flat plates at Mach numbers up to 8.5 for two values of R_{x_k}. Also shown on Figure 6(b) is the curve for Potter and Whitfield's work of Reference 13 which gives the roughness size necessary to move transition to the roughness position. The correlation given in Reference 13 is in a different form than presented in Figure 6(b). An inspection of Figures 3 and 6 indicates that while the values of $R_{k,eff}$ for flat plates are larger than for cones, transition is moved closer to the trip position on flat plates. The configuration (cone or plate) and trip position Reynolds number, as well as Mach number and wall temperature ratio, must be considered in the selection of $R_{k,eff}$ to minimize the drag and the flow distortions behind the trip (Refs. 7, 14).

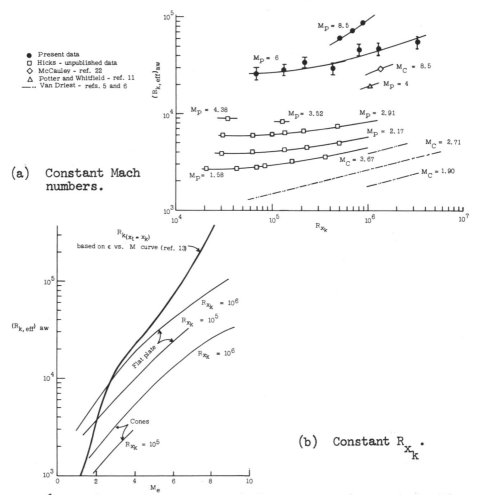

(a) Constant Mach numbers.

(b) Constant R_{x_k}.

Figure 6.- Variation of effective roughness Reynolds number with roughness position Reynolds number and Mach number for spherical roughness elements at adiabatic wall conditions. Subscripts C and P refer to cone and plate data respectively.

The previous discussion has been limited to effective roughness size (the "knee" of the curve). A correlation for the variation of transition position with change in roughness Reynolds
number, R_k, is given by Potter and Whitfield (Refs. 11-13, 15) where
the roughness Reynolds number is modified by the temperature function
previously discussed (eq. (2)). The modified roughness Reynolds
numbers are nondimensionalized by a parameter, ϵ, and then correlated
on a curve such that:

$$\frac{R_k{'}}{\epsilon} = f\left[\sqrt{\frac{x_t}{x_{to}}} - \sqrt{\frac{x_k}{x_{to}}}\left(\frac{R_k{'}}{\epsilon}\right)\right] \qquad (3)$$

The values of ϵ chosen for the data of the present paper presented
in Figure 7(a) (ϵ = 4650 for M_e = 6 and ϵ = 5700 for M_e = 8.5 as
compared with the values suggested in Reference 13 of ϵ = 3850 for
M_e = 6 and ϵ = 8800 for Mach 8.5) seem to give the best fit to the
suggested universal curve of Reference 12; however, the data correlate reasonably well over a wide range of values of ϵ. Also shown
on the figure as shaded symbols are the results of testing various-
shaped roughness elements. There appears to be no significant effect
of trip shape on transition position except for the pyramidal-shaped

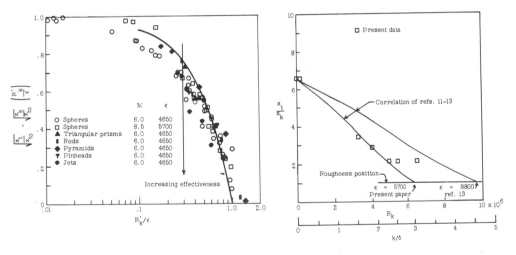

(a) Correlation of data. (b) Correlation used to predict transition
                          position $R_{x_k} \cong 0.9 \times 10^6$, x_k = 4.45 cm,

$$M_\infty = 8.5, \quad T_w/T_o = 0.4.$$

Figure 7.- Present data correlated by the method of Potter and
           Whitfield (Refs. 11-13), R_k for $k/\delta <1$ is based on
           local conditions inside the undisturbed laminar
           boundary layer at the top to the trip.

elements which are consistently poorer trips. One data point for the
pinhead roughness indicates substantially better tripping than the
other types. The reason for this is not known at this time. The
differences in the data for these two roughness types indicate that
a certain amount of volume (or blockage) is necessary at the top
of the trip to generate the flow disturbing vortices. Results obtained using sonic jets as a tripping device are also shown in
Figure 7(a), for which the jet penetration heights given by Torrance
(Ref. 16) are used as the roughness heights. While the jets appear
to be slightly more effective than the other types of trips, this
advantage is within the accuracy of the determination of the jet
penetration heights.

Potter and Whitfield have defined the parameter ϵ as the value
of R_k' for which transition is moved to the roughness position
($x_t = x_k$); however, artificial transition does not move to the
roughness position at hypersonic speeds (see Figs. 2 and 3) even
with the use of very large trips. Therefore, caution should be
exercised in applying the correlation (Refs. 11-13) to determine the
required trip size. This is particularly true at high Mach numbers
where spanwise distortions can become large if the trip size is too
large (Refs. 7 and 14). To better illustrate this, some data from
Figure 7(a) are replotted in Figure 7(b). An inspection of Figure
7(b) indicates that transition will not move to the trip position
even for fairly large trips. If the trip size were chosen on the
basis of R_k' equal to the ϵ given in Reference 13 (or even that
used in the present paper), a much larger trip than necessary would
be chosen which might induce large spanwise effects. For this
reason it is suggested that the effective roughness size ($R_{k,eff}$
in Fig. 6) based on the "knee" of the transition curve be used to
choose the required trip size. The correlation of Potter and Whitfield can be used for determining the transition position for
roughness sizes less than the effective roughness size if the proper
value of ϵ is known.

Element Drag Prediction

A serious problem in the use of tripping elements for force
tests in hypersonic wind tunnels is that the element drag adds an
extraneous and unknown component to the vehicle drag. Several
methods are available to predict element drag at supersonic speeds
(Ref. 18) which are not universally applicable at hypersonic conditions. In addition, a more accurate determination of the element
drag is required at hypersonic speeds because the effective element
size is much larger than the size needed at supersonic speeds. Based
on the results discussed earlier in this paper concerning the effect
of spacing on transition, the roughness drag tests in the present
investigation were tested at a lateral spacing equal to four times

the element width. A sketch of the model used in this investigation is shown in the insert of Figure 8. Two wedge models were employed, one with $\theta = 7.75°$ and the other with $\theta = 12.6°$. Local Mach numbers (M_e) on the inclined surface of the wedges were 5.50 and 4.71, respectively. Base pressure corrections applied to the data were obtained from two measurements made at the base of the wedge models. The elements were placed near the trailing edge of the model so that any skin-friction change due to the elements would be a negligible addition to the measured drag. A laminar boundary layer existed over both models at all conditions tested.

The spherical roughness drag data are shown in Figure 8. The drag of the elements C_{D_C} is obtained by subtracting the measured drag value for the model with no roughness from that value obtained when elements are present on the model. The data are obtained for two size elements at two local Mach numbers and various unit Reynolds numbers. If the drag coefficient is based on local dynamic pressure exterior to the boundary layer and the frontal area of the element, the C_{D_C} data are seen in Figure 8 to correlate with k/δ. Some scatter is evident, but k/δ is evidently the most important parameter.

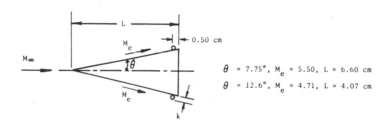

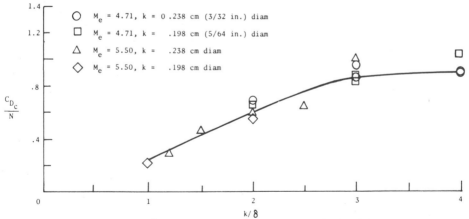

Figure 8.- Roughness drag correlation for spherical elements. $M_\infty = 6.8$. $R_{x_k} = 7.7 \times 10^4$ to 8.3×10^5.

The use of roughness element shapes other than spheres for tripping hypersonic boundary layers is of interest; so the drag characteristics of several other roughness types (triangular prisms, pinheads, and two types of vortex generators) were investigated. Sketches and dimensions of these elements are given in Figure 9. The vortex generators were set at 45° to the flow and were tested in pairs, one element angled to the left and the other to the right. In Figure 7 it was shown that the type of roughness element is not too important in moving hypersonic transition as long as much of the frontal area of the element is near the top. On this basis, the pinhead roughness element was thought to show promise. It was found to have a tripping effectiveness comparable or slightly better than other elements, yet its reduced frontal area suggested less drag.

The results of these tests are shown in Figure 9 for a k/δ range from 1 to 3, where C_{D_c} is based on conditions at the boundary-layer edge and the common frontal area of a circle with diameter equal to the roughness height. The elements generally exhibit the

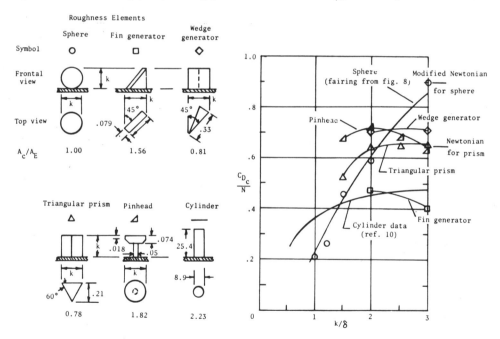

Figure 9   Roughness drag comparison for different element types

M_e = 5.5   k = 0.238 cm (3/32 inch)

All dimensions are in centimeters

R_{x_k} = 7.7 x 10^4 to 8.3 x 10^5

same trend with k/δ, that is, at the lower k/δ values, the drag coefficient shows a rapid initial increase with this parameter; as k/δ increases further, C_{D_C} levels off. The influence of the type of element on the C_{D_C} characteristics in Figure 9 is undoubtedly a result of the flow field about the element. For example, the flow diversion near the base of a sphere should be different from that for triangular prism.

Circular cylinders were not tested in this study, but the cylinder drag curve seen in Figure 9 was obtained from Reference 17 by integrating surface pressure data on the stagnation line of a cylinder placed normal to the surface. The use of a Newtonian pressure distribution around the cylinder was employed in the integration, based on the experimental results of Reference 17. These cylinder data were obtained under turbulent boundary-layer conditions, which could alter somewhat the trend of C_{D_C} for the lower k/δ values.

The major difference between the drag characteristics of the spheres, as compared to the other elements shown in Figure 9, is that over the range of k/δ values most often used for tripping hypersonic boundary layers (i.e., 1.5 to 3), all element types exhibit relatively constant drag values (20 percent change) except the sphere which shows a 100-percent increase in this k/δ range. The sphere drag data approach the inviscid modified Newtonian limit of $C_{D_C} = 0.9$ at $k/\delta = 3$, as indicated by the data fairing in Figure 8. This faired curve is repeated in Figure 9 to facilitate the comparison of the spherical element with the other element types.

Because the value of δ is often difficult to obtain experimentally or predict analytically on complex wind-tunnel models, the data of Figure 9 suggest that if any trip other than spheres is used, k/δ need not be known precisely because of the relative independence of element drag with k/δ. The inviscid Newtonian prediction of the drag coefficient of the triangular prism element is seen to closely predict the asymptotic value of this element type. The pinhead, with its promise as a low-drag trip, produces a drag value comparable to the other element types. The pinhead is thus neither markedly superior in tripping effectiveness nor in its drag characteristics, and is generally more difficult to machine and mount.

The measured incremental drag of sonic jets located on the wedge model was negligible at zero angle of attack. However, there might be normal forces created by the jet thrust, especially at angles of attack. This has not been investigated at this time.

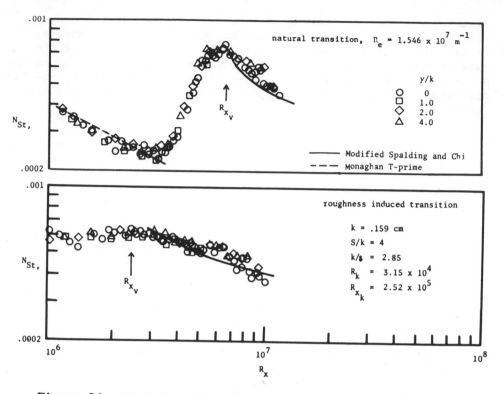

Figure 10.- Heat-transfer distribution without roughness
and with roughness. $M_\infty = 8.5$, $T_w/T_o = 0.4$.

Heat Transfer with Trips

Sterrett, et al. (Ref. 7) at Mach 6 showed that with properly
sized trips (about effective roughness size) the turbulent heating
is close to that from natural transition. They also showed that
if the roughness was large ($k/\delta \approx 5$), distortions occurred in the
heating downstream of the trip. Heating-rate distributions at
$M = 8.5$ on a plate with natural transition and roughness-induced
transition can be compared in Figure 10. Laminar theory (Ref. 19)
and modified Spalding-Chi turbulent theory (Refs. 20, 21) are shown
with the virtual origin for the turbulent theory assumed to be at
maximum heating. The data in each case are about 10 percent higher
than turbulent theory. There are no consistent spanwise differences
in the heating-rate distributions with roughness (Fig. 10(b)) and
the scatter is no greater than with natural transition. Transitional
heating rates with roughness are higher than for natural transition,
as previously reported (Ref. 7).

CONCLUSIONS

The mechanism of tripping at hypersonic speeds is apparently similar to that at supersonic speeds. Oil-flow photographs show that trips produce vortices in the separated region ahead of the trip. This suggests that the breakdown of these vortices introduces turbulence directly into the boundary layer.

The effective trip size for cones is found to be smaller than for flat plates; however, the transition position is moved closer to the roughness position on flat plates.

The type of configuration and the Reynolds number, based on the distance from the leading edge to the roughness position, as well as Mach number and wall temperature ratio, should be considered in choosing the smallest effective trip size. The effect of wall-to-total temperature ratio is found to be less than previously reported by Potter and Whitfield; however, Van Driest's prediction seems applicable at Mach 6.

Caution should be exercised in applying the correlation of Potter and Whitfield to determine the trip size. It is suggested that the effective roughness size data presented in this paper based on the "knee" of the transition curve be used to choose the required trip size. The correlation of Potter and Whitfield can be used for determining the transition position for roughness sizes smaller than the effective roughness size if the value of their roughness parameter is known.

There is only a small effect of trip shape on the position of transition at hypersonic speeds; however, certain shapes exhibit the advantageous characteristic of having drag coefficients which were relatively independent of roughness height for heights that have practical applications. Spheres exhibited the undesirable characteristic of a significant change in drag coefficient with a change in trip height.

NOMENCLATURE

A_c	area of circle with diameter equal to roughness height
A_E	frontal area of given roughness element
C_{D_c}	$\dfrac{D}{q_e A_c}$
D	drag of roughness elements

k   height of roughness element

M   Mach number

N   number of roughness elements

q   dynamic pressure

R_e $\dfrac{U_e}{v_e}$, Reynolds number per m

R_k $\dfrac{U_e k}{v_e}$, trip Reynolds number based on conditions at edge of boundary layer

$R_k{}'$ $R_k (T_k/T_w)^{\omega+0.5}$

$R_{k,eff}$ effective trip Reynolds number

R_x $\dfrac{U_e x}{v_e}$, Reynolds number based on distance from leading edge

$R_{xt,eff}$ Reynolds number based on distance from leading edge to position where boundary layer becomes turbulent for effective trip size

S   lateral spacing between elements, measured center-to-center

T   temperature

T_o total temperature

x   chordwise distance from leading edge

x_k chordwise distance from leading edge to roughness elements

x_t chordwise distance from leading edge to position where boundary layer becomes turbulent

x_{to} chordwise distance from leading edge to natural transition

y   spanwise distance from center line of model

δ undisturbed boundary-layer thickness at the location of roughness element

ϵ correlation parameter (see eq. (3))

θ half-angle of wedge model (see Fig. 7)

v dynamic viscosity

ω coefficient in temperature viscosity relationship

Subscripts

aw   at adiabatic wall conditions

C   cone

k   conditions in undisturbed flow at top of roughness

e   conditions at boundary-layer edge

eff   conditions at effective trip size

P   flat plate

W   wall

∞ free-stream condition

REFERENCES

1. Westkaemper, J. C., "Turbulent boundary-layer separation ahead of cylinders," *AIAA Journal*, Vol. 6, No. 7, 1352-1355 (July 1968).

2. Rainbird, W. J., Crabbe, R. S., Peake, D. J., and Meyer, Dr. R. F., "Some examples of separation in three-dimensional flows," *Canadian Aeronautics and Space Journal*, Vol. 12, No. 10, (December 1966).

3. Hall, Gordon R., "Interaction of the wake from bluff bodies with an initially laminar boundary layer," AIAA Third Aerospace Sciences Meeting, N.Y., N.Y., January 24-26, 1966, AIAA Paper No. 66-126.

4. Van Driest, E. R. and McCauley, W. D., "The effect of controlled three-dimensional roughness on boundary-layer transition at supersonic speeds," *Journal of the Aero/Space Sciences*, 261-271 and 303 (April 1960).

5. Van Driest, E. R. and Blumer, C. B., "Summary report on studies on boundary layer transition for years 1963-64," Space Sciences Laboratory, North American Aviation, Inc., SID 64-2191 (December 1964).

6. Klebanoff, P. S., Schubauer, G. B., and Tidstrom, K. D.,
    "Measurements of the effect of two-dimensional and three-
    dimensional roughness elements on boundary-layer transition,"
    Readers' Forum, National Bureau of Standards, Washington,
    D.C. (June 1955).

7. Sterrett, J. R., Morrisette, E. L., Whitehead, A. H., Jr., and
    Hicks, R. M., "Transition fixing for hypersonic flow," NASA
    TN D-4129 (October 1967).

8. Van Driest, E. R. and Blumer, C. B., "Boundary-layer transition
    at supersonic speeds - three-dimensional roughness effects
    (spheres)," Journal of Aero/Space Sciences, 909-916 (August
    1962).

9. Korkegi, Robert H., "Transition studies and skin-friction
    measurements on an insulated flat plate at a Mach number of
    5.8," Journal of the Aeronautical Sciences, 97-107 and
    192, (February 1956).

10. Holloway, Paul F. and Sterrett, James R., "Effect of controlled
    surface roughness on boundary-layer transition and heat
    transfer at Mach numbers of 4.8 and 6.0," NASA TN D-2054,
    (April 1964).

11. Potter, J. L. and Whitfield, J. D., "Effects of unit Reynolds
    number, nose bluntness, and roughness on boundary layer
    transition," AEDC-TR-60-5, (March 1960).

12. Potter, J. L. and Whitfield, J. D., "Effects of slight nose
    bluntness and roughness on boundary-layer transition in
    supersonic flows," Journal Fluid Mech., Vol. 12, Pt. 4,
    501-535, (1962).

13. Potter, J. L. and Whitfield, J. D., "Boundary-layer transition
    under hypersonic conditions," AGARDograph 97, Part III,
    "Recent developments in boundary layer research," (May 1965).

14. Stainback, P. Calvin, "Some effects of roughness and variable
    entropy on transition at a Mach number of 8," presented at
    the AIAA Fifth Aerospace Sciences Meeting, New York, New
    York, January 23-25, 1967.

15. Whitfield, J. D. and Iannuzzi, F. A., "Experiments on roughness
    effects on boundary-layer transition up to Mach 16," AIAA
    Third Aerodynamic Testing Conference, San Francisco, California,
    April 8-10, 1968, AIAA Paper No. 68-377.

16. Torrence, Marvin G., "Concentration measurements of an injected
     gas in a supersonic stream," NASA TN D-3860, (April 1967).

17. Price, E. A., Jr., and Stallings, R. L, Jr., "Investigation of
     turbulent separated flows in the vicinity of fin-type pro-
     tuberances at supersonic Mach numbers," NASA TN D-3804
     (February 1967).

18. Braslow, Albert L., Hicks, Raymond M., and Harris, Roy V., Jr.,
     "Use of grit-type boundary-layer-transition trips on wind-
     tunnel models," NASA TN D-3579 (September 1966).

19. Monaghan, R. J., "An approximate solution of the compressible
     laminar boundary layer on a flat plate," R.&M. No. 2760,
     Brit. A.R.C., (1953).

20. Spalding, D. B. and Chi, S. W., "The drag of a compressible
     turbulent boundary layer on a smooth flat plate with and
     without heat transfer," Journal Fluid Mech., Vol. 18,
     Pt. I, 117-143, (January 1964).

21. Bertram, Mitchel H. and Neal, Luther, Jr., "Recent experiments
     in hypersonic turbulent boundary layers," Presented at the
     AGARD Specialists Meeting on Recent Developments in Boundary-
     Layer Research, Naples, Italy, (May 10-14, 1965).

22. McCauley, W. D., Saydah, A., and Bueche, J., "The effect of
     controlled three-dimensional roughness on hypersonic laminar
     boundary layer transition," AIAA Paper No. 66-26, (January
     1966).

BALLISTICS RANGE BOUNDARY-LAYER TRANSITION MEASUREMENTS

ON CONES AT HYPERSONIC SPEEDS

Norman W. Sheetz, Jr.

U.S. Naval Ordnance Laboratory

ABSTRACT

A series of tests have been conducted in the ballistics ranges at the Naval Ordnance Laboratory to investigate the effect of a number of parameters on the boundary-layer transition on conical bodies. The parameters investigated include Mach number, cone angle, nose bluntness, and ratio of wall-to-recovery temperature. The tests were conducted on 3-, 5-, 6.3-, and 9-degree half-angle cones. The test Mach number varied from 3 to 15, and the ambient range temperature from 80°F to 800°F. The free-stream Reynolds number based on tip radius varied from near zero to 10^5.

The data show a stabilizing effect on the boundary layer as the free-stream Mach number is increased. In general, the increase in stability with increasing free-stream Mach number appears to be linear. However, when the data are viewed in terms of local properties, the local transition Reynolds number appears to increase with the 3.5 power of the local Mach number over the range investigated.

When the data are presented in terms of constant free-stream Mach number, it appears that the transition Reynolds number is a function of both the tip bluntness and cone angle. The data indicate that decreasing either the cone angle or the tip bluntness increases the transition Reynolds number. By presenting the data in terms of local Mach number, the transition Reynolds number appears to be independent of both the tip bluntness and cone angle.

The effect of the ratio of wall-to-recovery temperature was investigated at free-stream Mach numbers of 3, 5, and 8 on sharp 5-degree half-angle cones. Decreasing the temperature ratio produced

a destabilizing effect at Mach numbers 3 and 8. A destabilizing
effect was also obtained in the Mach number 5 tests at the higher
temperature ratios investigated. However, at temperature ratios
below approximately 0.13 it was observed that further decreases in
temperature ratio stabilized the boundary layer.

INTRODUCTION

Boundary-layer transition is influenced by a number of parameters. Some of the more important parameters include Mach number,
bluntness, heat-transfer rate, surface roughness, and angle of
attack. Due to the importance of boundary-layer transition in a
number of problems such as viscous drag, aerodynamic heating, ablation and mass injection, wake structure, and boundary-layer separation, it is necessary to know the effects of each of these parameters
on transition.

Perhaps one of the most interesting and controversial effects
is that of heat transfer. A theoretical study of a compressible
boundary layer by Lees (Ref. 1) indicated that a stabilizing effect
on the boundary layer is produced by increasing the rate of heat
transfer from the fluid to the body. This result has been generally
accepted in certain flow regimes. In addition, it has been suggested
(Refs. 1-4) that at certain Mach numbers the laminar boundary layer
can be completely stabilized by the presence of an appropriate
amount of cooling of the boundary layer regardless of the Reynolds
number. A large amount of experimental evidence substantiated this
predicted stabilizing effect for moderate rates of cooling (Refs. 5-8).
However, some more recent experiments (Refs. 9-15) have indicated
that this stabilizing effect does not exist at extremely high rates
of heat transfer. In these experiments it was observed that, for
certain test conditions, increasing the heat-transfer rate produced
a destabilizing effect on the boundary layer. This destabilizing
trend, termed "transition reversal," could not be satisfactorily
explained by the early stability theories.

In a recent theoretical investigation, Reshotko (Ref. 16) has
recalculated the temperature ratios required to stabilize completely
the boundary layer by considering the effects of temperature fluctuations and thermal boundary conditions. The recalculated values show
that there are two loops of complete stability in the usual diagram
(Ref. 4) of temperature ratio versus free-stream Mach number. The
trends suggested by the two loops of complete stability tend to
substantiate the experimentally observed "transition reversal"
phenomenon.

In addition to the "transition reversal" observed by some
experimentalists at high heat-transfer rates, a second reversal or
stabilizing trend has been obtained at even higher heat-transfer

rates under certain conditions (Refs. 12, 13, 17). The existence of
this "double reversal" can also be qualitatively explained by the
two-loop stability model defined by Reshotko. While all of the
experimental investigations previously mentioned showed a strong
dependency of boundary-layer transition on heat-transfer rate, a
number of tests (Refs. 18-20) at Mach numbers of approximately 10
have shown little or no dependency on heat-transfer rate.

Another area of controversy is the effect of bluntness on
boundary-layer transition. A number of investigators have observed
a downstream movement of transition as tip bluntness was increased
(Refs. 21-24). This movement has been partially explained by relating the movement of transition location with the reduction of the
unit Reynolds number within the inviscid shear layer caused by the
nose oblique shock. However, in other tests (Refs. 13, 26) both
favorable and adverse effects of bluntness were found, depending
upon both the shape and size of bluntness used.

The effect of Mach number on boundary-layer transition is also
of great importance. Some experimental wind-tunnel programs (Refs.
22,27) indicate that the Mach number effect is relatively small at
Mach numbers of less than 4. Other data (Refs. 17-19-28) from a
variety of facilities indicate that the effect becomes much greater
at Mach numbers above 4.

DESCRIPTION OF TESTS

Test Facilities

The tests were conducted in the NOL Pressurized Ballistics
Range (a 3-foot-diameter tube, 350 feet long), and in the NOL 1000-
foot Hyperballistics Range (Ref. 17) (a 10-foot-diameter tube,
1000 feet long). In addition to the "standard" range equipment
and instrumentation, a number of modifications recently have been
made to the ranges to increase the amount of information that could
be obtained.

Both new heating and cooling units have been obtained for the
21-foot-long temperature control section in the Pressurized Ballis-
tic Range. The heating unit has electrical resistance heaters that
are capable of varying the ambient temperature from 80°F to approximately 1200°F. The cryogenics unit uses liquid nitrogen and has an
operating range from 80°F down to approximately -300°F. The temperature control section is equipped with five pairs of orthogonal
data stations. These stations can be independently set to give

divergent shadowgraph, focused shadowgraph, or schlieren photographs.
The section is thermally insulated from the rest of the range by
doors at either end that remain closed until approximately one
second before firing.

Range Models

The models were 3-, 5-, 6.3-, and 9-degree half-angle cones.
The tip bluntness varied from mechanically sharp to a bluntness
ratio of 0.09. A photograph of the test configurations is shown in
Figure 1. The models were held in a soft lexan sabot while launching. The possibility of scratching the model surface with the soft
sabot material while launching has been investigated (Ref. 15) and
is considered very unlikely. A photograph of a typical model and
sabot is shown in Figure 2.

It was desirable to make the models as large as possible to
provide a long surface for boundary-layer observations. However,
the final size was limited by the capabilities of the launchers.
The base diameter varied from 1.2 inches for the Mach number 3 tests
to approximately 0.5 inch for the Mach number 15 tests. Extreme
care was taken to obtain and preserve a smooth surface on the models
prior to launching. The models were constructed of tool steel or
titanium and the surface was finished by grinding. It was found
that center-line average surface finishes of 1 to 6 microinches
could be obtained consistently by this method, and that further
attempts to improve the surface by polishing resulted only in introducing waviness in the surface.

Boundary-Layer Transition Determination

Both the Pressurized Ballistics Range and the 1000-foot
Hyperballistics Range are equipped with shadowgraph and schlieren
stations for flow observations. In general, the range photographs
have sufficient clarity and detail that accurate estimates can be
made of the boundary-layer transition location directly from the
photographs. In the shadowgraphs presented in Figure 3, it can be
seen that the location of boundary-layer transition can be clearly
defined for these test conditions. In these cases the transition
Reynolds number was obtained by measuring the length of laminar
flow in the boundary layer and determining the flow properties, such
as velocity, temperature, and pressure, from test conditions and
trajectory measurements in the range.

In the high Mach number tests, it was often not possible to
determine accurately the location of the boundary-layer transition
directly from the shadowgraph plates for a number of reasons. First,

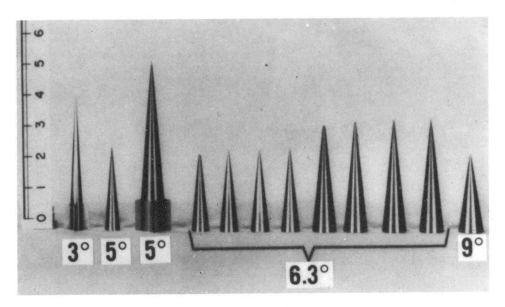

Figure 1.   Test configurations

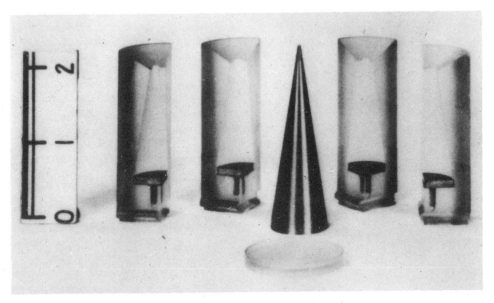

Figure 2.   Range model and sabot

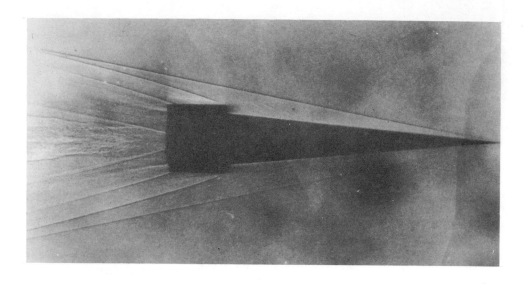

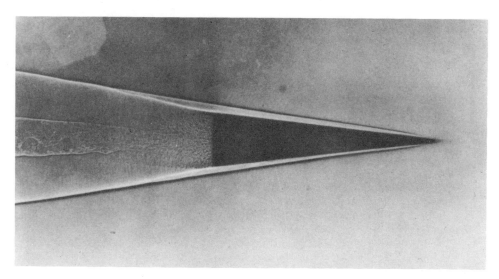

Figure 3.   Range shadowgraphs showing boundary layer transition

on slender bodies flying at high Mach numbers, the bow shock lies
so close to the body surface that the boundary layer is optically
distorted in the range photographs. Also, in order to achieve the
high-launch Mach number, the model size is somewhat reduced. This
also makes it more difficult to see the boundary layer. Finally,
at the relatively high pressures required to produce transition at
hypersonic Mach numbers, the nose region of the models is sometimes
luminous as a result of the extremely high aerodynamic heating rate.
As a result of the luminosity, the range pictures are further
reduced in quality. For these cases, transition was determined by
making a number of launchings over a wide range in Reynolds number
and monitoring changes in the drag coefficient and the nature of
the base flow from test to test. As the flow on the model surface
changed from all laminar, at the lower Reynolds numbers, to transitional, it was possible to detect a notable increase in the drag
coefficient, In addition, it was also possible to determine from
shadowgraphs of the base flow whether transition was occurring on
the body or not. Figure 4 presents shadowgraphs obtained from two
different tests at a Mach number of approximately 15. While details
of the boundary layer cannot be determined from these pictures, it
can be seen that the base flow is laminar in one case and turbulent
in the other. If transition could be seen in the wake, the flow
over the body was laminar. Conversely, a turbulent base flow indicates that transition has occurred on the body. By making a sufficient number of tests at different Reynolds numbers, conditions at
which transition was occurring right at the base of the body can be
determined.

Investigation of Effect of Wall-to-Recovery Temperature Ratio

        These tests were conducted on sharp 5-degree half-angle cones.
Data have been obtained at free-stream Mach numbers of 3, 5, and 8.
In order to vary the ratio of the wall-to-recovery temperature, a
21-foot temperature control section has been constructed for the
Pressurized Ballistics Range. The combination of the heating and
cooling units for this section provides an adjustable range in the
ambient temperature from approximately 160°R to nearly 1600°R.
This provides a possibility of varying the recovery temperature,
and thus the temperature ratio, at a constant Mach number by an
order of magnitude. However, as the ambient temperature is increased,
an increase in the launch velocity must also be made to maintain
a constant test Mach number due to the increase in the speed of
sound with temperature. For the higher test Mach numbers, the
maximum recovery temperature, or minimum temperature ratio obtainable was limited by the launch velocity and not the ambient temperature. After the desired ballistics range temperature and Mach number
are chosen, the ballistics range pressure can be varied to produce
the required unit Reynolds number. The range pressure can be varied

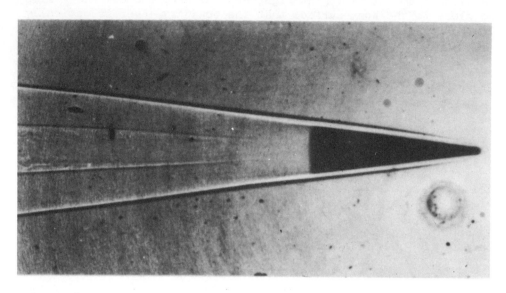

Figure 4a.   Laminar base flow
(θ_c = 6.3°, R_N = 0.036 ", M_∞ = 15, P_∞ = 401 mm Hg)

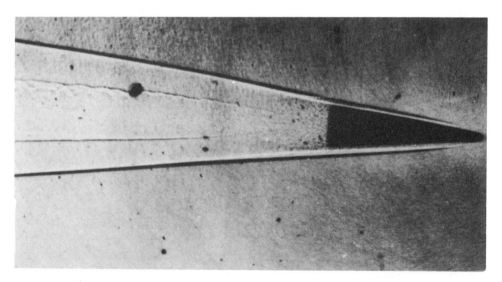

Figure 4b.   Turbulent base flow
(θ_c = 6.3°, R_N = 0.036 ", M_∞ = 15, P_∞ = 401 mm Hg)

from approximately 0.005 atmosphere to nearly 5 atmospheres. This
extremely large variation in free-stream pressure makes it possible
to obtain boundary-layer transition on the test model in any practical test condition.

Investigation of Mach Number and Body Geometry Effect

These tests were conducted on 3-, 6.3-, and 9-degree half-angle
cones with nose-to-base radius ratios of 0.015 to 0.09. Data have
been obtained at Mach numbers from 8 to 15. The tests were planned
so that the effects of Mach number, nose bluntness, and cone angle
could be determined independently of one another.

Series of tests were made with the 6.3-degree cones at bluntness ratios of 0.015, 0.03, 0.05, and 0.09 to determine the effect
of Mach number on boundary-layer transition with a constant body
configuration. Similar series of tests were also made with the
9-degree cones at a bluntness ratio of 0.05. The effect of varying the bluntness for a constant free-stream Mach number was investigated with the 6.3-degree cones at Mach numbers of 10 and 15.
Finally, the effect on boundary-layer transition of varying the
cone angle was investigated at constant Mach number and bluntness
ratio with 3-, 6.3-, and 9-degree cones.

DATA REDUCTION PROCEDURES

Transition Reynolds Number

Local transition Reynolds numbers were calculated, based on
local flow properties and both the length of laminar flow and the
boundary-layer momentum thickness at the location of transition.
They are, respectively:

$$(Re_{s,tr})_1 = \rho_1 U_1 S_{tr}/\mu_1 \tag{1}$$

$$(Re_{\theta,tr})_1 = \rho_1 U_1 \theta /\mu_1 \tag{2}$$

For the sharp cone tests, equation (1) was calculated by measuring
the length of laminar flow directly from the range shadowgraphs
and reducing the measured free-stream velocity, pressure, and temperature to the proper local properties with standard conical flow
tables (Ref. 29). To calculate the momentum thickness used in
equation (2) for the sharp cone tests, Mangler's transformation was
used to relate the cone momentum thickness to the momentum thickness
that would be obtained on a flat plate at the same local flow conditions, as follows.

$$\theta_{CONE} = 1/\sqrt{3} \; \theta_{FLAT \; PLATE} \qquad\qquad (3)$$

By integrating the momentum equation for a flat plate, the flat plate momentum thickness can be expressed in terms of the mean value of the skin friction coefficient.

$$\theta_{FLAT \; PLATE} = C_F \; X \; /2 \qquad\qquad (4)$$

The skin friction coefficient used in equation (4) was obtained from relations developed by van Driest (Ref. 30).

Even for the small amounts of bluntness used in the current blunted cone tests, the local flow conditions are considerably different from sharp cone conditions. For these tests, the transition Reynolds numbers, equations (1) and (2), were calculated by a momentum-integral method described by Wilson (Ref. 31). This method takes into account the curved bow shock wave that exists for slightly blunted slender bodies, and allows a variation in total pressure along the outer edge of the boundary layer on the conical portion of the body. It assumes, however, that the static pressure along the surface is constant and equal to the inviscid, sharp-nosed cone value.

DISCUSSION OF RESULTS

Factors Affecting Transition

While the primary purpose of the present paper is to make a parametric study of the effects of Mach number, bluntness, cone angle, and temperature ratio on boundary-layer transition, there are a number of other parameters that could affect the transition location. These include surface roughness, angle of attack, and ablation.

One of the parameters that has been studied in a great number of investigations is surface roughness. A number of tests (Refs. 22, 32-34) in which the surface roughness was varied in a controlled fashion have shown that transition can be created prematurely by increasing the surface roughness. However, other tests (Refs. 35, 36) show that small roughness can actually produce greater laminar runs than are obtained on a smooth surface. Since it did not seem possible to predict quantitatively the effects of surface roughness for the present tests, it was decided to minimize the effects by making the surface as smooth as practical. This approach seemed appropriate for another reason. At the high rates of heat transfer to the surface of the model that existed in these tests, the boundary layer was relatively thin. This would indicate that the effect of a particular size roughness would be more pronounced than in a case of small or no heat transfer. The maximum size of a discrete roughness protuberance found on the cones was approximately 120 microinches. In general, the maximum roughness height was usually less than 30 microinches. Using an approach presented by Lyons and Levensteins (Ref. 40), an analysis was made to determine if roughness of the order of 120 microinches would be expected to affect transition in the current tests. Using very conservative values, it was determined that for all test conditions the surface roughness was at least an order of magnitude less than that required to trip the boundary layer.

Perhaps the most undesirable element in a ballistics range transition program is control of the angle of attack of the model. For the present tests it was attempted to keep the angle of attack as low as possible. The sabots for the models were designed to give as small an initial angle of attack as possible. The aft portion of all of the models was made hollow, to shift the center of gravity as far forward as possible, and an internal ballast placed in the nose section. In addition, a finned cylindrical afterbody was placed on the back of the slender 3- and 5-degree cones. While in general the models did maintain small angles of attack, occasionally the angles did get sufficiently large to affect the boundary-layer transition drastically. To limit the effect of angle of attack on the present data, only data obtained at angles of attack of less than 1.5 degrees are presented. In general, the angle is less than 1.0 degree.

Due to the combination of high Mach numbers and high range pressures encountered in a number of the tests, the aerodynamic heating rate at times was quite high. This introduced the possibility that the tips of the models under these conditions could get sufficiently hot to melt or ablate. The resulting effect on the boundary layer would be difficult, if not presently impossible, to predict. Fortunately, both the Pressurized Ballistics Range and the 1000-foot Hyperballistics Range have in excess of 24 pairs each of shadowgraph and schlieren stations located along the length of the ranges. The first station is located approximately 40 feet downrange from the launcher. Over half of this distance is blast tank, which is maintained at a low pressure and, consequently, contributes little to the aerodynamic heating. By observing the results from all of the data stations, any change in the transition location as the temperature of the tip region increases can be detected. If a considerable change in transition location occurred during the flight, only data obtained prior to the change are used. Figure 5 shows the location of transition during a flight at a Mach number of approximately 11. At station 10, approximately 55 feet from the first data station, a sharp reduction in the length of laminar flow

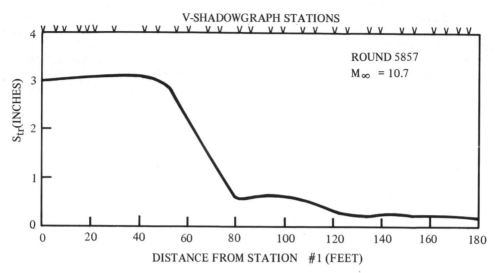

Figure 5.   Forward movement of transition
after tip starts to melt

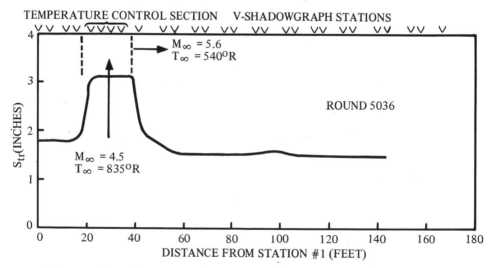

Figure 6.   Movement of transition as model passes through
temperature control section

begins. For this round, only data obtained prior to station 10 were used in the present analysis.

Determination of Transition Results

For nearly all test conditions the location of transition was determined optically from the range shadowgraph and schlieren photographs. Approximately 27 orthogonal pairs of photographs are obtained for each room-temperature test flight. Since there are only five pairs of data stations located within the temperature-controlled section of the range, the number of photographs obtained at elevated or lowered temperature is reduced. Figure 6 shows the movement of transition location as a model enters the temperature-control section of the range and then returns to the room-tempera-ture portion of the range for the remainder of its flight. The transition location was determined by averaging all transition locations obtained at angle of attack below one degree. If the location of transition changed noticeably, due to aerodynamic heating in the tip region, later data were neglected. The location of transition and the accompanying test conditions and calculated local flow properties (Ref. 31) are presented in Tables I and II. At some of the test conditions, the bow shock was so close to the surface of the model that it was not possible to determine the location of boundary-layer transition optically. For these conditions, transition was determined by the "drag and wake method" described earlier.

Effect of Temperature Ratio

The variation in the local transition Reynolds number with the ratio of wall-to-recovery temperature is shown in Figure 7. The dashed curve represents wind-tunnel data obtained at a free-stream Mach number of 3.12 with essentially the same test configuration. The portion of the wind-tunnel data presented shows a strong destabilizing or transition reversal effect on the transition Reynolds numbers obtained by decreasing the temperature ratio. Even though there are some effects of angle of attack reflected in the Mach 3 range data, there appears to be excellent agreement with the wind-tunnel data.

The Mach numbers 5 and 8 range data are also shown in Figure 7. The data points marked by an arrow indicate launchings for which the boundary layer remained completely laminar. In these cases, "minimum transition Reynolds numbers" were calculated and presented based on the length of the model. It should be noted that both the Mach number 5 and 8 data show the same destabilizing effect of increasing the heat-transfer rate. However, an additional effect was noted in the Mach number 5 data.

Table I
Test conditions and transition values
(temperature ratio investigations)

Shot No.	R_B (In.)	M_∞	P_∞ (mm Hg)	T_∞ (°R)	S_{tr} (In.)	$(Re_{\theta,tr})_1$	$(Re_{s,tr})_1 \times 10^{-6}$	M_1	T_w/T_r
4046	.60	3.24	754	821	3.04	688	3.57	3.1	.236
4047	.60	3.26	623	736	3.52	731	3.87	3.1	.261
4048	.60	3.23	630	774	5.32	776	5.62	3.1	.252
4050	.60	3.26	608	715	>6.85		>8.45	3.1	.269
4051	.60	3.17	695	801	2.02	662	2.35	3.0	.249
4056	.60	3.17	755	810	5.36	898	6.68	3.0	.246
4057	.60	3.08	762	779	5.36	785	6.04	2.9	.265
4058	.60	3.15	760	762	4.24	775	5.81	3.0	.264
4059	.60	3.16	755	811	3.18	823	3.96	3.0	.247
4060	.60	2.95	790	897	2.90	707	3.13	2.8	.243
5036	.40	4.53	764	829	3.12	865	5.46	4.3	.145
5037	.40	4.52	749	819	2.95	849	5.25	4.3	.147
5039	.40	5.15	455	535	4.40	1,092	9.23	4.9	.183
5040	.40	5.11	441	536	4.02	1,022	8.11	4.9	.185
5041	.40	4.85	737	770	2.94	843	5.25	4.5	.140
5042	.40	4.85	741	787	2.26	772	4.40	4.5	.137
5043	.40	4.86	600	535	3.51	1,095	9.20	4.5	.201
5049	.25	5.50	932	955	2.66	991	7.67	5.1	.092
5050	.25	5.17	1,224	1,013	2.12	848	5.36	4.9	.096
5051	.25	4.85	899	880	>2.88		>6.07	4.5	.123
5467	.40	4.89	1,051	970	2.38	821	4.98	4.7	.110
5468	.40	5.03	1,183	1,090	1.92	771	4.42	4.8	.093
5469	.40	4.44	893	860	2.55	826	4.91	4.2	.144
5470	.40	4.96	896	870	2.05	802	4.69	4.7	.120
5499	.25	5.20	1,313	1,160	>2.88		>6.94	4.9	.083
5462	.25	7.66	503	535	2.50	1,056	9.32	6.8	.092
5474	.25	8.29	538	533	2.53	1,161	11.56	7.4	.080
5475	.25	7.63	648	660	1.98	935	7.29	6.7	.075

Table II
Test conditions and transition values
(Mach number and body geometry investigations)

Shot No.	θ_c (Deg)	R_N (In.)	R_B (In.)	M_∞	P_∞ (mm Hg)	T_∞ (°R)	S_{tr} (In.)	$(Re_{\theta,tr})_1$	$(Re_{s,tr})_1 \times 10^{-6}$	M_1	$(Re_{R_N})_\infty \times 10^{-4}$	T_w/T_r
5697	5	.005	.4	6.7	428	540	3.3	1025	8.7	6.1	1.1	.116
5699	5	.005	.4	8.3	430	540	4.0	1245	14.2	7.6	1.3	.079
5707	5	.005	.4	8.7	330	540	4.0	1115	11.4	7.6	1.1	.072
5708	6.3	.012	.4	11.1	433	540	2.8	890	6.0	6.5	4.3	.046
5776	6.3	.020	.4	10.3	502	540	1.0	350	0.6	3.7	7.7	.052
5779	6.3	.010	.3	12.8	602	540	2.3	930	7.0	6.8	5.8	.035
5802	6.3	.005	.4	9.9	450	540	3.1	1145	12.1	7.8	1.7	.057
5836	.9	.020	.4	10.2	350	540	1.4	480	1.1	4.3	5.4	.054
5840	6.3	.020	.4	10.4	350	540	1.9	470	1.3	4.6	5.5	.052
5843	6.3	.005	.4	8.3	399	540	3.3	1120	11.1	7.1	1.2	.079
5857	6.3	.005	.4	10.7	472	610	3.1	1150	12.6	8.1	1.6	.043
5874	6.3	.036	.4	10.4	782	610	0.9	320	0.5	3.3	18.5	.045
5881	6.3	.020	.4	6.9	650	540	3.0	940	5.3	4.5	6.7	.110
5885	6.3	.005	.4	11.1	403	540	3.5	1250	15.2	8.4	1.7	.046
5895	3	.020	.2	10.2	520	540	3.0	590	1.9	4.6	8.0	.054

Table III
Test conditions and transition values
(drag method)

Shot No.	θ_c (Deg)	R_N (In.)	R_B (In.)	M_∞	P_∞ (mm Hg)	T_∞ (°R)	S_{tr} (In.)	$(Re_{\theta,tr})_1$	$(Re_{s,tr})_1 \times 10^{-6}$	M_1	$(Re_{R_N})_\infty \times 10^{-4}$	T_w/T_r
D1	6.3	.015	.5	9	290	540	4.2	950	6.8	6.2	2.9	.068
D2	6.3	.015	.5	13.3	280	540	4.2	920	6.8	7.0	4.2	.032
D3	6.3	.005	.3	15	580	540	2.6	1270	16.3	8.9	3.8	.026
D4	6.3	.012	.3	15	460	540	2.6	850	5.6	6.7	6.2	.026
D5	6.3	.020	.3	15	425	540	2.5	630	2.4	5.2	9.8	.026
D6	6.3	.036	.3	15	350	540	2.4	430	1.0	4.1	14.1	.026
D7	9	.031	.625	10	175	540	3.8	730	3.4	5.3	4.1	.055
D8	9	.013	.262	15	390	540	1.6	700	3.3	5.7	5.7	.026

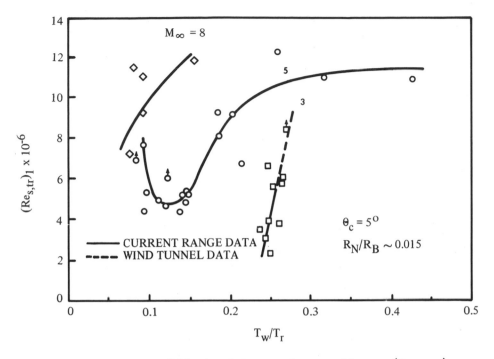

Figure 7.   Effect of temperature ratio on $(Re_{s,tr})_1$

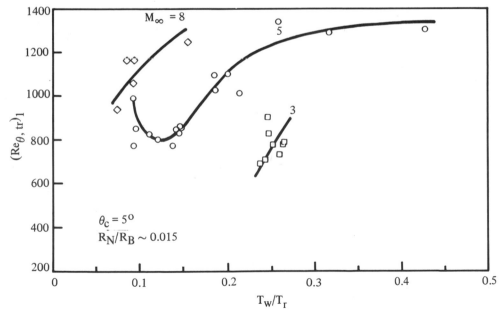

Figure 8.   Effect of temperature ratio on $(Re_{\theta,tr})_1$

The temperature ratio for the Mach number 5 tests varied from
approximately 0.43 to 0.08. For temperature ratios from approximately 0.25 to 0.12, a destabilizing effect of decreasing temperature ratio on transition Reynolds number, very similar to that
observed in the Mach number 3 test, was obtained. However, the
slope of the data as presented in Figure 7 is different, and there
is less scatter in the data. This is partially due to the more
stable finned model used in the Mach numbers 5 and 8 tests. At
temperature ratios of less that 0.13, the destabilizing effect was
not noticed in the Mach number 5 range data. Instead, further
decreases in the temperature ratio produced a stabilizing effect,
or a "double reversal" effect, in the boundary layer. This is
similar to the effect observed by Wisniewski and Jack (Ref. 38)
and by Stetson and Rushton (Ref. 13). However, the double reversal
observed in the current tests was obtained at considerably lower
temperature ratio. For the Mach number 5 tests, no well-defined
effect of temperature ratio can be determined from the present data
at temperature ratios from 0.25 to 0.45. Additional data are
required to define this region better.

Reynolds numbers based on local flow properties and the momentum thickness at the location of transition were also calculated
for the temperature ratio tests. The results of these calculations
are shown in Figure 8. In general, these data show the same trends
as illustrated in Figure 7.

Effect of Mach Number and Body Geometry

The variation of the free-stream transition Reynolds number
with the free-stream Mach number is shown in Figure 9. In general,
it is seen that increasing the Mach number increases the transition
Reynolds number for all configurations investigated. Also, increasing either the tip bluntness or cone angle tends to decrease the
free-stream transition Reynolds number. However, there appears to
be a relatively large amount of scatter in the data when they are
presented in these terms. One possible source of the scatter is
that as the free-stream Mach number is increased the recovery temperature also increases, since the ambient range temperature was
essentially constant for all of these tests. This results in a
variation in the ratio of the wall-to-recovery temperature, which
has been shown to have a strong influence on transition. Another
source of scatter originates from the relatively large variation in
the local Mach number along the surface due to the tip blunting.
Thus, even for a constant free-stream Mach number, the local Mach
number at transition is a function of where transition occurs on
the body.

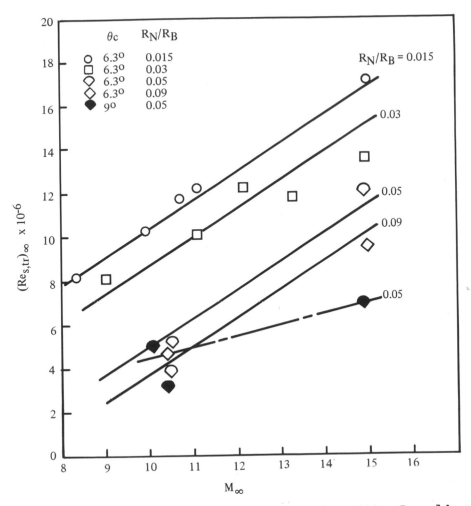

Figure 9.   Variation of free stream transition Reynolds
number with free stream Mach number

The variation of the local transition Reynolds number with the local Mach number at transition is shown in Figure 10. By presenting the data in this fashion, the problems associated with the previous figure can be better understood. First, it should be noted that the local transition Reynolds number at transition has a strong effect on the local transition Reynolds number. In fact, in the region investigated, the local transition Reynolds number varies with approximately the 3.5 power of the local Mach number. The effect of temperature ratio on these data can also be observed. The open symbols represent tests in which the temperature ratio was approximately 0.050. This corresponds to free-stream Mach numbers of about 9 to 11. The half-filled symbols represent temperature

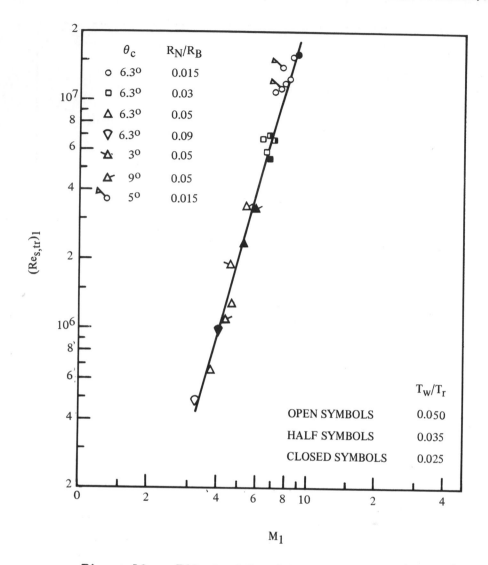

Figure 10.   Effect of local Mach number on $(Re_{s,tr})_1$

ratios of approximately 0.035 and free-stream Mach numbers near 13, while the solid symbols represent the Mach number 15 tests and a temperature ratio of about 0.025. With few exceptions the data vary in an orderly fashion in terms of temperature ratio. A curve has been fitted through the data with a temperature ratio of about 0.035, with the lower temperature ratio data below the curve and the higher temperature ratio data above the curve. Such a pattern shows that for a constant local Mach number the local transition Reynolds number increases with increasing temperature ratio. This is similar to the transition reversal observed on the sharp 5-degree cones at higher temperature ratios and lower free-stream Mach numbers.

Another point of interest that can be obtained from Figure 10 is that for a constant temperature ratio, i.e., constant free-stream Mach number, it does not appear important how the local Mach number at transition is produced. Consider the data obtained at a free-stream Mach number of 10 and indicated by the open symbols. Even though the physical tip bluntness varies by a factor of 6, and the cone angle from 3 degrees to 9 degrees, the data all correlate in terms of local Mach number. Figure 11 presents the variation of the local Reynolds number based on the momentum thickness at transition with local Mach number. A similar, strong dependence of momentum thickness Reynolds number at transition with local Mach number is obtained. Again it is noted that, for a constant local Mach number, increasing the temperature ratio increases the momentum thickness Reynolds number.

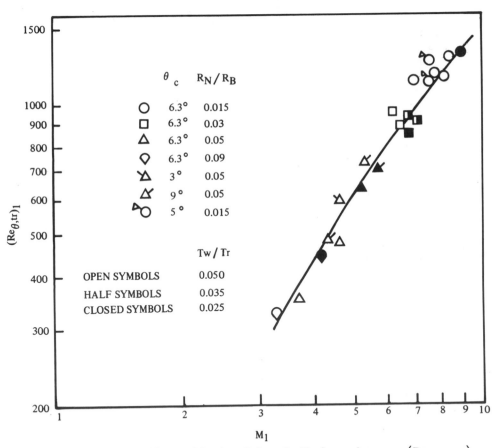

Figure 11. Effect of local Mach number on $\left(Re_{\theta, tr}\right)_1$

The variation of the local transition Reynolds number with the
free-stream Reynolds number based on tip radius is shown in Figure
12. The majority of the data has been obtained with 6.3-degree
cones and is indicated by open symbols. The limited amount of 9-
degree cone data indicated by the solid symbols has been included
for completeness. Note that when the data are grouped in terms of
free-stream Mach number, the local transition Reynolds number is a
function of both the bluntness Reynolds number and the cone angle.
Also the data imply that, as the bluntness increases, the local
transition Reynolds number decreases. This implication will be
discussed more fully later.

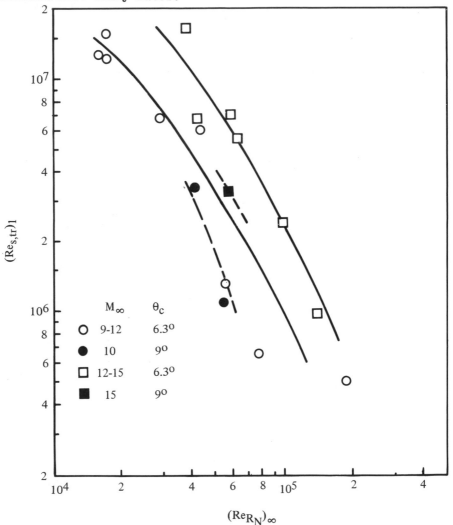

Figure 12.   Effect of bluntness on $(Re_{s,tr})_1$

(expressed in terms of M_∞)

The same data are presented again in Figure 13 and separated
into two groups of essentially constant temperature ratio by a heavy,
dashed line. Above the line and to the right, the variation in the
temperature ratio for the data is only 0.026 to 0.035. The data
shown below the line and to the left were obtained at temperature
ratios from 0.046 to 0.068. The local Mach number at the location
of transition is shown beside each point. If the data are grouped
in terms of local Mach number within each region of essentially
constant temperature ratio, it is seen that the local transition
Reynolds number is no longer a function of either cone angle or

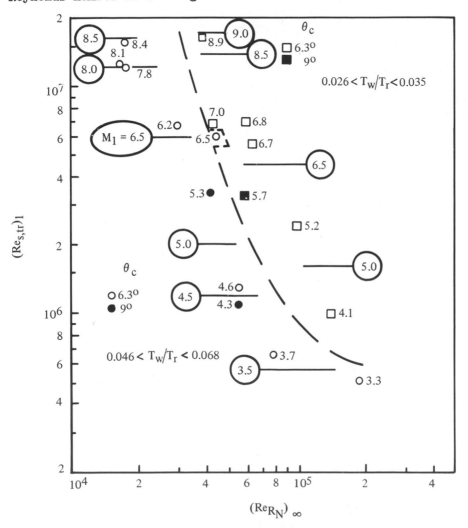

Figure 13.   Effect of bluntness on $(\mathrm{Re}_{s,tr})_1$
(expressed in terms of M_1)

tip bluntness. It can also be seen that for a constant bluntness
Reynolds number large variations in local transition Reynolds numbers are obtained with variations in the local Mach number and
temperature ratio. This indicates that for the range of parameters
considered, varying the bluntness does not change the stability
but only the distribution of local Reynolds number and local Mach
number over the body. That is, the local transition Reynolds number can be correlated in terms of local Mach number and temperature
ratio regardless of bluntness.

     An interesting presentation of bluntness data has been made by
Stetson and Rushton (Ref. 13) in which they show the variation of
the local transition Reynolds number with the ratio of the length
of laminar flow to the entropy gradient swallowing distance. The
swallowing distance is defined by Stetson and Rushton as the distance
along the cone surface from the cone tip to the location where the
outer edge conditions of the boundary layer approach those of an
equivalent sharp cone. It is assumed that these conditions are met
when the local Mach number reaches 95 percent of the cone Mach number. A similar plot for the current data is shown in Figure 14.

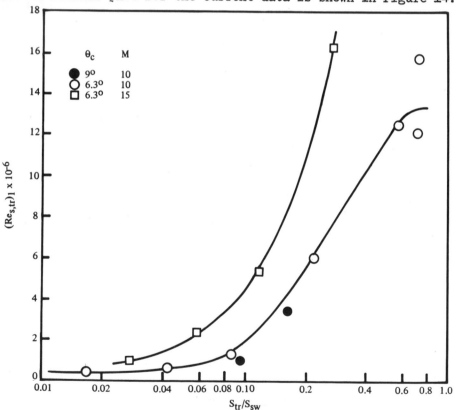

Figure 14.   Effect of swallowing length on local
             transition Reynolds number

Stetson and Rushton defined three types of transition. They are
blunt body transition where transition occurs well within the region
influenced by the curved portion of the bow shock, sharp body transition where transition occurs outside the region influenced by the
curved shock, and an intermediate value. From Figure 14, it appears
that the present data are characteristic of blunt body transition
for S_{tr}/S_{sw} less than 0.05. For the Mach number 15 data, the local
Mach number never exceeds 80 percent of the cone Mach number. This
would indicate that sharp body transition is not obtained in the
current tests at Mach number 15. However, in two of the Mach number 10 tests at values of S_{tr}/S_{sw} greater than 0.6, the local Mach
number was only slightly less than 95 percent of the cone Mach number. Therefore, it is reasonable to consider these points as sharp
body transition, and the curve has been faired accordingly. The
variation of the momentum thickness Reynolds number at transition
with S_{tr}/S_{sw} is presented in Figure 15 and shows a similar variation
as seen in Figure 14.

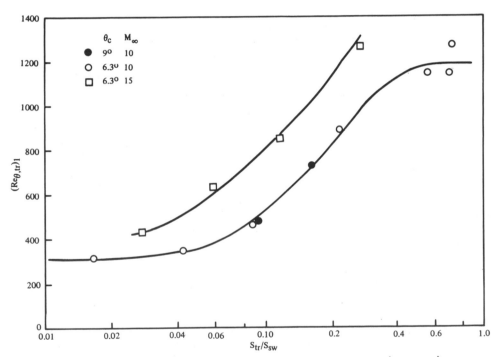

Figure 15.   Effect of swallowing length on $(Re_{\theta,tr})_1$

A compilation of all of the data obtained in these tests is presented in Figure 16. The figure shows the variation of the local transition Reynolds number with the temperature ratio. The data are correlated in terms of local Mach number at the location of transition. It is seen that, in general, the data show a destabilizing or transition reversal trend produced by decreasing the temperature ratio. The exception is the double reversal obtained at temperature ratios below 0.13 in the Mach number 5 tests on the sharp 5-degree cone. It is interesting to note that, if the destabilizing branch of the Mach number 5 tests were extrapolated to the lower temperature ratios, it would correlate with the data obtained on the higher free-stream Mach number blunted cones. This has been done with the dashed curve at $M_1 = 4.7$ in Figure 16.

A similar correlation of the data in terms of the local momentum thickness Reynolds number, local Mach number, and temperature ratio is shown in Figure 17. While curves have been drawn in Figures 16 and 17 describing the relation between local Reynolds numbers and the local Mach numbers at transition over a wide range in temperature ratio, it is realized that considerably more data are needed to define these curves more accurately. However, it is felt that the data are providing a good description of conditions at transition in a region of realistic temperature ratios encountered in free flight, and can be very useful in predicting transition for such flights.

The transition values presented in the previous figures were obtained from the early part of the test flights before any indication of tip melting due to aerodynamic heating was observed. As can be seen in Figure 5, at the higher test Mach numbers and range pressures, some of the models showed definite indications of tip melting in the latter portions of their flights. This was demonstrated both by a very clear forward movement of transition and by an apparent change in the tip configuration as observed in the range photographs. In Figure 18, transition values obtained before tip melting was observed are compared with values obtained immediately after an indication of melting was observed. These later values do not consider any change in body contour due to melting. For selected values of the local Mach number at transition, transition zones have been presented where the upper limit of the zones represents transition Reynolds numbers obtained before melting began and the "lower limit" represents transition Reynolds numbers obtained immediately after an indication of melting was observed. While this "lower limit" does not reflect the maximum effect tip melting can have on transition, it does indicate the degree to which a very small amount of tip melting can influence transition. As can be seen, even these small amounts of tip melting can have a pronounced effect on the boundary-layer stability. In Figure 18, the data have been separated into three plots to prevent an overlapping of zones obtained at different local Mach numbers.

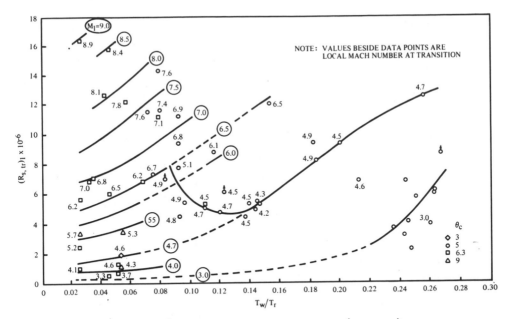

Figure 16. General variation of $(Re_{s,tr})_1$

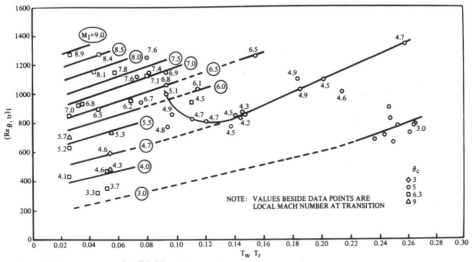

Figure 17. General variation of $(Re_{\theta,tr})_1$

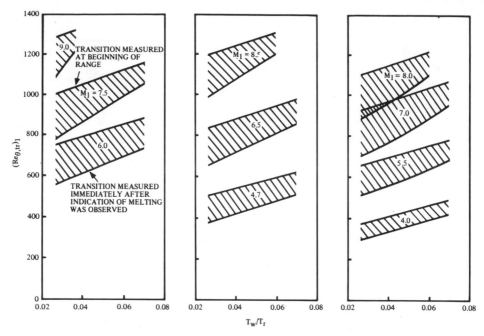

Figure 18.   Effect of melting on transition

CONCLUSIONS

Experimental range tests have been conducted on slender cones to determine the effects of Mach number, cone angle, bluntness, and wall-to-recovery temperature ratio on boundary-layer transition.

The temperature ratio tests were conducted on sharp 5-degree half-angle cones at nominal Mach numbers of 3, 5, and 8. Decreasing the temperature ratio produced a destabilizing, or transitional reversal, effect at all three Mach numbers. However, an additional effect was noted in the Mach number 5 tests. At temperature ratios below 0.12 a stabilizing, or double reversal, effect was produced by further reduction of the temperature ratio.

The investigation of the effects of Mach number and body geometry was made with 3-, 6.3-, and 9-degree cones. When transition is viewed in terms of free-stream quantities, it appears to be strongly affected by free-stream Mach number and body geometry. In general, an increase in the free-stream transition Reynolds number was obtained by increasing the free-stream Mach number. An increase in free-stream transition Reynolds number was also obtained by either decreasing the bluntness or decreasing the cone angle. However, when the results are correlated in terms of local properties, transition appears to be a function of only the local Mach number and the temperature ratio for the test conditions investigated. The local transition Reynolds number, based on wetted length, increases with approximately the 3.5 power of the local Mach number.

As the free-stream Reynolds number based on tip radius is increased, the local transition Reynolds number based on wetted length decreases. This appears to be caused by a change in distribution of local properties as the bluntness is varied. The same decrease is observed in the local transition Reynolds number based on momentum thickness. On the basis of the swallowing length concept described by Stetson and Rushton, it appears that sharp cone transition data were obtained at Mach number 10. Blunt body and intermediate transition data were obtained at Mach numbers 10 and 15.

ACKNOWLEDGMENTS

The author would like to acknowledge the work performed by Messrs. Leonard Crogan and Stuart Hanlein who designed the models and sabots used in these tests. Appreciation is expressed to Miss Amy Chamberlin who performed many of the numerical calculations used in the reduction and analysis of the data, to Mrs. Jeanne Jusino and Mr. David Bixler for assisting in planning and conducting a large number of the tests, and to Mr. Hensel Brown for coding the computer programs used in the analysis of the data.

NOMENCLATURE

C_D	Drag coefficient
C_F	Mean skin-friction coefficient
M	Mach number
P	Static pressure
R_B	Model base radius
R_N	Model nose radius
$(Re_{R_N})_\infty$	Free-stream Reynolds number based on nose radius
$(Re_{s,tr})_l$	Local Reynolds number based on length of laminar boundary-layer flow
$(Re_{\theta,tr})_l$	Local Reynolds number based on boundary-layer momentum thickness

T	Absolute temperature
T_r	Recovery temperature
T_w	Temperature of the model surface
U	Velocity
S_{sw}	Swallowing distance - distance from tip to location where M_1 equals 95 percent sharp cone value
S_{tr}	Length along surface of laminar boundary-layer flow
θ	Boundary-layer momentum thickness
θ_c	Cone half-angle
μ	Viscosity
ρ	Density

REFERENCES

1. Lees, L., "The Stability of the Laminar Boundary Layer in a Compressible Fluid," NACA Report No. 876, 1947

2. van Driest, E. R., "Calculation of the Stability of the Laminar Boundary Layer in Compressible Fluid on a Flat Plate with Heat Transfer," Journal of the Aeronautical Sciences, Vol 19, No. 12, Dec. 1952, pp 801-812

3. van Driest, E. R., "The Laminary Boundary Layer with Variable Fluid Properties," Report No. AL-1866, North American Aviation, Inc., Downey, Calif., Jan. 1954

4. Dunn, D. W., and Lin, C. C., "On the Stability of the Laminar Boundary Layer in a Compressible Fluid," Journal of the Aeronautical Sciences, Vol 22, No. 7, 1955, pp 455-477

5. Higgins, R. W., and Pappas, C. C., "An Experimental Investigation of the Effect of Surface Heating on Boundary-Layer Transition on a Flat Plate in Supersonic Flow," NACA TN 2351, Apr. 1951

6. Czarnecki, K. R., and Sinclair, C. R., "An Extension of the Investigation of the Effects of Heat Transfer on Boundary-Layer Transition on a Parabolic Body of Revolution (NACA RM-10) at a Mach Number of 1.61," NACA TN 3166, Apr. 1954

7. van Driest, E. R., and Bolson, J. L., "Research on Stability
    and Transition of the Laminar Boundary Layer," Report No.
    AL-2196, North American Aviation, Inc., Downey, Calif.,
    Sep. 1955

8. Browning, A. C., Crane, J. T. W., and Monaghan, R. J.,
    "Measurements of the Effect of Surface Cooling on Boundary-
    Layer Transition on a 15-Degree Cone," Part I, Technical
    Note No. Aero-2527, Royal Aircraft Establishment, Farn-
    borough, Sep. 1957

9. Jack, J. R., Wisniewski, R. J., and Diaconis, N. S.,
    "Effects of Extreme Surface Cooling on Boundary-Layer
    Transition," NACA TN 4094, Oct. 1957

10. Diaconis, N. S., Wisniewski, R. J., and Jack, J. R., "Heat
    Transfer and Boundary-Layer Transition on Two Blunt Bodies
    at Mach Number 3.12," NACA TN 4099, Oct. 1957

11. Cooper, M., Mayo, E. E., and Julius, J. E., "The Influence
    of Low Wall Temperature on Boundary-Layer Transition and
    Local Heat Transfer on 2-inch-Diameter Hemispheres at a Mach
    Number of 4.95 and a Reynolds Number per Foot of 73.2 x 10^6,"
    NASA TN D-391, Jul. 1960

12. Richards, B. E., and Stollery, J. L., "Natural Transition
    Measurements on a Cold Flat Plate in a Hypersonic Gun
    Tunnel," Aeronautical Research Council ARC 26405, Dec. 1964

13. Stetson, Kenneth F., and Rushton, George H., "A Shock Tunnel
    Investigation of the Effects of Nose Bluntness, Angle of
    Attack and Boundary Layer Cooling on Boundary-Layer Transi-
    tion at a Mach Number of 5.5," AIAA Preprint No. 66-495,
    Jun. 1966

14. Wilson, Donald M., "Measurement of Hypersonic Turbulent
    Heat Transfer on Cooled Cones," Proceedings of 1966 Heat
    Transfer and Fluid Mechanics Inst., Jun. 1966

15. Lyons, W. C., Jr., and Sheetz, N. W., Jr., "Free Flight
    Experimental Investigations of the Effect of Boundary
    Layer Cooling on Transition," NOL TR 61-83, Sep. 1961

16. Reshotko, Eli, "Transition Reversal and Tollmien-Schlichting
    Instability," Journal of the Physics of Fluids, Vol 6, No. 3
    1963, pp 335-342

17.   Sheetz, N. W., Jr., "Free-Flight Boundary-Layer Transition
      Investigations at Hypersonic Speeds," AIAA Preprint No.
      65-127, 1965

18.   Nagamatsu, H. T., Sheer, R. E., Jr., and Wisler, D. C.,
      "Wall Cooling Effects on Hypersonic Boundary-Layer Transi-
      tion, M = 7.5-15," General Electric Report BSD-TR-66-229,
      Aug. 1966

19.   Deem, Ralph E., and Murphy, James S., "Flat Plate Boundary-
      Layer Transition at Hypersonic Speeds," AIAA Preprint No.
      65-128, Jan. 1965

20.   Sanator, R. J., DeCarlo, J. P., and Torrillo, D. T.,
      "Hypersonic Boundary-Layer Transition Data for a Cold-Wall
      Slender Cone," AIAA Journal, Vol 3, Apr. 1965, pp 758-760

21.   Nagamatsu, H. T., Graber, B. C., and Sheer, R. E., Jr.,
      "Combined Effects of Roughness, Bluntness, and Angle of
      Attack on Hypersonic Boundary-Layer Transition, M = 8.5
      to 10.5," General Electric Res. & Dev. Center Rept.
      65-C-011, Sep. 1965

22.   Potter, J. L., and Whitfield, J. D., "Effects of Unit
      Reynolds Number, Nose Bluntness, and Roughness on Boundary-
      Layer Transition," AEDC-TR-60-5, Mar. 1960

23.   Diaconis, N. S., Jack, J. R., and Wisniewski, R. J.,
      "Boundary-Layer Transition at Mach 3.12 as Affected by
      Cooling and Nose Blunting," NACA TN 3928, Jan. 1957

24.   Brinich, Paul F., "Effect of Leading-Edge Geometry on
      Boundary-Layer Transition at Mach 3.1," NACA TN 3659, Mar. 1956

25.   Moeckel, N. E., "Some Effects of Bluntness on Boundary-
      Layer Transition and Heat Transfer at Supersonic Speeds,"
      NACA Rept 1312, 1957

26.   Brinich, Paul F., and Sands, Norman, "Effect of Bluntness
      on Transition for a Cone and a Hollow Cylinder at Mach 3.1,"
      NACA TN 3979, May 1957

27.   Czarnecki, K. R., and Jackson, M. W., "Effects of Cone
      Angle, Mach Number, and Nose Blunting on Transition at
      Supersonic Speeds," NASA TN D-634, Jan. 1961

28.   Potter, J. Leith, and Whitfield, Jack D., "Boundary-Layer
      Transition under Hypersonic Conditions," AEDC-TR-65-99,
      May 1965

29. Ames Research Staff, "Equations, Tables, and Charts for
     Compressible Flow," NACA Report 1135, 1953

30. van Driest, E. R., "Investigation of the Laminar Boundary
     Layer in Compressible Fluids Using the Crocco Method,"
     Report No. AL-1183, North American Aviation, Inc., Los
     Angeles, Calif., Jan.1951

31. Wilson, R. E. "Laminar Boundary Layer Growth on Slightly-
     Blunted Cones at Hypersonic Speeds," J. Spacecraft Rockets,
     Vol 2, No. 4, Jul.-Aug. 1965

32. van Driest, E. R., and McCauley, W. D., "The Effect of
     Controlled Three-Dimensional Roughness on Boundary-Layer
     Transition at Supersonic Speeds," NAA Report MD 59-115,
     Nov. 1958

33. van Driest, E. R., and Blumer, C. B., "Boundary-Layer
     Transition at Supersonic Speeds - Three-Dimensional
     Roughness Effects (Spheres)," NAA Report SID 61-275, Aug.1961

34. McCauley, W. D., Saydah, A., and Bueche, J., "The Effect of
     Controlled Three-Dimensional Roughness on Hypersonic Laminar
     Boundary-Layer Transition," AIAA Preprint No. 66-26, Jan.1966

35. James, C. S., "Boundary-Layer Transition on Hollow Cylinders
     in Supersonic Free Flight as Affected by Mach Number and a
     Screwthread Type of Surface Roughness," NASA Memo 1-20-59A,
     Feb.1959

36. Holloway, P. F., and Sterret, J. R., "Effect of Controlled
     Surface Roughness on Boundary-Layer Transition and Heat
     Transfer at Mach Numbers of 4.8 and 6.0," NASA TN D-2054,
     Apr. 1964

37. Lyons, W. C., Jr., and Levensteins, Z. J., "The Determination
     of Critical Roughness Height for Boundary-Layer Transition,"
     U. S. Naval Ordnance Laboratory NOLTR 61-87, Dec.1962

38. Wisniewski, R. J., and Jack, J. R., "Recent Studies on the
     Effect of Cooling on Boundary-Layer Transition at Mach 4,"
     Journal of the Aerospace Sciences, Vol 28, No. 3, Mar.1961,
     p 250

AMPLIFIED LAMINAR BOUNDARY LAYER OSCILLATIONS AND TRANSITION AT THE FRONT ATTACHMENT LINE OF A 45° SWEPT FLAT-NOSED WING WITH AND WITHOUT BOUNDARY LAYER SUCTION

W. Pfenninger* and J. W. Bacon, Jr.

Northrop Corporation

ABSTRACT

Transition was observed in the Northrop 7 x 10 ft tunnel at the attachment line of a 45° swept flat-nosed wing with and without suction through closely spaced chordwise slots, starting with an undisturbed laminar initial boundary layer at the apex stagnation point. Wind tunnel screen turbulence induced regular amplified attachment line boundary layer oscillations. Their frequencies correlated with theoretical values for the most strongly amplified attachment line boundary layer oscillations. They were generally modulated and superimposed over random low frequency oscillations induced presumably by free-stream larger scale eddies. Slightly off the attachment line the high frequency boundary layer velocity fluctuations grew to several percent, causing finally turbulent spots in combination with the random low frequency oscillations. Without suction, transition started at $Re_{\theta a.l.T} = 240$ and 310 at $(\frac{WZ}{\nu}) = 5.5 \times 10^6$ and 3.5×10^6, respectively. Boundary layer suction rapidly increased these transition Reynolds numbers. They are substantially higher than in the presence of large disturbances which induce turbulent spots directly. However, $Re_{\theta a.l.T}$ was much lower than on flat plates, explainable by the destabilizing influence of transverse disturbance vortex stretching in the diverging flow field of the attachment line region and the large growth factor $e^{\alpha c_i t}$ of attachment line boundary layer oscillations, resulting from the relatively large C_i and α values $(\alpha \sim \frac{1}{\theta_{a.l.}})$.

*Currently with the Boeing Company

INTRODUCTION, PREVIOUS WORK, FORMULATION OF THE PROBLEM

Turbulent bursts at the front attachment line of swept wings, which cause premature transition on the wing, result either directly from large surface disturbances, residual turbulent attachment line boundary layer and free stream eddies, etc. or from amplified attachment line boundary layer oscillations induced by weak disturbances (free-stream turbulence, noise) or a combination of both types of disturbances. The lowest attachment line boundary layer transition Reynolds numbers $Re_{\theta a.1.T}$ = 90 to 95 (without suction) were observed in the presence of a large attachment line surface roughness or a turbulent attachment line boundary layer at the up-stream end of the attachment line (Refs. 1,2). Relaminarizing the attachment line boundary layer by suction, leading edge extensions, suction fences, etc., delayed spanwise turbulent contamination to higher $Re_{\theta a.1.}$'s (Refs. 1-3). With decreasing disturbance size at the location where laminar attachment line flow was reestablished $Re_{\theta a.1.T}$ increased (Ref. 4). The highest $Re_{\theta a.1.T}$'s ($\sim$240) resulted by eliminating large disturbances which caused transition directly, especially residual turbulent attachment line boundary layer eddies. This was accomplished by laminarized leading edge suction fences (Ref. 4), leading edge extensions, attachment line boundary layer suction, or starting with an undisturbed laminar wing apex stagnation point boundary layer from which the wing is swept back in both directions (Ref. 5). Amplified attachment line boundary layer oscillations induced by wind tunnel turbulence and noise were then primarily responsible for transition (Ref. 5). Due to transverse disturbance vortex stretching in the 3-dimensional diverging flow field of the attachment line region, the attachment line boundary layer, according to Brown (Ref. 7), using Stuart's linearized boundary layer disturbance equations (Ref. 6), is less stable than on flat plates (Figs. 2, 7); furthermore, the small $\theta_{a.1.}$'s lead to large disturbance growth factors $e^{\alpha c i t}$. Therefore, $Re_{\theta a.1.T}$ is substantially lower than on flat plates.

Besides thinning the attachment line boundary layer, area suction changes the shape of the attachment line boundary layer profiles (Fig. 1, Table 1) such as to increase their stability limit Reynolds number with increasing suction (Fig. 2) according to Brown (Ref. 7). To verify the theoretically predicted stabilizing influence of area suction on the attachment line boundary layer of swept wings and better understand the transition mechanism involved, transition experiments were conducted on the aerodynamically smooth attachment line of a 45° swept wing in the Norair 7 x 10 ft tunnel, with area suction in the attachment line region approached by suction through closely spaced chordwise slots.

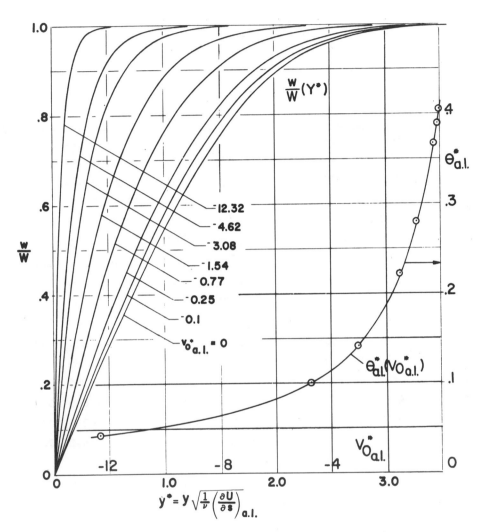

FIGURE 1.   ATTACHMENT LINE BOUNDARY LAYER PROFILES

TABLE I

ASYMPTOTIC SUCTION PROFILES

$$y\sqrt{\frac{1}{\nu}\left(\frac{\partial U}{\partial S}\right)_{a.\ell.}}$$

$$v^*_{o_{a.\ell.}} =$$

$\frac{w}{W}$	0	-0.77	-1.54	-3.08	-4.62	-12.32	-0.1	-0.25
0.9975	3.5424	2.8165	2.2700	1.5636	1.1607	0.4812	3.444	3.290
0.9900	3.0571	2.3618	1.8578	1.2395	0.9054	0.3682	2.961	2.813
0.9775	2.7422	2.0715	1.6003	1.0445	0.7551	0.3036	2.649	2.504
0.9600	2.4962	1.8484	1.4058	0.9014	0.6466	0.2579	2.405	2.264
0.9375	2.2882	1.6625	1.2467	0.7872	0.5611	0.2224	2.198	2.062
0.9100	2.1039	1.5005	1.1103	0.6917	0.4903	0.1933	2.016	1.884
0.8775	1.9354	1.3550	0.9900	0.6091	0.4298	0.1687	1.850	1.722
0.8400	1.7781	1.2216	0.8816	0.5363	0.3768	0.1474	1.695	1.572
0.7975	1.6286	1.0974	0.7824	0.4709	0.3297	0.1285	1.549	1.492
0.7500	1.4843	0.9803	0.6906	0.4116	0.2872	0.1116	1.407	1.293
0.6975	1.3435	0.8688	0.6049	0.3571	0.2485	0.0963	1.270	1.161
0.6400	1.2045	0.7618	0.5243	0.3068	0.2129	0.0823	1.135	1.033
0.5775	1.0660	0.6586	0.4481	0.2600	0.1800	0.0694	1.000	0.905
0.5100	0.9265	0.5584	0.3756	0.2163	0.1493	0.0575	0.866	0.779
0.4375	0.7850	0.4607	0.3064	0.1752	0.1207	0.0464	0.730	0.653
0.3600	0.6400	0.3651	0.2402	0.1364	0.0938	0.0360	0.592	0.506
0.2775	0.4903	0.2714	0.1767	0.0997	0.0684	0.0262	0.451	0.398
0.1900	0.3345	0.1794	0.1156	0.0648	0.0444	0.0170	0.306	0.267
0.0975	0.1714	0.0889	0.0567	0.0316	0.0217	0.0083	0.156	0.135
0	0	0	0	0	0	0	0	0
$\theta^*_{a.\ell.}$	0.4045	0.2971	0.2231	0.1412	0.1008	0.0400	0.3899	0.3669

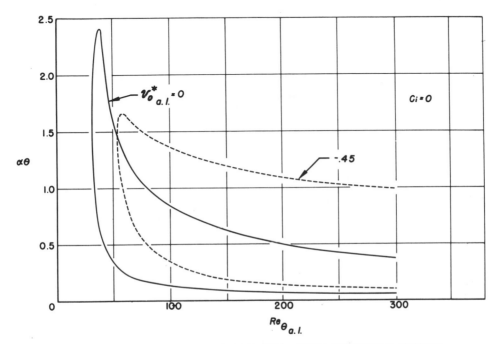

FIGURE 2.   NEUTRAL STABILITY LIMIT REYNOLDS NUMBER
             AT ATTACHMENT LINE OF A 33° SWEPT WING

EXPERIMENTAL SETUP

Figure 3a shows a 3-view drawing of this wing, swept backwards 45° in both directions from a common wing apex stagnation point, where an undisturbed laminar boundary layer started. Figures 3b and 3c show a cross section of the wing and suction slot details. The rather thick flat-nosed wing with a small chordwise velocity gradient $(\frac{\partial U}{\partial s})_{a.1.}$ enabled relatively high $Re_{\theta a.1.}$'s at low tunnel speeds and correspondingly reduced turbulence and noise levels (Ref. 5). To control the attachment line boundary layer along the span, the spanwise suction distribution could be varied by subdividing suction into zones 1 to 5 (Fig. 3a), whose suction rates were individually controlled and measured.

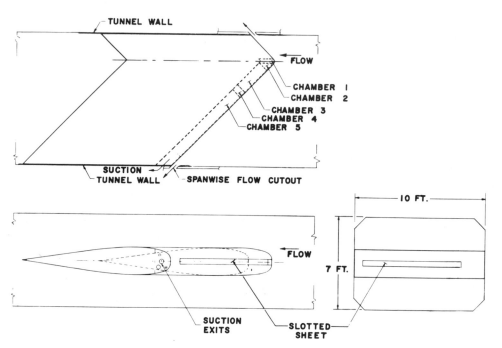

FIGURE 3a   THREE-VIEW DRAWING OF 45° SWEPT FLAT-NOSED WING IN NORTHROP TUNNEL

Suction was applied through 0.002 to 0.0025 inch wide slots of 2.5 inch chordwise length and 0.232 inch spacing. Disturbances due to slot wakes were eliminated by maintaining purely viscous slot wakes; over most of the test region the slot flow Reynolds number was kept below 100, using a single row of suction holes in the plenum chambers. Shallow plenum chambers with two rows of suction holes, located symmetrically with respect to the slot,

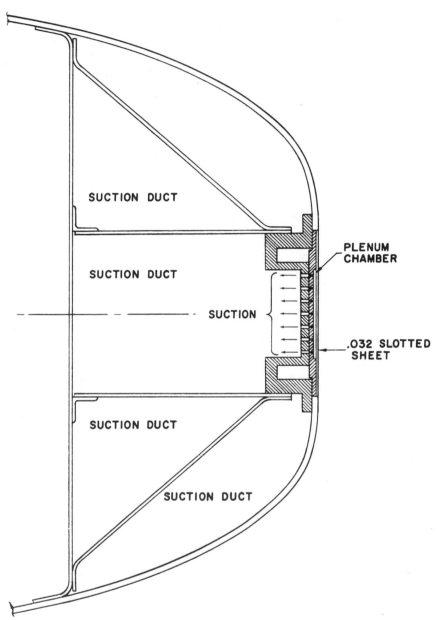

FIGURE 3b   LEADING EDGE CROSS SECTION OF A 45°SWEPT WING

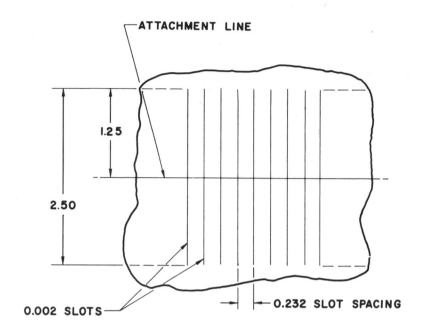

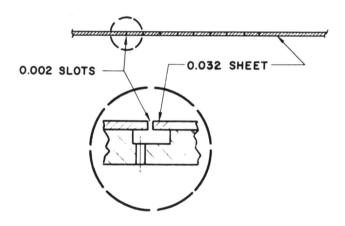

FIGURE 3c   SLOTTED SHEET DETAIL

were used to enable undisturbed slot flow up to slot flow Reynolds numbers of 200, when locally increased suction was required to re-laminarize the attachment line boundary layer, after having become turbulent by surface roughness.

The attachment line boundary layer profiles and $Re_{\theta a.1.}$ were evaluated for various equivalent area suction velocities $V_{0a.1.}$ from the measured W- and $(\frac{\partial u}{\partial S})_{a.1.}$-values, using theoretical results for the fully developed spanwise attachment line boundary layer. Figure 4 shows the measured spanwise pressure distribution along the attachment line. The theoretical spanwise growth of the attachment line boundary layer, starting from zero thickness (corresponding approximately to the case with strong initial suction in zones 1-3), is shown in Figure 5 and Table II, indicating asymptotic attachment line flow within a short spanwise distance.

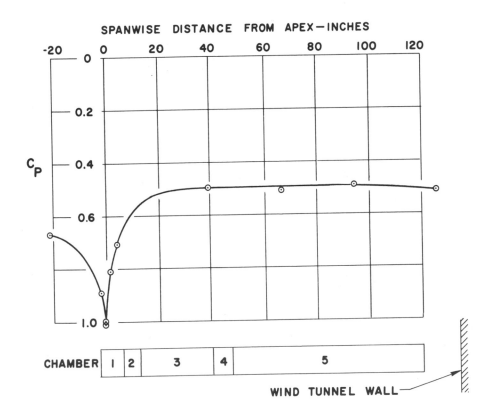

FIGURE 4   SPANWISE PRESSURE DISTRIBUTION ALONG ATTACHMENT LINE

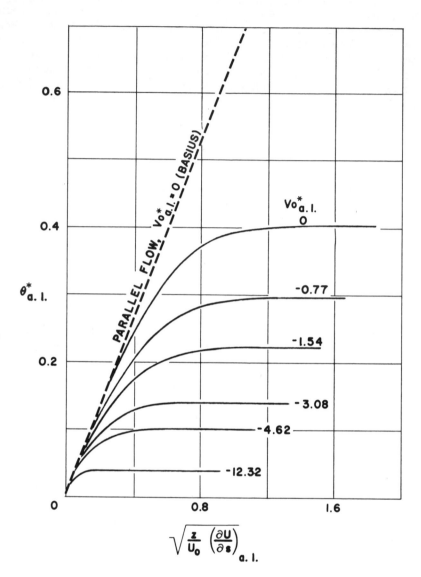

FIGURE 5   ATTACHMENT LINE BOUNDARY LAYER GROWTH FROM
            ZERO THICKNESS (IN SPANWISE DIRECTION)
            45° WING SWEEP

TABLE II

ATTACHMENT LINE BOUNDARY LAYER GROWTH FROM ZERO THICKNESS

$$\theta_{a.l.}\sqrt{\frac{1}{\nu}\left(\frac{\partial U}{\partial s}\right)_{a.l.}}$$

$$v^*_{o_{a.l.}} =$$

$\sqrt{\dfrac{z}{U_o}\left(\dfrac{\partial U}{\partial s}\right)_{a.l.}}$	0	-0.77	-1.54	-3.08	-4.62	-12.32
0	0	0	0	0	0	0
0.0386	0.0256	0.0252	0.0248	0.0240	0.0232	0.0201
0.0772	0.0511	0.0493	0.0476	0.0444	0.0414	0.0299
0.1158	0.0764	0.0724	0.0688	0.0621	0.0561	0.0354
0.1931	0.1257	0.1153	0.1059	0.0897	0.0765	0.0391
0.2703	0.1727	0.1532	0.1363	0.1090	0.0883	0.0397
0.3476	0.2164	0.1861	0.1607	0.1218	0.0948	0.0398
0.4248	0.2560	0.2137	0.1796	0.1301	0.0980	0.0399
0.5021	0.2906	0.2362	0.1937	0.1351	0.0996	0.0400
0.5793	0.3198	0.2540	0.2039	0.1380	0.1002	
0.6566	0.3436	0.2675	0.2110	0.1396	0.1005	
0.7338	0.3631	0.2775	0.2158	0.1404	0.1006	
0.8110	0.3760	0.2845	0.2188	0.1408	0.1007	
0.8882	0.3860	0.2893	0.2207	0.1410	0.1007	
0.9655	0.3928	0.2924	0.2218	0.1410	0.1007	
1.0427	0.3974	0.2944	0.2224	0.1411	0.1007	
1.1200	0.4003	0.2956	0.2228	0.1411	0.1008	
1.1972	0.4021	0.2963	0.2230	0.1412		
1.2745	0.4032	0.2967	0.2231			
1.3517	0.4038	0.2970				
1.4290	0.4041	0.2971				
1.5061	0.4043					
1.5834	0.4044					
1.6607	0.4045	0.2971	0.2231	0.1412	0.1008	0.0400

EXPERIMENTAL RESULTS

Regular sinusoidal laminar boundary layer oscillations were observed by hot wires at several spanwise stations in the attachment line region at various tunnel speeds and suction rates (Fig. 6). They were often modulated and generally superimposed over much slower random fluctuations which, except at large amplitudes, did not seem to be correlated with the high frequency oscillations. In the clean wind tunnel the high frequency oscillations at wing station 110 inch from the apex started at $Re_{\theta a.l.} = 227$ $(v_{oa.l.}^* = 0)$, growing first slowly and increasingly more rapidly as the start of transition at $Re_{\theta a.l.T} = 252$ was approached. At the 47-inch wing station laminar high frequency oscillations started at $Re_{a.l.} = 255$, with $Re_{\theta a.l.T} = 310$ to 320 (growth of the oscillations with $Re_{\theta a.l.}$ see Figure 6a-d). A 0.032-inch diameter turbulence wire mounted vertical to and 36.5 inches upstream of the 25-inch wing station induced the first high frequency oscillations at wing station 110 inch at $Re_{\theta a.l.} = 209$, with $Re_{\theta a.l.T} = 240$. A 45° swept 0.032-inch diameter wire mounted parallel to and 3 feet upstream of the wing induced reasonably regular attachment line boundary layer oscillations at $Re_{\theta a.l.} = 120$, with $Re_{\theta a.l.T} = 155$.

With suction, the high frequency boundary layer oscillations were similar as on the impervious leading edge covered with a thin rubber sheet, indicating that disturbances induced by suction through the 0.232 inch spaced slots could not have caused these oscillations. They rapidly decreased with increasing suction, while the random low frequency oscillations were much less affected by suction. With increasing chordwise distance, s, from the attachment line the high frequency oscillations grew considerably from $\frac{w'}{W} = 1.18$ percent (100 to 5000 c/s) and 1.07 percent (1000 to 5000 c/s) for S = 0 to 3.59 percent (100 to 5000 c/s) and 3.39 percent (1000 to 5000 c/s) for s = 0.8 inch at y = 0.010 inch (wing station 61 inch from apex, $v_{oa.l.}^* = 0$, $Re_{\theta a.l.} = 270$).

Since the high frequency boundary layer oscillations developed only at sufficiently high tunnel speeds and $Re_{\theta a.l.}$ when turbulent wake flow developed downstream of the wind tunnel screens, the observed boundary layer oscillations apparently were induced by the wind tunnel screen turbulence. To verify whether or not they were identical with those predicted by stability theory, the frequency of the experimentally observed regular attachment line boundary layer oscillations was compared with Brown's theoretical frequencies for the most strongly amplified attachment line boundary layer oscillations. Figure 7 shows a plot of Brown's nondimensional oscillation frequency $\frac{\beta r \cdot \nu}{W^2}$ versus $Re_{\theta a.l.}$ for various amplification parameters c_i for the laminar attachment line boundary layer of a 33° swept wing without suction, assuming infinitely small 2-dimensional

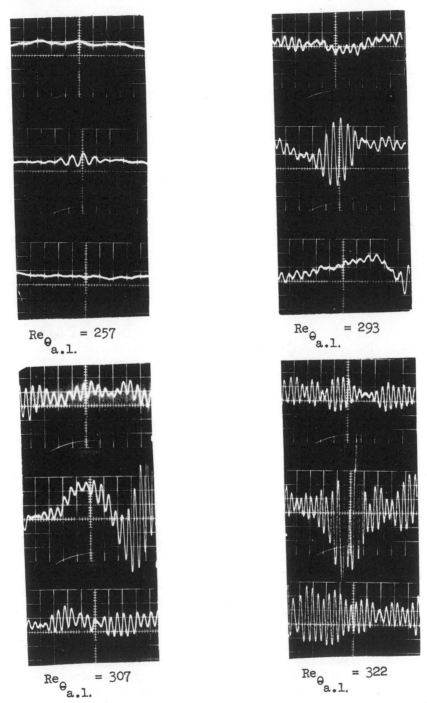

$Re_{\theta_{a.l.}} = 257$ $Re_{\theta_{a.l.}} = 293$

$Re_{\theta_{a.l.}} = 307$ $Re_{\theta_{a.l.}} = 322$

FIGURE 6   HOT WIRE OSCILIATIONS IN LAMINAR ATTACHMENT LINE BOUNDARY
LAYER AT THE 47 INCH WING STATION, NO SUCTION

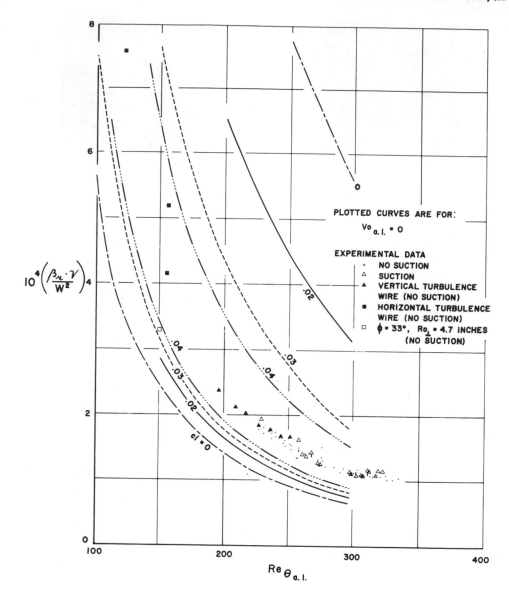

FIGURE 7   COMPARISON OF EXPERIMENTAL BOUNDARY LAYER OSCILLATION
           FREQUENCY WITH STABILITY THEORY

disturbances.   The included experimentally observed frequencies
closely agree with the theoretical values for the most strongly
amplified 2-dimensional attachment line boundary layer oscillations.

Thus, the observed high frequency oscillations apparently are
amplified laminar attachment line boundary layer oscillations induced probably by the small scale wake turbulence of the wind
tunnel screens. Two hot wires, located at the same spanwise station
and displaced by 0.3 inch in chordwise direction, showed no phase
shift; i.e., the disturbance waves were essentially 2-dimensional,
when the oscillations were weak. Phase shifts between the two wires
at larger oscillation amplitudes indicated an increasing 3-dimensional
distortion of the disturbance waves with larger amplitudes.

With increasing $Re_{\theta a.l.}$, for given spanwise distances z from
the apex, the attachment line boundary layer oscillations grew
first slowly and increasingly more rapidly as transition was
approached (Fig. 8). Off the attachment line they grew to larger

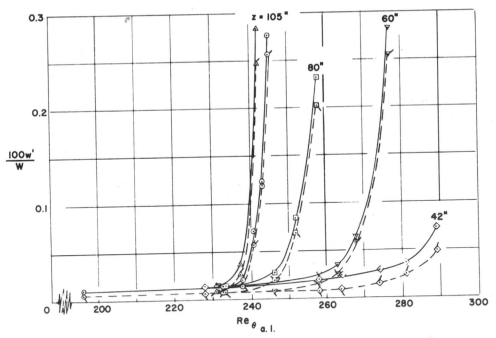

FIGURE 8   VELOCITY FLUCTUATIONS VERSUS ATTACHMENT LINE REYNOLDS NUMBER

amplitudes than on the attachment line itself. The experimentally observed growth of the oscillations seems smaller than that theoretically predicted, partially explainable by the presence of initial low frequency oscillations which did not contribute to amplified boundary layer oscillations. One might question Brown's low stability limit Reynolds numbers and his relatively large c_i-values in the range of amplified oscillations; it is also uncertain what distance Δz to use over which boundary layer oscillations grow. The fact that amplified boundary layer oscillations were previously observed at the attachment line of a 33° swept non-suction wing ($R_{O_\perp}$ = 4.7 inches leading edge radius) at $Re_{\theta a.l.}$ = 150 (Fig. 7) below the minimum stability limit Re_θ = 280 of the same boundary layer profile in parallel flow, indicates that transverse disturbance vortex stretching indeed destabilizes the attachment line boundary layer of swept wings. Experiments with controlled disturbances are desirable to check Brown's theoretical stability limit Reynolds numbers and amplification parameters.

The start of turbulent spots in the aerodynamically smooth attachment line region was observed with hot wires for various tunnel speeds and suction rates at different chordwise distances s from the attachment line. At a given spanwise station, turbulent spots were generally observed simultaneously over the whole attachment line strip, along which turbulent spanwise contamination can develop. Sometimes they were slightly more numerous and of longer duration at larger s-values; i.e., they apparently originated primarily from areas off the attachment line where preceding amplified laminar boundary layer oscillations were strongest. Prior to transition the laminar oscillations at the outer edge of the attachment line strip grew to values comparable with the velocity fluctuations in the following turbulent spot. Thus, turbulent spots apparently resulted from amplified high frequency attachment line boundary layer oscillations induced by wind tunnel screen turbulence in combination with random low frequency oscillations induced presumably by free-stream eddies of larger scale. At higher tunnel speeds and correspondingly increased tunnel turbulence, turbulent spots in the attachment line region could not be fully suppressed by increasing suction. Presumably, when free stream eddies approach the wing stagnation region they may be sufficiently intensified by stretching in aligning their axis of rotation with that of the external flow (according to Schuh) to induce turbulent spots at higher tunnel speeds and $Re_{\theta a.l.}$, in combination with amplified boundary layer oscillations induced by wind tunnel screen turbulence. Such freestream eddies at higher tunnel speeds induce a highly 3-dimensional nonlinear boundary layer disturbance motion with longitudinal disturbance vortex stretching and strong instantaneous velocity fluctuations, against which the change of the mean boundary layer profile by suction is relatively insignificant. Suction then appears ineffective in completely suppressing the formation of turbulent spots induced by such free-stream eddies.

Figure 9 shows $Re_{\theta}a.l._T$ at the start of transition versus the spanwise length Reynolds number $\frac{Wz}{\nu}$ for various nondimensional equivalent area suction velocities $V_{Oa.l.}^*$ in the test region.   The tagged symbols indicate uniform spanwise suction (excluding chamber 1), the regular symbols apply to strong suction in chambers 1, 2, 3 preceding the test region of chambers 4, 5.   The spanwise length z and the corresponding length Reynolds number $\frac{Wz}{\nu}$ were evaluated for an equivalent attachment line boundary layer of constant thickness.   The experimental scatter is probably due to variation of wind tunnel turbulence over the wind tunnel test section as well as temperature fluctuations in the tunnel under different atmospheric conditions.   The highest transition Reynolds numbers were usually observed during cloudy overcast days at lower temperatures early in the morning.

With suction, $Re_{\theta}a.l._T$ increased from 240 at $\frac{Wz}{\nu} = 5.5 \times 10^6$ to 310 to 320 at $\frac{Wz}{\nu} = 3.5 \times 10^6$. With suction, $Re_{\theta}a.l._T$ increased with decreasing $\frac{Wz}{\nu}$ in a similar manner. With increasing suction, $Re_{\theta}a.l._T$ increased rapidly, as long as transition was caused by amplified boundary layer oscillations induced by weak disturbances.

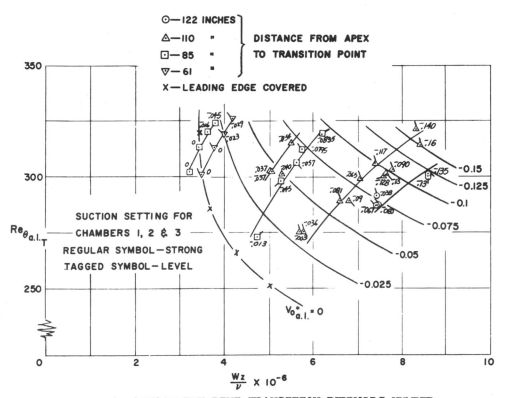

FIGURE 9   ATTACHMENT LINE TRANSITION REYNOLDS NUMBER

With the exception of attachment line transition results on a 33° swept 10 ft chord suction wing in the Ames 12 ft tunnel and Russian flight results on a 35° swept low drag suction wing panel of 4 meters span, the above described $Re_{\theta a.l.T}$-values are substantially higher than previous results. However, $Re_{\theta a.l.T}$ is much lower than on flat plates, explainable by the destabilizing influence of transverse disturbance vortex stretching in the diverging flow field of the attachment line region and the large growth factor $e^{\alpha c_i t}$ of attachment line boundary layer oscillations, resulting from the relatively large c_i and α-values $(\alpha \sim \frac{1}{\theta_{a.l.}})$.

The reported $Re_{\theta a.l.T}$-values are similar to those obtained on the above mentioned 33° swept low drag suction wing ($Re_{\theta a.l.T}$ = 240, $v^*_{oa.l.}$ = 0), with an undisturbed initial laminar attachment line boundary layer established by means of a laminarized leading edge suction fence. The corresponding transition length Reynolds number $(\frac{Wz}{\nu})$ = 17.5 x 10^6, however, was about 3 times larger than in the Northrop tunnel, presumably due to the lower turbulence and noise level of the Ames 12 ft tunnel. Thus, substantially higher attachment line transition Reynolds numbers appear feasible by minimizing external disturbances and the resultant attachment line boundary layer oscillations. Since atmospheric turbulence generally affects transition less than the microscale turbulence of low turbulence tunnels, due to their larger scale, further increased attachment line transition Reynolds numbers appear basically possible in flight, provided aerodynamic and acoustic disturbances generated by the airplane and propulsion system are minimized.

FIGURES

1   Attachment line boundary layer profiles $\frac{w}{W} = f\left[y\sqrt{\frac{1}{\nu}\left(\frac{\partial U}{\partial S}\right)_{a.\ell.}} \right]$

for various nondimensional area suction velocities

$v^*_{oa.\ell.} \equiv \dfrac{v_{oa.\ell.}}{\sqrt{\gamma(\partial U/\partial S)_{a.\ell.}}}$ and nondimensional attachment line

boundary layer momentum thickness $\theta^*_{a.\ell.} \equiv \theta_{a.\ell.}\sqrt{\frac{1}{\nu}\left(\frac{\partial U}{\partial S}\right)_{a.\ell.}}$

versus $v^*_{oa.\ell.} \equiv \dfrac{v_{oa.\ell.}}{\sqrt{\nu\left(\frac{\partial U}{\partial S}\right)_{a.\ell.}}}$

2   Stability Reynolds numbers $Re_{\theta_{a.\ell.}} = f(\alpha\theta_{a.1.})$ at attachment line of 33° swept wing for $v^*_{oa.\ell.}$ = 0, and -0.45

3a   Three-view drawing of 45° swept flat-nosed wing in Northrop 7 x 10 ft tunnel

3b   Leading edge cross section of a 45° swept wing

3c   Suction slot details of a 45° swept wing

4   Spanwise pressure distribution along attachment line

5   Nondimensional spanwise attachment line boundary layer

growth $\theta_{a.l.}^{*} \equiv \theta_{a.l.} \sqrt{\dfrac{1}{\nu} \left(\dfrac{\partial U}{\partial S}\right)_{a.l.}} = f \sqrt{\dfrac{z}{u_0} \left(\dfrac{\partial U}{\partial S}\right)_{a.l.}}$

from zero thickness on 45° swept wing for various $v_{oa.l.}^{*}$.

6a-d   Hot wire velocity fluctuations in laminar attachment line
            boundary layer at the 47 inch wing station, no suction
            1 div. = 0.001 sec   a)   b)   c)   d)

                        $Re_{\theta a.l.}$ 257   293   307   322

7   Nondimensional frequency $\dfrac{\beta r \cdot \nu}{W^2}$ of the experimentally

observed high frequency boundary layer oscillations versus
$Re_{\theta a.l.}$ with and without suction, comparison with Brown's
theoretical dimensionless frequency $\dfrac{\beta r \cdot \nu}{W^2}$ of amplified
attachment line boundary layer oscillations without suction

8   Laminar attachment line boundary layer velocity fluctua-

tions $\dfrac{w'}{W} = f \ (Re_{\theta})_{a.l.}$ without suction at y = 0.010
inch for different z's

9   Variation of $Re_{\theta a.l._T}$ at the start of turbulent spots

versus $\left(\dfrac{Wz}{\nu}\right)_T$ for different $v_{oa.l.}^{*}$.

                        NOMENCLATURE

C_p pressure coefficient based on free stream dynamic
            pressure (with reference to free stream static pressure)

C_i amplification parameter of boundary layer oscillations

$Re_{\theta a.l.}$ momentum thickness Reynolds number at attachment line =
                     $\dfrac{W \theta_{a.l.}}{\nu}$

Re_z length Reynolds number along attachment line = $\dfrac{Wz}{\nu}$

t	time
U	component of potential flow velocity in a plane perpendicular to the leading edge
U_o	component of free-stream velocity perpendicular to the wing leading edge
$\left(\frac{\partial U}{\partial S}\right)_{a.l.}$	potential flow velocity gradient at attachment line perpendicular to the leading edge
s	surface distance from attachment line measured in plane perpendicular to leading edge
$v_{o_{a.l.}}$	equivalent attachment line area suction velocity
$v^*_{o_{a.l.}}$	nondimensional equivalent area velocity $\equiv \dfrac{v_{o_{a.l.}}}{\sqrt{\upsilon\left(\frac{\partial U}{\partial S}\right)_{a.l.}}}$
w	boundary layer velocity
w'	rms boundary layer velocity fluctuation at the attachment line in z-direction
W	potential flow velocity at the attachment line in z-direction
y	normal distance from surface
z	distance along the wing attachment line
ρ	density
$\theta_{a.l.}$	momentum thickness of the spanwise attachment line boundary layer
$\theta^*_{a.l.}$	nondimensional boundary layer momentum thickness $= \theta\sqrt{\frac{1}{\nu}\left(\frac{\partial U}{\partial S}\right)_{a.l.}}$
β_r	angular frequency of boundary layer oscillations
α	wave number of boundary layer oscillations $= \frac{2\pi}{\lambda}$
λ	wave length of boundary layer oscillations
ν	kinematic viscosity

Index a.1.   attachment line

T   start of transition

REFERENCES

1 W. Pfenninger, "Flow Phenomena at the Leading Edge of Swept Wings,"
AGARDograph 97, Part IV, Recent Developments in Boundary Layer
Research, May 1965

2 N. Gregory, "Laminar Flow on a Swept Leading Edge," Second Progress
Report, NPL Aero Memo 12, 1964

3 M. Gaster, "On the Flow Along Swept Leading Edges," College of
Aeronautics, Note Aero 167, 1965

4 W. Pfenninger, "Flow Problems of Swept Low Drag Suction Wings of
Practical Construction at High Reynolds Numbers," Lecture presented
at Subsonic Aeronautics Meeting, New York, April 1967

5 John W. Bacon, Jr. and W. Pfenninger, "Transition Experiments at
the Front Attachment Line of a 45° Swept Wing with a Blunt Leading
Edge," Technical Report AFFDL-TR-67-33, Wright-Patterson Air Force
Base, Ohio, April 1967

6 N. Gregory, J. T. Stuart, and W. S. Walker, "On the Stability of
Three-Dimensional Boundary Layers with Application to the Flow Due
to a Rotating Disc," Philosophical Transactions of the Royal Society
of London, A 248, 1955

7 W. B. Brown, "Stability of the Laminar Boundary Layer at the Attachment Line of a 33° Swept Wing;" Northrop Rep. NCL-68-48R, 1968

8 W. Pfenninger, J. Bacon, and J. Goldsmith, "Flow Disturbances Induced
by Low-Drag Boundary-Layer Suction Through Slots," Boundary Layers
and Turbulence, IUGG-IUTAM Symposium, 1966

THE ONSET OF DILUTE POLYMER SOLUTION PHENOMENA

P. S. Virk and E. W. Merrill

Massachusetts Institute of Technology

ABSTRACT

It is shown that in dilute polymer solution flows anomalous behaviour begins — onsets — abruptly. The experimental evidence concerning onset in turbulent pipe flow is reviewed and the observed effects of flow and polymeric parameters summarized. Theoretical approaches to pipe flow onset are analysed and three types of onset hypotheses are evaluated against experimental data. A semi-empirical correlation is presented for onset in pipes. Onset results are used to derive the ratios of macromolecular/eddy length and time scales. The possible influence of steric factors is noted.

INTRODUCTION

Dilute solutions of high molecular weight polymers frequently exhibit flow phenomena strikingly different from their solvents. This was first systematically demonstrated by Toms (Ref. 1) who showed that in turbulent pipe flow the polymeric solutions required considerably less energy expenditure per unit of volumetric flow rate. Toms' phenomenon in turbulent flow through pipes has since been amply confirmed. Further, dilute polymer solution phenomena — in which these solutions behave very differently from solvent — have been reported in many flow configurations; e.g., smooth pipes (Refs. 2-7), rough pipes (Refs. 8, 9), Couette flow (Refs. 10, 11), spinning discs (Refs. 12, 13), heat and mass transport from pipe walls (Refs. 14-17), Pitot tubes (Refs. 18-20), crossflow heat transfer from wires (Refs. 19, 21).

A noteworthy feature of all dilute polymer solution phenomena is the abruptness of their onset. This is illustrated in Fig. 1 which shows data obtained in our laboratory with 100 wppm of a polyethylene oxide, MW $\sim 6 \times 10^6$, in water. The x-axis on Fig. 1, common to all parts, is average (or free stream) velocity, U; y-axes all represent fluxes relevant to the individual cases. Fig. 1A refers to laminar flow through a capillary. Both with polymer solution and with solvent the wall shear stress increases linearly with average velocity. Both fluids follow Poiseuille's law; the constant, parallel, shift of the polymer solution with respect to the solvent reflects the relative viscosity ($\eta r \sim 1.20$) of the former. Such behaviour is typical; dilute polymer solutions are essentially Newtonian in Poiseuille flow. Figs. 1B, 1C, 1D, show, respectively, the wall shear stress in turbulent flow through a 3.21 cm i.d. pipe; the stagnation pressure attained with a 0.051 cm o.d. square ended Pitot tube; the average heat transfer coefficient from a 0.0025 cm o.d. hot film cylinder in crossflow. In all of these cases a common pattern is evident; at the lowest velocities, results in the polymer solution are practically identical with those in solvent; at the highest velocities, the fluxes in polymer solution are nearly an order of magnitude lower than in solvent. There is a sharp demarcation between the zone of normal, solvent-like behaviour and that of reduced transport. This point of "onset" of dilute polymer solution phenomena is the subject of the present paper. The data of Fig. 1 also point to an interesting generalization - namely that the anomalous effects are only observed in flow configurations with non-vanishing Lagrangian (or material) derivatives; i.e., in cases where a fluid particle (and the macromolecules contained therein) experiences changing conditions in its passage past the region of interest.

Although onsets occur in a variety of flow configurations and there are intriguing commonalities between them (for instance, in Figs. 1B and 1C, the shear rate at the 3.21 cm i.d. pipe wall and the stagnation strain rate on the face of the 0.051 cm o.d. Pitot tube at their respective onsets are about equal), pipe flow is the only configuration for which enough meaningful information is presently available. Our review will, therefore, be limited to onset in pipe flow. In pursuing this review, we will:

(i)   Outline, very briefly, the physics of dilute polymer solution pipe flow.

(ii)   Examine the available experimental onset data and summarize the observed effects of flow and polymeric parameters.

(iii)   Analyse the theoretical approaches taken towards predicting onset, compare them with the experimental findings, and use the results to present a semi-empirical onset correlation.

(iv)   Interpret some aspects of onset in physical terms and
        briefly discuss these.

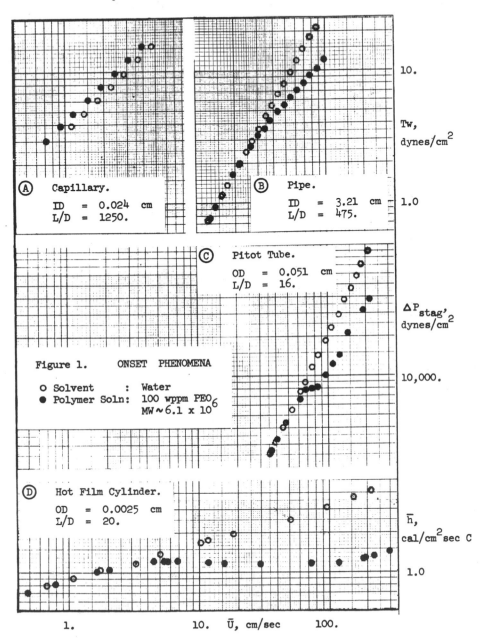

Figure 1.   Onset Phenomena

PIPE FLOW

In order to appreciate the ensueing discussion concerning
onset, a knowledge of the various flow regimes encountered in the
pipe flow of dilute polymer solutions is helpful. These are
illustrated in Fig. 2, a flow diagram — showing wall shear stress,
Tw, vs. volumetric flow rate, Q — obtained by the present authors
for 500 wppm of a polyethylene oxide, MW $\sim$ 0.76 x 10^6, flowing
through a 0.292 cm i.d. pipe. In order of increasing flow rate,
the segments are (Ref. 7):

AT - Laminar flow; the polymer solution obeys Poiseuille's law.
     The parallel shift relative to solvent reflects the slight
     increase in viscosity ($\eta_r \sim 1.20$) caused by polymer addition.

TF - Transition region; this appears as a blank in Fig. 2 since
     the intermittency makes it difficult to obtain stable measure-
     ments. It is interesting to note that at T, the transition
     point, the Reynolds number in polymer solution is, in this
     case, the same as in solvent.

FO - Fully developed turbulent flow without drag reduction; the
     polymer solution exhibits a normal, solvent-like behaviour.

 O - Onset point (superscript * hereafter). This depends both on
     the flow and on the polymeric solute.

OM - Turbulent flow, with drag reduction; the polymer solution
     exhibits Toms' phenomenon. The extent of drag reduction
     depends on polymeric parameters — concentration, molecular
     weight, species, solvent.

MH - Turbulent flow along maximum drag reduction asymptote, inde-
     pendent of polymeric parameters.

It should be noted that Fig. 2 illustrates the completely general
case of drag reduction; often, experimental data do not cover one
or more of the regions described. With respect to onset in particular,
considerable confusion arises when the onset shear stress, Tw*,
lies in the transition region or is lower than the transitional
wall shear stress, Tw_T. In this event (Refs. 22, 23) drag reduction
occurs immediately as turbulent flow is attained, segment FO and
part of OM being absent; in extreme cases transition occurs directly
from laminar flow to the maximum drag reduction asymptote (path ACH).

In neither of the above is an onset point observed, nor can it reliably be estimated; indeed back-extrapolation of polymer solution data to the solvent line in such cases can lead to large errors. For the purposes of this paper we have tried to select, as far as possible, data which exhibit an unambiguous onset — i.e. a region like FO <u>without</u> drag reduction followed by one, like OM, with drag reduction.

Also, Fig. 2 is characteristic of polymer solutions that are dilute in the thermodynamic sense (Ref. 24). Physically this implies a concentration of polymer low enough to avoid any significant overlapping of the individual macromolecular random coils. Practically, the "dilute" criterion amounts to the polymer solution viscosity being less than about twice that of the solvent — $\eta r \leq 2$ — and only such data as comply with this are considered in our review.

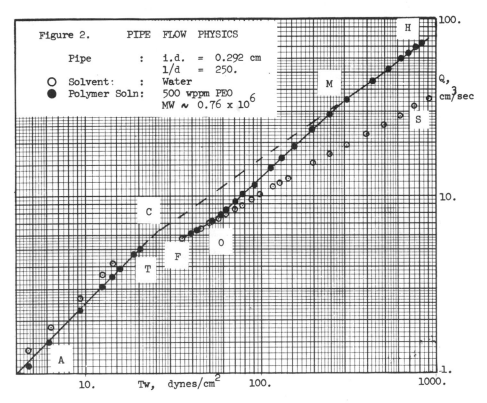

Figure 2.   Pipe Flow Physics

THE EXPERIMENTAL EVIDENCE

The onset point appears indicative of incipient interaction between the turbulent flow field and the macromolecule in solution. In assessing the available experimental information it is therefore desirable to determine separately the dependence of onset on "flow" and "polymeric" parameters. Such parametric dependences as can presently be ascertained are itemized next.

Effect of Flow Parameters

Flow parameters are those required to characterize a Newtonian pipe flow; for instance wall shear stress, Tw, pipe inside diameter, D, and solvent physical properties like density, ρ, and kinematic viscosity, ν.

Wall Shear Stress. The effect of wall shear stress has already been shown in Fig. 2; the onset of drag reduction occurs at a well-defined value, Tw*, termed the onset wall shear stress. Tw* is characteristic of onset; its dependence on other variables will be examined in what follows. Instead of using Tw* directly, it is often convenient to employ a derivative parameter, (Ut^*/ν), that incorporates Tw* via the onset friction velocity, Ut* where $Ut = \sqrt{Tw/\rho}$. (Ut^*/ν) has dimensions of inverse length and will be called the onset wavenumber, Wn*.

Pipe Diameter. The effect of pipe diameter on onset is shown in Table 1, wherein values of Wn* vs. D, derived from four investigations (Refs. 6, 7, 13, 25), are listed. For each of the three polymer-solvent combinations the variation in Wn* is small compared with the range of D, indicating that the onset wavenumber is approximately independent of pipe diameter.

Solvent Physical Properties. Drag reduction has been reported in a variety of solvents. However, most of these have been "thin" liquids with physical properties affecting flow, ν and ρ, essentially akin to water. Hence no obvious trends can presently be discerned. It is worth pointing out, though, that the effect of a solvent is complicated by the fact that it influences drag reduction both through its physical properties, which affect the flow, and its chemical structure which affects the macromolecule in solution. This latter aspect is considered in the following section.

TABLE 1   EFFECT OF PIPE DIAMETER

Polymer Solvent MW x 10^{-6}	PEO Water 6.0		GGM Water 0.60		PMM Toluene 1.02	
	Dia	(u_T^*/ν)	Dia	(u_T^*/ν)	Dia	(u_T^*/ν)
	0.292	MDR	1.22	700	0.081	2900
	0.945	240	2.22	700	0.117	2300
	3.210	210	3.22	690	1.290	3000
	5.080	140	5.07	690	2.540	2200
Source	(7,25)		(13)		(6)	

Note: Pipe diameters are in cm.

Units of (u_T^*/ν) are cm^{-1}.

MDR indicates that maximum drag reduction
asymptote was followed without onset.

Effect of Polymeric Parameters

The polymeric parameters that have investigated in
connection with onset are concentration, molecular weight, monomeric
unit, and solvent power. While these would seem to describe a
dilute polymer solution completely, the properties explicitly relevant
to drag reduction are not yet clear.

Concentration. Fig. 3. shows data obtained by four separate investigators (Refs. 1, 13, 25, 26) under widely different circumstances.
In each case, polymer concentration is the only variable, pipe
diameter and polymer/solution combination being fixed. Further,
even the highest concentrations qualify as being "dilute."
It may be observed that concentration variations from 10 to 100
fold do not significantly alter the value of the onset shear stress,
Tw*, or the onset wavenumber (Ut*/ν). This concentration independence of onset is particularly significant in that it permits
the direct association of Tw* with a given polymer/solvent pair.
However, two reservations should be kept in mind. First, despite
the impressive range of concentrations over which Tw* is constant,
the behaviour at exceedingly low concentrations C → 0, is still
uncertain owing to experimental difficulties. Second, the characteristic concentration independent Tw* type of behaviour is
universally exhibited by solutions of random-coiling polymers
but there is some indication (Ref. 14) that solutions of weak polyelectrolytes (e.g. substituted poly-acrylic acid derivatives)
behave differently.

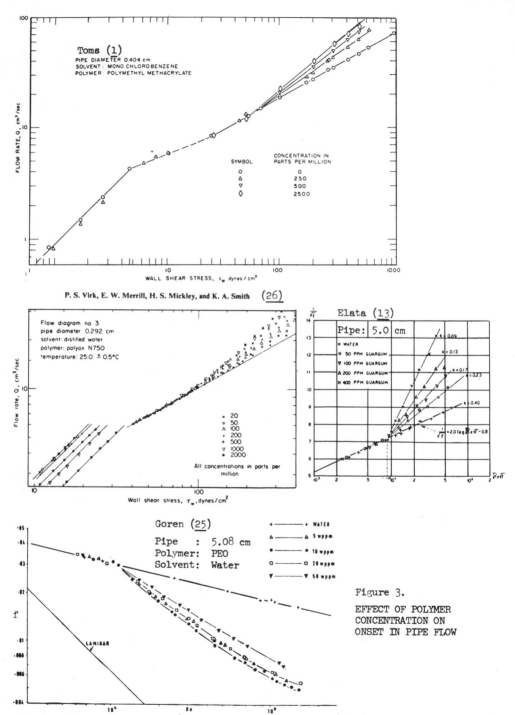

Figure 3.

EFFECT OF POLYMER
CONCENTRATION ON
ONSET IN PIPE FLOW

Figure 3.   Effect of Polymer Concentration on Onset in Pipe Flow

Molecular Weight. The effect of molecular weight (strictly speaking, degree of polymerization) is best observed with a given polymer homologous series-solvent combination in a single pipe. Data of several investigators (Refs. 7, 27, 28) for the polyethylene oxide-water system and one (Ref. 29) for the polyisobutylene-kerosene with increasing molecular weight. Within each polymer/solvent series, Tw* appears to be approximately inversely proportional to molecular weight.

Monomeric Unit. The effect of the monomeric unit, i.e. of polymer species, has not been systematically investigated thus far but some idea of its importance may be gained by considering onset shear stresses for equal molecular weight polymers in similar sized pipes. Such a tabulation is provided in Table 2 which shows values of the onset wavenumber in approximately 1.0 cm pipes for several polymers having molecular weights of about 1×10^6 and 5×10^6 respectively. Striking disparities are evident; PEO in water is seen to start reducing drag at a wall shear stress nearly forty times lower than a comparable molecular weight PMMA in toluene. In interpreting such differences it should be recognized that they can result from factors involving both monomeric structure (configuration) and monomer/solvent interaction (conformation). As an example of the latter, note the results for PIB in kerosene, a poorer solvent than cyclohexane. However, PEO, PIB, and PMMA all have a carbon-carbon type of backbone and water, cyclohexane and toluene are all respectively "good" solvents for these. Thus in these cases the differences in Wn* should be due primarily to configurational factors. Following this logic, column 5 of Table 2 shows calculated values of molecular weight per backbone chain link; comparison with column 3 indicates that the onset of drag reduction is strongly related to the number of links in the macromolecular backbone. Molecular weight per backbone link is, of course, the crudest con- figurational parameter and other such factors - steric hindrances, tacticity - are also possibly relevant.

Solvent. The form assumed by macromolecule in dilute solution, termed its conformation, depends on the nature of the solvent/ monomer interaction. For a given random coiling polymer, the effective linear dimension of the macromolecular coil varies according to the solvent: "good" solvents tend to expand while "poor" solvents tend to compact the size of coil. Two investigators (Refs. 6, 28) have studied the effect of solvent on drag reduction. In each case the onset of drag reduction in the poorer solvent occurred at a significantly higher wall shear stress indicating the relevance of effective coil size. These results further suggest that in characterizing polymers for drag reduction, a conformational parameter, such as rms radius of gyration in solution, Rg, would be preferable to a purely configurational parameter such as molecular weight.

TABLE 2   EFFECT OF MONOMERIC UNIT

Pipe i.d. = 1.0 cm

Polymer MW x 10^{-6}		60	5.0	MW per backbone chain link	
Species	Solvent	Wn*	Wn*		Source
PEO	Water	500	250	14.7	(7,27)
GGM	Water	1000			(4,13)
PIB	Cyclohexane	1300		28.0	(6,30)
PIB	Kerosene	2000	1000		(29)
PMM	Toluene	3000		50.0	(6)

Note: Onset wavenumbers, Wn*, are in cm^{-1}

             Values have been interpolated in some cases.

To summarize this section, the best currently available experimental data for the onset of drag reduction in pipe flow are presented in Table 3. (The last four columns in this table contain information pertinent to the next section and will be referred to therein.) Onset wavenumbers, Wn*, have been employed to characterize the flow at onset; values listed have been obtained directly from the sources referenced. The polymer characterization is, in all except two cases (entries 32, 33 which are based on approximate molecular weights), based on quoted experimental intrinsic vis- cosities. From these, molecular weights have been obtained via well-established values of the relevant Mark-Houwink constants (Refs. 31, 32, 33). RMS radii of gyration have, wherever possible, been obtained from light-scattering data. This applies to the PEO-water (Ref. 33), PIB-cyclohexane (Refs. 33, 34), Guargum-water (Ref. 35), and PAM-water (Ref. 11) systems. In all other cases, values of Rg have been derived from intrinsic viscosity and molecular weight by the use of Flory's universal constant, Φ (Ref. 24).

ENTRY	POLYMER	SOLVENT	DIA CM	ETA DL/G	MW-6	RG+8 CM	WN* 1/CM	CL	TM+3 SEC	SR*-3 1/SEC	CT	SOURCE	REF
1	PMM	C6H5CL	0.128	3.90	2.30	600.	1030.	0.0124	0.0860	7.29	0.63	TOMS	1
2			0.404	3.90	2.30	600.	1100.	0.0132	0.0860	8.37	0.71		
3	PMM	TOLUENE	0.081	1.70	1.02	380.	2900.	0.0220	0.0147	50.66	0.75	HERSHEY	6
4			0.117	1.70	1.02	380.	2300.	0.0175	0.0147	31.86	0.47		
5			1.290	1.70	1.02	380.	3000.	0.0228	0.0147	54.21	0.80		
6			2.540	1.70	1.02	380.	2200.	0.0167	0.0147	29.15	0.43		
7	PIB	CYCLOHEX	0.081	3.43	0.93	680.	1700.	0.0231	0.1471	32.94	4.85		
8			0.117	3.43	0.93	680.	1550.	0.0211	0.1471	27.38	4.03		
9			1.290	3.43	0.93	680.	1300.	0.0177	0.1471	19.26	2.83		
10			2.540	3.43	0.93	680.	1150.	0.0156	0.1471	15.07	2.22		
11	PIB	CYCLOHEX	1.290	6.64	2.41	1130.	880.	0.0199	0.6752	8.83	5.96	RODRI-	30
12	PIB	TOLUENE	0.160	4.20	2.41	720.	1900.	0.0274	0.1001	21.74	2.18	GUEZ	
13			1.790	4.20	2.41	720.	700.	0.0101	0.1001	2.95	0.30		
14			2.540	4.20	2.41	720.	1050.	0.0151	0.1001	6.64	0.66		
15	PIB	BENZENE	1.290	0.82	0.93	275.	3500.	0.0192	0.0067	85.05	0.57	HERSHEY	6
16			2.540	0.82	0.93	275.	2900.	0.0159	0.0067	58.39	0.39		
17	PIB	KEROSENE	0.315	3.92	1.40	570.	1650.	0.C188	0.1107	49.32	5.46	RAM	29
18			0.580	3.97	1.40	570.	1850.	0.0211	0.1107	62.00	6.86		
19			1.020	3.92	1.40	570.	1850.	0.0211	0.1107	67.00	6.86		
20			0.315	5.62	2.50	770.	1450.	0.0223	0.2779	38.00	10.40		
21			0.580	5.62	2.50	770.	1300.	0.0200	0.2729	30.62	8.36		
22			1.020	5.62	2.50	770.	1600.	0.0246	0.2729	46.38	12.66		
23			0.315	8.51	5.00	1110.	1050.	0.0233	0.8176	19.97	12.33		
24			0.580	8.51	5.00	1110.	1050.	0.0233	0.8176	19.97	16.33		
25			1.020	8.51	5.00	1110.	950.	0.0211	0.8176	16.35	13.17		
26			1.370	8.51	5.00	1110.	950.	0.0211	0.8176	16.35	13.37		
27	GGM	WATER	1.220	7.00	0.60	515.	700.	0.0072	0.0643	4.39	0.28	ELATA	13
28			2.220	7.00	0.60	515.	700.	0.0072	0.0643	4.39	0.28		
29			3.220	7.00	0.60	515.	690.	0.0071	0.0643	4.27	0.27		
30			5.070	7.00	0.60	515.	690.	0.0071	0.0643	4.27	0.27		
31	GGM	WATER	1.650	20.00	1.93	1070.	350.	0.0075	0.5765	1.10	0.63	WELLS	4
32	PAM	WATER	1.890	7.00	2.50	1400.	470.	0.0132	1.2913	1.98	2.56	GUPTA	15
33	PAM	WATER	1.200	7.00	2.50	1400.	530.	0.0148	1.2913	2.52	3.25	MARUCCI	16
34	PEO	WATER	5.080	20.00	6.00	2350.	140.	0.0066	6.1074	0.18	1.07	GOREN	25
35	PEO	WATER	0.953	2.81	0.50	755.	453.	0.0068	0.2025	1.82	0.37	LITTLE	27
36			0.953	4.43	0.89	980.	340.	0.0067	0.4429	1.04	0.46		
37	PEO	WATER	0.851	4.25	0.85	960.	370.	0.0071	0.4164	1.23	0.51	PRESTON	9
38	PEO	WATER	0.457	1.96	0.23	630.	750.	0.0094	0.1177	5.04	0.59	PRUIT'	28
39			0.457	3.82	0.55	930.	650.	0.0121	0.3785	3.79	1.43		
40	PEO	.6MK2SO4	0.457	0.73	0.23	455.	1290.	0.0117	0.0443	14.92	0.66		
41			0.457	1.33	0.55	655.	920.	0.0121	0.1322	7.59	1.00		
42			0.457	2.81	1.60	1025.	840.	0.0172	0.5068	6.33	3.21		
43	PEO	WATER	3.210	0.66	0.08	315.	2240.	0.0141	0.0147	44.99	0.66	VIRK	7
44			0.292	0.73	0.09	350.	2100.	0.0147	0.0202	39.54	0.80		
45			0.292	1.75	0.28	795.	1000.	0.0159	0.2365	8.97	2.12		
46			0.292	3.38	0.63	835.	940.	0.0157	0.2740	7.92	2.17		
47			3.210	3.61	0.69	875.	830.	0.0145	0.3153	6.18	1.95		
48			0.292	3.90	0.76	910.	790.	0.0144	0.3546	5.60	1.98		
49			0.945	18.00	5.10	2200.	235.	0.0103	5.0109	0.50	2.48		
50			3.210	20.00	6.10	2350.	210.	0.0099	6.1074	0.40	2.42		
	MEAN							0.0154			3.38		
	STANDARD DEVIATION							0.0057			4.38		

PMM	POLYMETHYLMETHACRYLATE	PIB	POLYISOBUTYLENE		GGM	GUAR GUM	
PAM	POLYACRYLAMIDE	PEO	POLYETHYLENEOXIDE				
DIA	PIPE INSIDE DIAMETER	RG	RMS RADIUS OF GYRATION		TM	TERMINAL RELAXATION TIME, (39)	
ETA	INTRINSIC VISCOSITY	WN*	ONSET WAVENUMBER (UT*/V)		SR*	ONSET SHEAR RATE	
MW	MOLECULAR WEIGHT	CL	ONSET CONSTANT, LENGTH		CT	ONSET CONSTANT, TIME	

INTEGERS FOLLOWING SOME SYMBOLS INDICATE MULTIPLICATION BY CORRESPONDING POWER OF 10.

Table 3. Onset Data

A brief note concerning the errors associated with the entries in Table 3. The percentage error in Wn*, to 95% confidence, is typically ±20% and varies from ±10% at very best to ±50%. These large errors stem from the fact that onset is defined by the intersection of experimentally ascertained lines, each subject to uncertainity. Further, as a molecular weight (and/or concentration) is decreased, the polymer solution flow lines approach the solvent line (on Fig. 2, OM → OS) and it becomes increasingly difficult to locate their intersection. As regards the macromolecular parameters, it should be noted that all of the data reported in Table 3 were obtained with commercial polymer samples. These have fairly wide (and generally unknown) molecular weight distributions making for considerable uncertainty in their characterization. Intrinsic viscosities are, typically, good to ±10%, thus ±20% precision can be expected of molecular weights derived therefrom. Radii of gyration for the PEO-water and PIB-cyclohexane systems are accurate to about ±10%. Rg values for Guargum-water and PAM-water are each internally consistent but their absolute magnitudes have unknown systematic errors of order ±20%. Values of Rg derived from intrinsic viscosity via Flory's method are estimated accurate to ±20%. In comparing these, it should be kept in mind that light scattering yields Z-average values which weight the high molecular weights more strongly than does the $M[\eta]$ product in Flory's method. Thus systematic discrepancies, depending on the molecular weight distributions of the polymers, can be expected between the experimental and estimated values of Rg; the former will tend to be somewhat larger.

THEORETICAL APPROACHES

The absence of anomalous effects in the laminar regime and the abruptness of the onset of drag reduction in turbulent pipe flow suggests an explicit connection between the turbulent flow field and the macromolecule in solution. Although the basic nature of the polymer/turbulence interaction is still unclear, three hypotheses have been advanced regarding onset. In accordance with their physical bases, these will be referred to as the hypotheses of

(1) Length (Refs. 7, 26)
(2) Time (Refs. 6, 22, 36)
(3) Strain Energy (Ref. 37).

The logical structure of the length and time based hypotheses is virtually identical even though the entities concerned differ. The basic, intuitive notion involved in both cases is that, at onset, the ratio of corresponding macromolecular and the turbulence scales should be constant. It might further be expected that the relevant macromolecular scales would be characteristic of a polymer molecule in dilute solution while the proper turbulence scales would be those associated with flow near the pipe wall, where energetic process dominate. In connection with the turbulence it has been noted that the polymer solutions exhibit normal, solvent-like, behaviour until the onset point; therefore the usual Newtonian "law of the wall" parameters, Ut and ν, should serve to scale the turbulent flow field at onset. At this juncture the length and time hypotheses diverge. In the length hypothesis (Ref. 26), the rms radius of gyration, Rg was chosen as the macromolecular scale while (Ut/ν), a wavenumber with dimension of inverse length was used to scale the turbulence. In the time hypotheses, (Refs. 6, 22, 36) terminal relaxation time, Tm, was used to characterize the polymer while wall shear rate, (Ut^2/ν), a frequency, with dimensions of inverse time was chosen to scale the turbulence. However, the polymer solutions involved are so dilute that their relaxation times are not experimentally accessible (unlike Rg), hence in all cases Tm has to be obtained from theories of dilute polymer solution viscoelasticity (Refs. 38, 39).

The third, strain energy, hypothesis (Ref. 37) is considerably more sophisticated than the previous two in that it is based on a mechanism of polymer/turbulence interaction. Briefly, the concept involved is that the polymer molecules store energy when strained; thus there exists the possibility of convective transport of strain energy from the highly strained wall region to the essentially unstrained core of the pipe flow. This provides an energy supply mechanism for sustaining the turbulent core in addition to the usual supply mode of kinetic energy diffusion. While all the consequences of this are not obvious, the physical idea is that drag reduction appears when strain energy convection becomes comparable to kinetic energy diffusion. Thus, some value of their non-dimensional ratio becomes a criterion for onset. Strain and kinetic energies per unit of solution are each evaluated from dimensional considerations. Turbulent kinetic energy is, of course, scaled by Ut^2. Strain energy is the product of the number of macromolecules per unit of solution times the strain energy per molecule. The latter is estimated by modelling the macromolecule as a Hookean spring. In the final result the strain energy per unit of solution is scaled by the group

$$c[\eta] \ . \ \frac{M[\eta] \ \eta s.}{RT} \ \nu \, (Ut^2/\nu)^2 .$$

To facilitate comparison, the structures of the three types of onset hypotheses are shown in Table 4. In each case the $L_H S$ has been broken up to show the polymeric and turbulence scales employed while the $R_H S$ represents their nondimensional product which should, according to hypothesis, remain constant at onset. The $(M[\eta]\ \eta s)/RT$ term in (2) and (3) will be recognized as a relaxation time at infinite dilution. The numerical factors, (2, 0.422, 8) are not especially relevant, but have been retained as originally proposed.

Comparison with Experiment

In testing the onset hypotheses proposed against the experimental observations we note that all three forms employ "wall" type of parameters Ut and ν to scale the turbulent flow. Since the flow structure in the wall region is independent of pipe diameter, all forms predict an onset wall shear stress independent of pipe size. This is in accord with experiment. The data in Table 3 show no trend with diameter though they are limited to rather small diameter pipes; in Table 3, 5 cm is the largest pipe ID, 90% of the data is in pipes less than 3 cm ID and 50% in pipes under 1 cm ID.

TABLE 4   STRUCTURE OF ONSET HYPOTHESES

Hypothesis Type			Scales		Universal Constant
			Polymer	Flow Field	
Length (26, 7)	:	2.0	$\cdot$ Rg	$\cdot$ $(Ut*/\nu)$	$=$	Cl
Time (6, 22, 36)	:	0.42	$\cdot$ $\dfrac{M[\eta]\ \eta s}{RT}$	$\cdot$ $(Ut*^2/\nu)$	$=$	Ct
Strain Energy (37)	:	8.0	$\cdot$ $c[\eta]$ $\cdot$ $\dfrac{M[\eta]\ \eta s}{RT}$	$\cdot$ $(Ut*^2/\nu)$	$=$	Cs

The hypotheses differ in their predictions concerning solvent physical properties. For a given macromolecular conformation, the length hypothesis predicts an onset wall shear stress, Tw* varying as $\rho\nu^2$ while the time and strain energy hypotheses predict Tw* to be independent of solvent physical properties. This evidently provides a way to discriminate between hypotheses. Unfortunately, as pointed out earlier, the available onset data is all in solvents with closely similar physical properties. It is interesting to note, nevertheless, that both cyclohexane (Refs. 6, 30) and kerosene (Ref. 29) have been employed as solvents for PIB; these have density, kinematic viscosity values of 0.78 gm/cm^3, 0.011 cm^2/sec and 0.69 gm/cm^3, 0.018 cm^2/sec respectively. If we now compare onsets at constant Rg (which presumably accounts for macromolecular conformation) e.g. entries 11 and 25 in Table 3, it is seen that $Wn*$ is essentially constant (~ 900 for the example cited) in both solvents. This is as predicted by the length hypothesis (and contrary to the predictions of the time hypothesis). It must be emphasized that, in the case considered, the uncertainty in $Ut*/\nu$ is of the same order as the variation in the physical properties so the results are only indicative.

Consider next the predicted effect of polymer concentration. The length and time hypotheses are essentially concentration independent if one neglects the very weak concentration dependence caused in each case by changes in relative viscosity. The strain energy hypothesis predicts an onset shear stress inversely proportional to concentration. Experimentally, $Tw*$ was seen (Fig. 3) to be concentration independent over 10 to 100 fold ranges of concentration which agrees with the length and time hypotheses but sharply contradicts the strain energy hypothesis. This would appear to eliminate the last named as a viable hypothesis for practical purposes. Strictly speaking, however, the strain energy hypothesis as originally proposed was restricted to exceedingly dilute solutions ($c[\eta] < 0.03$) and no definitive onset measurements are available under such conditions.

Lastly, we take up the relationship between the flow field and the macromolecule. The length hypothesis predicts an onset wavenumber, $Wn*$, inversely proportional to polymer rms radius of gyration, Rg. For a given polymer/solvent system, $Wn*$ is proportional to the square root of the onset wall shear stress, $Tw*$; whence, according to the length hypothesis, $Tw*^{1/2} \propto Rg^{-1}$. The time hypothesis predicts an onset frequency, $Fr*$, inversely proportional to terminal relaxation time, Tm. For a given system, the onset frequency, $Fr*$ (or shear rate Ut^2/ν), is proportional to $Tw*$. The relaxation time, Tm, while experimentally inaccessible is, according to linear viscoelasticity theory, proportional to the product of polymer molecular weight, M, and intrinsic viscosity, $[\eta]$. This $M[\eta]$ product is classically interpreted as a volume per macromolecule, proportional to Rg^3. Consequently, the time hypothesis predicts that $Tw*^{1/2} \propto Rg^{-3/2}$. The length and time hypotheses thus yield power law relationships between $Tw*^{1/2}$ and Rg that differ in the Rg exponent: the former predicts -1, the latter -3/2. Qualitatively, both hypotheses predict lower onset shear stresses for larger molecules — as is, of course, observed experimentally. The functional relationship between $Tw*$ and Rg can be tested by following onset for several homologous polymers in a given solvent.

For two systems in which polymer molecular weight was varied
over considerable ranges — PIB in kerosene (Ref. 29) and PEO
in water (Ref. 7) — the variation of $Tw*^{1/2}$ is closer to the
-1 power or Rg than the -3/2 power.

Recall, finally, that each of the onset hypotheses postulates
a universal onset constant (the RHS in Table 4) involving the
nondimensional product (or ratio) of macromolecular and turbulence
scales at onset. The overall validity of an onset hypothesis
can therefore be assessed by the universality of its experimentally
ascertained onset constant. The length and time based hypotheses
are evaluated on this basis in Table 3; columns headed by Rg, Wn*
and Cl pertain to the length hypothesis while those headed by
Tm, Fr* and Ct refer to the time hypothesis.

Perusal of the Cl column reveals values of the length based
onset constant from 0.007 to 0.027 with a mean of 0.0154 and a
standard deviation of 0.0057. The 95% confidence limits on Cl
thus amount to about 70% of its absolute value. Clearly, therfore,
Cl is constant within a factor of two of the mean obtained from
the present set of data. Further, it will be recalled that the
errors in $(Ut*/\nu)$ and Rg were each of order 20%; whence the
observed constancy of Cl is essentially as good as can be expected
with the precision of the present data. Considering the variety
of experimental systems and the exclusive use of commercial,
unfractionated polymer samples, this constancy of the length onset
constant is mildly remarkable.

In evaluating the time hypothesis, onset frequencies
(column Fr* in Table 3) have been obtained directly from experimental data. Terminal relaxations times (column Tm) have been
calculated from the Zimm theory (Ref. 39) with one difference.
In the expression for Tm, the $M[\eta]$ product has, whenever
experimental Rg values were available, been substituted by 30.9 x
10^{21} Rg, using Flory's relation (Ref. 24). Relaxation times so
calculated (i.e. Z-averaged) were found to cause somewhat less
overall scatter in Ct than values calculated directly from the
listed $M[\eta]$ figures. Examination of the Ct column in Table 3
reveals values of the time based onset constant ranging from 0.27
to 16.3 with a mean value of 3.38 and a standard deviation of 4.38.
In viewing these apparently excessive variations it must be
realized that the entities employed in the time hypotheses cover
much greater ranges, numerically, than the corresponding length
variables. The relaxation time, Tm varies as Rg^3 while the onset
frequency goes as Tw*; thus Ct is effectively a product of
$(Rg^3 Tw*)$ while Cl is a product of $(RgTw*^{1/2}/\nu\rho^{1/2})$. Therefore,
over small ranges of solvent physical properties — as presently —
Ct is rather more severely tested by experimental onset data. To
compare the length and time hypotheses over similar ranges of

variables, the length constant, C_1, should more properly be viewed against the square root of Ct; $\sqrt{Ct}$ amounts to a product of $(Rg^{3/2}Tw*^{1/2})$ and can readily be calculated. The results of such a comparison are shown in Table 5. From the last row in Table 5 it is seen that experimental values of the length based onset constant have about half the scatter shown by $\sqrt{Ct}$, the "equivalent" time based constant. Which indicates that, overall, the onset data obey the length hypothesis rather better than the time hypothesis.

Onset Correlation

From the foregoing comparison between theory and experiment it is evident that, while the scatter encountered in the experimental data is too great to permit any definitive distinction between length and time hypotheses, the length hypothesis is more promising for the empirical prediction of onset. A semi-empirical correlation, based on the length hypothesis, is presented next. In Fig. 4, the experimental data tabulated in Table 3 are displayed graphically on double logarithmic coordinates of polymer rms radius of gyration, Rg, vs, onset wavenumber, $Ut*/\nu$. Individual polymer species are indicated by different symbols but no attempt has been made to differentiate between solvents. The solid line represents the length type onset relation

$$(Ut*/\nu) = 0.0077 \ Rg^{-1}$$

TABLE 5   COMPARISON OF ONSET CONSTANTS

	C_1	Ct	$\sqrt{Ct}$
Mean	0.0154	3.38	1.54
Standard Deviation	0.0057	4.38	1.02
(Std Dev/Mean)	0.3700	1.30	0.66

obtained by using the experimentally ascertained mean value of 0.0154 for C_1; the dashed lines show the corresponding 95% confidence limits.

It is possible to "fit" the data of Fig. 4 better than shown — the best fit, least square, straight line has a slope of -1.15 (vs. -1.0 for the present correlation and -1.50 predicted by the time hypothesis). However, close scrutiny of the figure reveals that the data are grouped by species; essentially all the PIB points lie above the mean line while all the PEO points fall below. Rather than destroy such information as is contained in this fine

structure by a lumped "best fit" it is preferable to ascertain
Cl values for individual species. These are shown in Table 6.
For each species, the (standard deviation/mean) ratio is lower
than the overall value of 0.37 indicating that the differences
in Cl, while small, are statistically significant. Empirically,
the individual Cl values will slightly improve the precision with
which onset can be predicted for the species concerned. Theoretically,
the small differences in Cl between polymer species are of interest
because they probably reflect the influence of configurational
factors on onset.

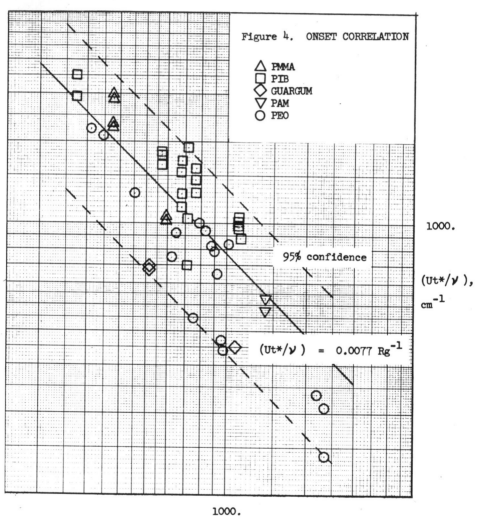

Figure 4. Onset Correlation

DISCUSSION

It is interesting to interpret the numerical magnitudes of the length and time onset constants in physical terms. To do so, the macromolecular and turbulence scales chosen must each be related to the physical reality — a rather more difficult task than the dimensional analysis involved in choosing the scales.

At conditions corresponding to onset, both theoretical calculations as well as very recent experiments (Ref. 34) show that the polymer molecules are only slightly elongated. Therefore the macromolecular scales can, at least initially, be accepted at face value. Thus Rg is considered a macromolecular radius and Tm a true relaxation time. The turbulence scales — Ut/ν and Ut^2/ν — can be related to pipe flow structure in two steps. First, a characteristic radial location has to be chosen. Since drag reduction is an energetic effect, and the dominant energetic processes occur (Ref. 40) in the so called 'buffer' layer, $y^+ \simeq 10$ is a location possessing physical significance. Second, characteristic "eddy" length and time scales have to be found at $y^+ \simeq 10$. By mixing length type of reasoning, the largest eddies in this region will have a radial dimension, Le, of the order of distance from the wall. The rms turbulent velocity, V', is of the order of the friction velocity, Ut. Hence the turbulence Reynolds number, (LeV'/ν), at $y^+ \simeq 10$ is of order y^+, i.e. 10^1. At such low values there is considerable spectral overlap between the regions of turbulent energy production and dissipation. Hence the energetic and dissipative eddies can be expected to **possess length scales of the same** order of magnitude. This expectation is borne out by Laufer's data (Ref. 40) from which, using available turbulence theory (Ref. 41), it can be shown (Ref. 42) that the dissipative eddy size, Ld, is of order 10^1. ν/Ut. Thus the length scale, Lt, characteristic of the turbulent eddies at $y^+ \simeq 10$ is such that $(LtUt/\nu) \sim 10^1$. Corresponding to this it can easily be shown that the eddy time scale, Tt, is such that $(TtUt^2/\nu) \sim 10^1$.

From the foregoing, the ratio of macromolecular to eddy length scales is

$$(Rg/Lt) = (RgUt/\nu)/(LtUt/\nu) \sim 10^{-3}$$

while the ratio of time scales is

$$(Tm/Tt) = (TmUt^2/\nu)/(TtUt^2/\nu) \sim 10^0.$$

In words, at onset, the radius of the macromolecule is several
orders of magnitude smaller than the turbulent eddy size but the
macromolecular relaxation time is of the same order as the turbulent time scale. On physical grounds, therefore, it is easier to
conceive of an interaction between the polymer and the turbulence
in the time domain. Which leads to a curious dilemna: the
experimental data tend to obey the length based onset hypothesis
but the time based hypothesis is conceptually more appealing.
Our concluding remarks are addressed to this subject.

Clearly the physical interaction between the macromolecule
and the turbulence — however it occurs — is independent of the
parameters used to describe it. Therefore the present authors feel
that the length and time hypotheses must, ultimately, be reconcil-
able. The present divergence seems due to the inability of the
scales employed to adequately represent all of the factors involved
in onset. Whilst major improvements must await fuller understanding
of the onset mechanism, some of the limitations of Rg and Tm as
macromolecular scales are worth pointing out.

In describing onset, the rms radius of gyration, Rg, evidently
provides a good first approximation to whatever polymeric scale is
relevant. However, a small but significant segregation of onset
constants by polymer species was noted earlier. From Table 6,
PEO and PIB have Cl values of 0.012 and 0.020 respectively (other
species have too few entries to interpret confidently). And it is
known, from independent intrinsic viscosity measurements in theta
solvents, that the PEO chain has lesser steric hindrances, i.e.
is more flexible, than the PIB chain: their respective 'steric
factors' (Ref. 24) are 1.40 and 1.95. Which implies that in
addition to Rg, configurational factors like chain flexibility
might also influence onset. Ideally, chain flexibility should be
accounted for in the macromolecular relaxation time, Tm, since,
physically, flexibility implies longer relaxation times. However,
the major problem with Tm is its proper evaluation. No experimental
methods are available for dilute polymer solutions. And the estimates provided by linear viscoelasticity theory do not include the
effect of chain structure. Further, since linear viscoelasticity
ascribes all retardation to solvent drag, neglecting steric
restrictions (the so-called "internal viscosity"), the dependence
it predicts for Tm on solvent viscosity is also suspect — the
more so for "rigid" chains in "thin" solvents.

It can thus be anticipated that both length and time hypotheses
would benefit from the incorporation of configurational information
into their respective molecular scales. When this — and other —
improvements are effected, the two hypotheses should tend to
equivalence. In which event the time hypothesis could, conceiv-
ably, possess the greater physical significance owing to the closer
correpondence between polymeric and flow time scales.

SUMMARY

In this paper we have:

(1) Demonstrated experimentally that an abrupt onset is a characteristic feature in the anomalous flow behaviour of dilute polymer
solutions.

(2) Reviewed the experimental evidence regarding onset in
turbulent pipe flow, summarized the observed effects of various flow
and polymeric parameters and presented a 50 entry tabulation of
the best available onset data. Pipe wall shear stress and macromolecular rms radius of gyration in solution appear, respectively,
to be the flow and polymeric parameters most relevant to onset.

(3) Analysed the logical structures of three types of onset
hypotheses and compared their predictions with experimental results.
It was found that all hypotheses predict an onset wall shear stress
independent of pipe diameter, in accord with experiment. The
hypotheses differ in their predictions regarding the effect of solvent physical properties on onset but these cannot conclusively
be tested by the available data. Experiments show that onset is
essentially independent of polymer concentration for dilute solutions;
this is in agreement with the length and time type of onset hypotheses
but contradicts the hypothesis based on strain energy arguments.
Overall, statistical analysis of the data indicates that the
length hypothesis is better obeyed than the time hypothesis; however
the data scatter too much to permit definitive discrimination.

(4) Presented a semi-empirical onset correlation based on the length
hypothesis.

(5) Interpreted the experimental onset data to show that, at onset,
the macromolecular radius is much smaller than the turbulent eddy
size but that the polymeric and eddy time scales are of comparable
magnitudes.

(6) Discussed some of the deficiencies in the macromolecular
scales presently employed to characterize onset and pointed out
the possible significance of steric factors.

TABLE 6   ONSET CONSTANTS FOR INDIVIDUAL POLYMER SPECIES

	Entries	Mean Cl	Std Dev	Ratio
PIT - Polyisobutylene	6	0.0174	0.0043	0.25
PMM - Polymethylmethacrylate	20	0.0201	0.0039	0.19
GGM - Guar Gum	5	0.0072	0.0002	0.02
PAM - Polyacrylamide	2	0.0140	0.0012	0.08
PEO - Polyethyleneoxide	17	0.0117	0.0035	0.30
Overall	50	0.0154	0.0057	0.37

REFERENCES

1.   Toms, B. A., Proc. 1st Intnl. Congress on Rheology, (North Holland Publ. Co., Amsterdam, Holland, 1948), Vol. 2, p. 135

2.   Savins, J. G., Soc. Petrol. Eng. Journal, 4, 203 (1964)

3.   Fabula, A. G., Proc. 4th Intnl. Congress on Rheology, (Interscience, New York, 1965), Vol. 3, p. 455

4.   Wells, C. S., A. I. A. A. Journal, 3, 1800 (1965)

5.   Hoyt, J. W., In Symposium on Rheology, A. W. Marris & J. T. S. Wang, Ed., (ASME, New York, 1965), p. 71

6.   Hershey, H. C., & J. L. Zakin, Chem. Eng. Sci., 22, 1847 (1967)

7.   Virk, P. S., et. al., J. Fluid Mech., 30, 305 (1967)

8.   Lindgren, E. R., Clearinghouse Ad 621070 (1965)

9.   Preston, J. L., "The Toms Phenomenon in a Rough Pipe", S.B. Thesis, M.IT.T, Cambridge, Mass. (1967)

10. Merrill, E. W., K. A. Smith, H. Shin, & H. S. Mickley, Trans. Soc. Rheology, 10, 335 (1966)

11. Lee. T. S., "Turbulent Flow of Dilute Polymer Solutions - Studies in Couette Flow", SC.D Thesis, M.I.T., Cambridge, Mass. (1966)

12. Hoyt, J. W., & A. G. Fabula, Paper to the 5th Symposium on Naval Hydrodynamics. Bergen, Norway (1964)

13. Elata, C., & J. Tirosh, Isreal J. Technol., $\underline{3}$, 1 (1965)

14. Pruitt, G. T., N. F. Whitsitt & H. R. Crawford, Rept. NAS 7-369, The Western Co. Res. Div., Dallas Tex. (1967)

15. Gupta, M. K., A. B. Metzner & J. P. Hartnett, Intnl J. Heat & Mass Transfer, $\underline{10}$, 1211 (1967)

16. Marucci, G. & G. Astarita, Ind. Eng. Chem. Fund., $\underline{6}$, 471 (1967)

17. Suraiya, T., "Mass Transfer to Dilute Polymer Solutions in Turbulent Pipe Flow", S.B. Thesis, M.I.T., Cambridge, Mass. (1967)

18. Astarita, G. & L. Nicodemo. A.I.Ch.E. Journal, $\underline{12}$, 478 (1966)

19. Smith, K. A., E. W. Merrill, H. S. Mickley & P. S. Virk, Chem. Eng. Sci., $\underline{22}$, 619 (1967)

20. Brennen, C., & G. E. Gadd, Nature, $\underline{215}$, 1368 (1967)

21. James, D. F., Ph.D. Thesis Research Quoted by Metzner, A. B., & G. Astarita, A.I.Ch.E. Journal, $\underline{13}$, 550, (1967)

22. Fabula, A. G., J. L. Lumley & D. W. Taylor, In The Mechanics of Continua, S. Eskinazi, Ed., (Academic Press, New York 1966), p. 145

23. Hershey, H. C., & J. L. Zakin, Ind. Eng. Chem. Fund., $\underline{6}$, 381 (1967)

24. Flory, P. J., Principles of Polymer Chemistry, (Cornell Univ. Press. Ithaca, N. Y. 1953)

25. Goren, Y., & J. F. Norbury, A.S.M.E. J. Basic Eng., $\underline{89}$, 814 (1967)

26. Virk, P. S., E. W. Merrill, H. S. Mickley & K. A. Smith in The Mechanics of Continua, S. Eskinazi, Ed., (Academic Press, New York 1966), p. 37

27. Little, R. C., Clearinghouse Ad 654160 (1967)

28. Pruitt, G. T., B. Rosen & H. R. Crawford, Clearinghouse Ad 642441 (1966)

29. Ram. A., E. Finklestein & C. Elata, Ind. Eng. Chem. Proc Des. Dev., 6, 309 (1967)

30. Rodriguez, J. M., J. L. Zakin & G. K. Patterson, Soc. Petrol. Eng. J., 7, 325 (1967)

31. Kurata, M., & W. H. Stockmayer, Fortschr. Hochpolymer Forsh., 3, 192 (1963) ·

32. Bailey, F. E., & R. W. Callard, J. Appl. Poly. Sci., 1, 56 (1959)

33. Shin, H., "Reduction of Drag in Turbulence by Dilute Polymer Solutions" Sc.D. Thesis, M.I.T., Cambridge, Mass. (1965)

34. Cottrell, F. R., "The Conformation of Polyisobutylene in a Hydrodynamic Shear Field", Sc.D. Thesis, M.I.T., Cambridge, Mass. (1968)

35. Deb, S. K., & S. N. Mukherjee, Indian J. Chem, 1, 413 (1963)

36. Elata, C., J. Lehrer & A. Kahanovitz, Isreal J. Technol., 4, 87 (1966)

37. Walsh, M., "On The Turbulent Flow of Dilute Polymer Solutions", Ph.D. Thesis, Calif. Inst. Tech., Pasadena, Calif. (1967)

38. Rouse, P. E., J. Chem. Phys., 21, 1272 (1953)

39. Zimm, B. H., J. Chem. Phys., 24, 264 (1956)

40. Laufer, J., N.A.C.A. Report 1174 (1954)

41. Hinze, J. O., Turbulence, (McRaw-Hill, New York 1959)

42. Virk, P. S., "The Toms Phenomenon - Turbulent Flow of Dilute Polymer Solutions" Sc.D. Thesis, M.I.T., Cambridge, Mass. (1966)

STUDIES OF VISCOUS DRAG REDUCTION WITH POLYMERS INCLUDING TURBULENCE

MEASUREMENTS AND ROUGHNESS EFFECTS

J. G. Spangler

LTV Research Center

ABSTRACT

Recent results of turbulence measurements in very effective drag-reducing fluids are presented. Effects of the polymer on turbulence intensity are found to not be directly related to friction reduction. Turbulence intensity is found to be a function of Reynolds number, polymer concentration, and location in the flow field and may be locally higher or lower than for Newtonian flow. Turbulence spectral measurements show moderate effects in both macroscale and microscale for polymer solutions suggesting a possible elasticity effect which is not related to the drag-reduction phenomenon.

Friction factors for flow of a very effective drag-reducing dilute polymer solution in uniformly rough pipes are presented. The onset of "fully rough" effects is found to occur at higher Reynolds numbers in the polymer solution than in water in accordance with predictions based on the sublayer thickening effect of the polymer. The friction factors are found to be less for the polymer than for water in the roughness transition regime, but there is an indication that in the fully rough regime no drag-reduction will be realized. The data are analyzed in terms of a roughness function based on the effects of the polymer and the roughness on the law of the wall velocity profile.

INTRODUCTION

The understanding of the mechanics of non-Newtonian fluid flow has increased significantly in recent years. The mean flow characteristics of fully developed turbulent shear flows have been well documented by several investigators for numerous drag-reducing

131

fluids (Refs.1-5). A friction factor - Reynolds number correlation
has been developed by Meyer (Ref. 6) which adequately predicts friction losses in pipes of different sizes for dilute polymer solutions
when two particular fluid characteristics are known. This correlation has made it possible to derive mass and energy transport expressions for both internal and external shear flows from the
momentum transport characteristics of drag-reducing fluids in turbulent pipe flow by means of the Reynolds-Prandtl analogy (Refs. 7,
8, and 9).   These and other developments have provided a fairly
comprehensive picture of the results to be expected for viscous
shear flows of drag-reducing non-Newtonian fluids. Still to be
answered are the questions concerning the actual mechanisms which
control the non-Newtonian effects.

    Comparisons of various effective drag-reducing polymers point
out several interesting facts. Friction drag reduction only occurs
in turbulent flow. The degree of friction drag reduction increases
with increasing molecular weight. Polymer solutions that are effective drag reducers in low concentrations appear to be slightly
elastic while having viscous properties which are essentially Newtonian. Considerable attention has been given to the role that
elasticity may play in the drag reduction phenomenon, but recent
results of at least one investigation, (Ref. 10), have shown that
elasticity disappears with aging of polymer solutions while the
drag-reduction effectiveness remains unchanged. No measurements
of turbulence effects due to the time dependency of the elasticity
were mentioned in this case.

    It grows increasingly apparent that in order to identify and
understand the mechanism by which friction drag is reduced it will
be necessary to examine as many aspects of the flow as possible.
Two particular points are of current interest to those presently
active in the field, one primarily of a fundamental nature and the
other of a practical nature in the application of the drag-reduction
phenomenon. These are, respectively; (1) the relationship between
polymer effects on the turbulence structure of the flow and the
friction drag,and (2) the effects of surface roughness on friction
drag reduction and polymer stability.

    Several investigations of turbulence effects have been re-
ported. The studies of Wells, Harkness, and Meyer, (Ref. 11),
Virk (Ref. 12), and Johnson and Barchi (Ref. 13), have shown
effects on both the rms intensity and the spectral distribution of
turbulent energy for the axial turbulent velocity component in
turbulent pipe flow. In Reference 11 the fluid tested was a
500 wppm solution of carboxymethylcellulose in water, a moderately
effective drag reducer (friction factor reduction of about 30
percent). The changes in the turbulence structure were small.
The turbulence intensity in the core of the flow, when normalized

with friction velocity, was found to be independent of Reynolds number. The turbulent energy at low frequencies was found to be slightly reduced and at high frequencies slightly increased compared to measurements in water at the same Reynolds numbers. In all cases the effects of the polymer additive on the turbulence structure were too vague to be conclusive. These measurements were made with a total pressure probe whereas the measurements in Reference 12 and some of those in Reference 13 were made with conical hot film anemometers. The results of Reference 11 suggest extending that investigation to a much more effective drag-reducing solution in order to enhance the connection, if any, between the turbulence effects and friction effects caused by the polymer additive.

In the consideration of surface roughness the experiments of White (Ref. 14) have shown anomalous results with guar gum and poly(ethylene oxide) in a very rough pipe. The guar gum caused no apparent change in the frictional characteristics of rough pipe flow compared to water results while the more effective Polyox showed a friction reduction at sufficiently large Reynolds numbers and concentrations. The roughness was so extreme that fully rough flow was apparently established immediately above the threshold of turbulent flow and no transition roughness regime was detected.

This paper describes a set of experiments similar to those of References 11 and 14. Two concentrations of a very effective drag-reducing polymer additive were studied in a smooth pipe to determine the effects of the additive on the turbulence field and the relation between turbulence effects and friction effects for conditions of both large and small drag reduction. The same polymer additive was also tested in a dilute concentration in three rough pipes of geometrically similar but different sized roughness to investigate the effectiveness in reducing friction drag on moderately rough surfaces.

The polymer additive was a commercial product of the Stein, Hall and Co. designated as P-295 and commonly called Polyhall. This is an anionic copolymer of polyacrylamide and polyacrylic acid with a molecular weight of 5-6 million. Solution concentrations of 31 and 100 wppm were tested and the effects on friction reduction, turbulence intensity, and spectral energy density are presented as functions of concentration and Reynolds number. Roughness effects are analyzed in terms of a roughness function derived from fluid properties and the law of the wall velocity profile correlation.

EXPERIMENTAL FACILITY AND INSTRUMENTATION

All of the tests described in this paper were conducted in the

Pipe Flow Facility of the LTV Research Center. This is a blow-down
type of system in which liquids from a 600-gallon pressurized
reservoir are forced through tubes of various sizes at a steady rate.
Flow rates are determined by the size of an orifice at the discharge
end of the tube and by the hydrostatic pressure controlled by air
pressure regulators at the reservoir. A sharp edged orifice at the
tube entrance assures turbulent flow at relatively low Reynolds
numbers. Run times are of 10-minute duration or greater depending
on the flow rate. A more detailed description of the facility may
be found in a paper by Ernst (Ref. 15). The smooth test section
used in this study was made of honed stainless steel tubing 0.761
inches in diameter. The roughness test sections were made by threading the inside of extruded brass tubing with specially made taps.
The brass tubing was 0.750 inches in diameter prior to threading.

Four 1/32-inch diameter static pressure ports were located on
a 2-foot spacing center to center in the smooth tube with the first
port 150 tube diameters from the test section entrance. A port in
the wall of the smooth tube just downstream of the static pressure
ports was used for installation of traversable pitot probes for
both mean and instantaneous velocity measurements.

The threaded roughness sections were made with specially
ground taps to produce sharp edged threads with a 90-degree included angle such that the thread faces were at ± 45 degrees to the
flow. The three rough test sections had 24, 48, and 96 threads
per inch with designed roughness heights of 0.0208, 0.0104, and
0.0052 inches respectively. The 24 and 48 threads per inch sections were single thread types but the 96 threads per inch section
was made by using a double-threaded 48 thread per inch tap set to
cut half depth with the two thread sets spaced one-half cycle out
of phase so that full-depth 96 threads per inch were produced. The
threaded brass tubing was made in 1-foot sections joined with 0.10-
inch thick smooth collars each with a 1/32-inch diameter static
pressure port.

All steady pressure measurements were made with a variable-
reluctance transducer driven by a carrier amplifier. The transducer output was displayed on a digital voltmeter. The pressure
drop down the tube and the mean velocity measurements were taken
in this way. The pitot probe had a round tip 0.014-inch o.d. with
a 0.010-inch i.d. and could be traversed from the tube centerline
to the wall with a positioning accuracy of ± 0.0005 inches.

The pitot probe used for instantaneous total pressure fluctuations was similar in size and utility to the pitot probe used
for mean measurements. The total pressure fluctuations were
sensed by a piezoelectric crystal mounted in the probe strut. A
0.002-inch bleed hole in the base of the pitot probe allowed a

slight continuous bleeding of the probe cavity to prevent air from
becoming entrapped. A more detailed description may be found in
Reference 11. A second piezoelectric crystal was mounted in the
tube wall in the same plane with the pitot probe tip to sense
static pressure fluctuations at the wall. The signals from the two
crystals were subtracted through a high impedance differential
electrometer amplifier in order to remove acoustical noise from the
turbulence signal, the idea being that long wave-length acoustical
pressure fluctuations would correlate at the two sensor locations
and thus could be algebraically cancelled. The frequency response
of the probe is good from approximately 0.1 - 6000 Hertz. The
signal from the crystal is on the order of 100 millivolts and thus
requires little amplification, having a signal to noise ratio of
better than 100 to 1.

The operating procedure involved pre-mixing of the polymer
solutions in a large open tank and then transfering the solutions
to the pressurized reservoir. This involved a single pass through
a centrifugal pump. The flow through the test section was controlled by a ball valve at the exit of the tube. Mass flow rates
were determined by measuring the time required to accumulate a
given weight sample of fluid from the tube discharge. Pressure
drop data were measured with the single transducer through a manifold
system. The viscosity of tested solutions was determined from discharge samples in a Contraves rotational concentric cylinder viscometer, the data being fitted to a power law viscosity expression.
An on-line wave analyzer (Technical Products Model 627) and an RMS
voltmeter (B&K Model 2417) in series with a variable band-pass
filter (Krohn-Hite Model 330-A) were used to record turbulence data
for the longitudinal component of turbulence only.

DATA ANALYSIS

Turbulence Analysis

Turbulent friction factor data were analyzed in terms of the
correlation of Meyer (Ref. 6) which is based on the observation
that the outer or turbulent portions of the velocity profiles in
pipe flow for very dilute drag-reducing polymer solutions are
correlated by the universal law of the wall in the form:

$$\phi = A \log_{10} \eta + B \tag{1}$$

where $\phi = u/u_*$, $\quad \eta = \dfrac{yu_*}{\nu_w}$, $\quad A = 5.75$, $\quad B = 5.5 + \alpha \log_{10} \dfrac{u_*}{u_{*crit}} \tag{2}$

The parameters α and $u*_{crit}$ are respectively measures of the drag-reducing effectiveness and the onset wall shear stress above which drag reduction occurs and they are constants for a given fluid. The effect of these parameters on the velocity profile is shown as a shift in the logarithmic portion with no change in slope. This indicates an effective thickening of the viscous sublayer with no apparent change in the mixing length distribution. Thus a correlation for friction factor with Reynolds number using these parameters can be established for flow in pipes of varying sizes and the resulting expression for friction factor as a function of Reynolds number is

$$\frac{1}{\sqrt{f}} = (4 + \frac{\alpha}{\sqrt{2}})\ (\frac{n}{2-n})\log_{10} Re_{w.}\sqrt{f}\ -\ .394$$

$$-\ \frac{\alpha}{\sqrt{2}}\ \log_{10}\left[\frac{u*_{crit}(D)^{\frac{n}{2-n}}\ (2)^{\frac{n}{2(2-n)}}}{(a/\rho)^{\frac{1}{2-n}}}\right] \tag{3}$$

Smooth pipe data for solutions of 31 and 100 wppm of P-295 in water are shown in Figure 1(a) as the law of the wall velocity profile and in Figure 1(b) as the friction factor - Reynolds number correlation.

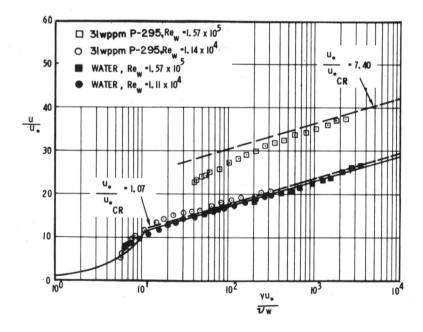

Figure 1(a)   Law of the Wall Velocity Profiles for P-295.

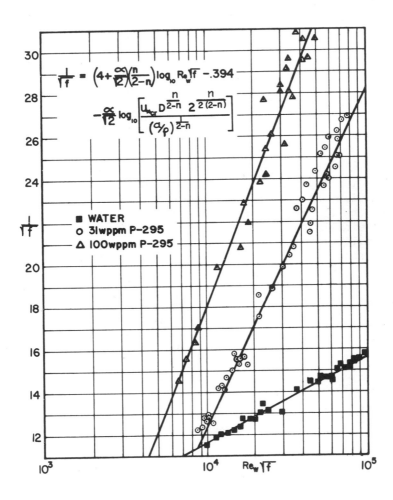

Figure 1(b) Friction Factor - Reynolds Number Correlation for P-295 in a 0.761-inch Pipe.

An explanation and analysis of the method of determining turbulent velocity fluctuations from total pressure fluctuations will
not be given in detail in this paper but this can be found in
Reference 11. An integration of Euler's equation leads to the result:

$$\frac{[\overline{(u')^2}]^{1/2}}{u} = \frac{[\overline{(p_t')^2}]^{1/2}}{\rho u^2} \tag{4}$$

The turbulence data in this paper are presented in two ways,
the total longitudinal turbulence intensity as a function of spatial position and the spectral distribution of longitudinal turbulent energy. The turbulent energy spectra are presented as the
non-dimensionalized turbulent energy per unit bandwidth versus non-
dimensionalized wave number, kD as rationalized in Reference 11. The
dimensionless energy is then expressible as

$$\bar{E}(kD) = \frac{\overline{\Delta(u')^2}}{\Delta k} \frac{1}{\overline{(u')^2}D} \tag{5}$$

where $\quad k = \dfrac{2\pi f}{u_L}$ $\tag{6}$

The integral over kD of all spectra in this form is thus unity and
direct comparisons of polymer solution and solvent spectra will
show any changes in energy distribution. Due to the normalization
with total intensity, changes in the energy amplitude will not be
apparent but any effects of the polymer additive on turbulence
scales can be determined. The macroscale, or inertial range turbulence scale, is expressed as

$$\Lambda = \int_0^\infty \frac{\bar{E}(kD)}{kD} \, d\,(kD) \tag{7}$$

The microscale, or dissipative range turbulence scale, is determined
by the value of kD at which the quantity $(kD)^2 \bar{E}(kD)$ is maximum.

Roughness Analysis

The roughness experiments involved the measurement of friction factor versus Reynolds number for three sizes of uniform roughness. Data for water and for a 31 wppm solution of P-295 are presented. The water data were used to determine the effective roughness size from the Newtonian data of Nikuradse (Ref. 16) for sand grain roughness in pipes. A roughness function was then defined for the P-295 data in a manner similar to Fenter (Ref. 17) by simply adding terms to the law of the wall velocity profile expression to account for roughness effects and sublayer thickening effects of the polymer additive. Allowing the roughness function to possibly be dependent on fluid properties as well as roughness the law of the wall can be written as

$$\phi = A \log_{10} \eta + B - F, \quad \text{for } u_* \geq u_{*crit} \tag{8}$$

where the sublayer thickening effect is included in B and from Equation (2)

$$B = 5.5 + \alpha \log_{10} \frac{u_*}{u_{*crit}}$$

F is assumed to be a function of η_k, α, and u_{*crit}. Evaluation of Equation (8) at the tube centerline gives

$$\frac{u_{max}}{u_*} = 5.77 \log_{10} \frac{R u_*}{\nu_w} + 5.5 + \alpha \log_{10} \frac{u_*}{u_{*crit}} - F \tag{9}$$

For fully developed turbulent pipe flow of Newtonian fluids and dilute solutions of drag-reducing fluids

$$u_{max} = \bar{u} + 4.07 u_* \tag{10}$$

Substitution of Equation (10) into Equation (9), converting shear velocity to friction factor, and introducing the Reynolds number leads to

$$\sqrt{\frac{2}{f}} = -4.07 + 5.5 + 5.77 \log_{10} Re_w \sqrt{f} + 5.77 \log_{10} \frac{1}{2\sqrt{2}}$$

$$- \alpha \log_{10} \frac{u_{*crit} \sqrt{2}}{\bar{u} \sqrt{f}} - F \tag{11}$$

Further manipulation and adjustment of the constants gives

$$F = \sqrt{2} \left\{ (4 + \frac{\alpha}{\sqrt{2}}) \log_{10} Re_w \sqrt{f} - \frac{1}{\sqrt{f}} \right.$$

$$\left. - .394 - \frac{\alpha}{\sqrt{2}} \log_{10} \frac{\sqrt{2} D u_{*crit}}{\nu_w} \right\} \tag{12}$$

Equation (12) allows the determination of the value of the roughness function for a drag-reducing fluid from friction factor – Reynolds number data taken in a rough pipe when α and $u*_{crit}$ for the fluid are known. In this equation the roughness function is defined to account for the deviation between the law of the wall velocity profiles for flow of drag-reducing fluids in smooth and rough pipes similar to the roughness function for Newtonian fluids that accounts for the deviation in the law of the wall for smooth and rough pipes in Newtonian flow.

RESULTS AND DISCUSSION

Turbulence Effects

The purpose of the turbulence experiments was to study the effects of the polymer additive on the turbulence field during a condition of reduced friction in order to see if the friction re- duction was a simple consequence of reduced turbulence as has been suggested by some investigators. This is essentially a continua- tion of the investigation reported in Reference 11 since the CMC solution used in the previous work showed no significant differences in turbulence structure from that of pure water. The CMC was only a moderately effective friction reducer (30 percent). The P-295 additive was known to be much more effective in reducing friction and it was decided to study the turbulence field for conditions of relatively large and small friction reduction for two solution con- centrations, 31 and 100 wppm.

Turbulence intensities were measured at the tube centerline for each solution of P-295 as well as for water over a range of Reynolds numbers. These data are shown in Figure 2. When non- dimensionalized with u_* the 31 wppm P-295 centerline turbulence intensity shows almost a constant value over the range of Re_w tested as does the water data. However, in this case the P-295 data are higher than the water data instead of having the same non-dimension- alized value as did the CMC data of Reference 11, indicating the

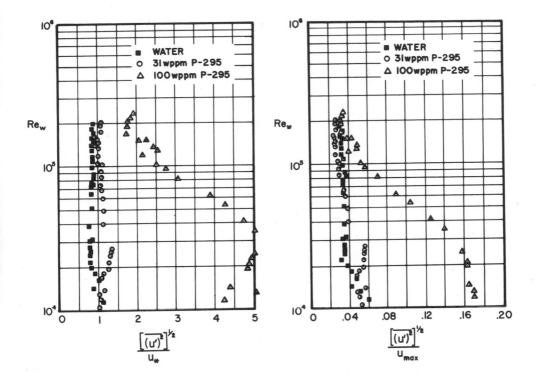

Figure 2 Turbulence Intensity at Pipe Centerline.

stronger effect of the P-295 on u_*. When non-dimensionalized with
u_{max} the 31 wppm P-295 data show a slight reduction in centerline
intensity (15-20 percent) compared to water at high Re_w or large
friction reduction (60 percent), and at low Re_w or small friction
reduction (16 percent) the P-295 intensity is slightly higher (20
percent) than that of water.

The centerline turbulence intensities for the 100 wppm P-295
solution show much stronger effects. The data non-dimensionalized
with u_{max} show no difference from water at the highest Re_w but
the intensity increases very strongly as Re_w decreases, becoming
three times that of water at the lowest Re_w. The friction reduction
for the 100 wppm P-295 solution at these two extremes was 78 and
55 percent respectively. The same data non-dimensionalized with
u_* show the effect of the larger friction reduction by being shifted
farther to the right on the graph.

Turbulence intensity profiles were measured for both P-295
solutions near the upper and lower extremes of the range of Re_w

previously mentioned. The data show some very interesting and somewhat puzzling trends as seen in Figure 3. Comparisons are made with
water at approximately the same values of Re_w and u_*. It will be
noticed that there is no appreciable Reynolds number effect on the
profiles as evidenced by the water data.

The turbulence intensity for the 31 wppm P-295 solution shows
only slight differences from that of water throughout the turbulent
core when non-dimensionalized with either the local velocity, u_L,
which is a variable, or u_* which is constant, for both high and low
Re_w (large and small friction reduction). In the buffer zone near
the wall the intensity for this concentration solution increases
above that of water at high Re_w and decreases at low Re_w in both nondimensional forms. Since the sublayer and buffer zone regions are
believed to control the polymer friction reduction phenomenon (Ref.
18) it is apparent that the friction reduction is due to something
more complex than just a simple reduction in turbulence intensity.

The turbulence intensity profiles for the 100 wppm solution of
P-295 further cloud the friction reduction - turbulence reduction
question. At high Re_w the 100 wppm data agree well with the 31
wppm data throughout the turbulent core when non-dimensionalized
with u_L, but in the buffer region the 100 wppm data lie considerably
below the water data while the 31 wppm are higher than the water
data. When non-dimensionalized with u_* the 100 wppm data show an
overall upward shift due to the large friction reduction, and the
trend to lower intensity as the wall is approached is more obvious.
It is also obvious that the location of the maximum intensity is
shifted farther from the wall. At low Re_w the 100 wppm data show a
very large increase in intensity throughout the turbulent core in
both plots and a very sharp reduction near the wall.

It should be mentioned that some significant errors in pitot
probe measurements were found with the 100 wppm solution. This
showed up in the mean velocity profile. When the measured profiles
were integrated and compared to the measured mass flow rates an
error of -14 percent at the high Re_w and -29 percent at the low
Re_w were found which are believed attributable to elastic effects.
The mean velocity data were corrected accordingly but no correction
was applied to the instantaneous velocity measurements and no
corrections were applied to any of the 31 wppm data as the maximum
errors found in mass flow rate comparisons for this solution were
less than five percent. It has been suggested (Ref. 19) that for
frequencies less than the reciprocal of the relaxation time of the
fluid molecules the response of a pitot probe will not be significantly affected. Oliver (Ref. 20) estimates a relaxation time of
10^{-4} sec. for dilute solutions of additives like P-295 which would
give a frequency limit of approximately 10^4 Hertz. Since this is
an order of magnitude greater than the frequency band containing the

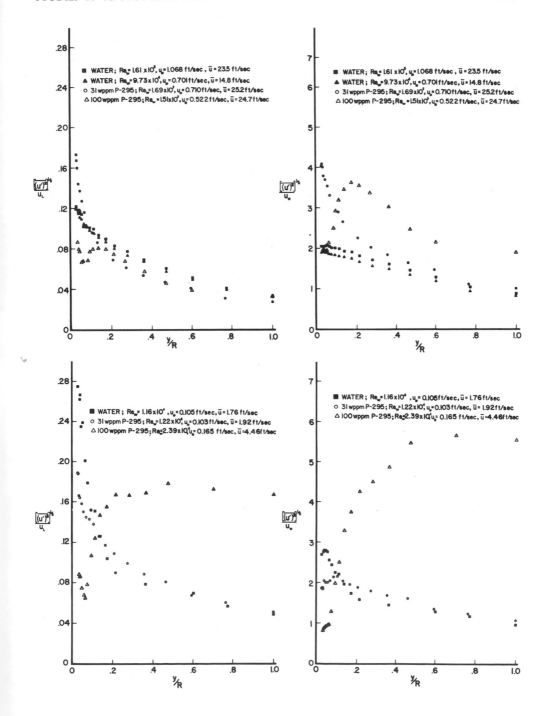

Figure   3   Turbulence Intensity Profiles.

bulk of the energy in these experiments the pitot response to the
fluctuations is assumed to be unaffected. Any correction would be
such as to raise the intensity level even higher than is shown.

Turbulent energy spectra were also measured for both P-295
solutions and for water at approximately the same conditions as
those of the intensity profiles. These data are shown in Figure 4.

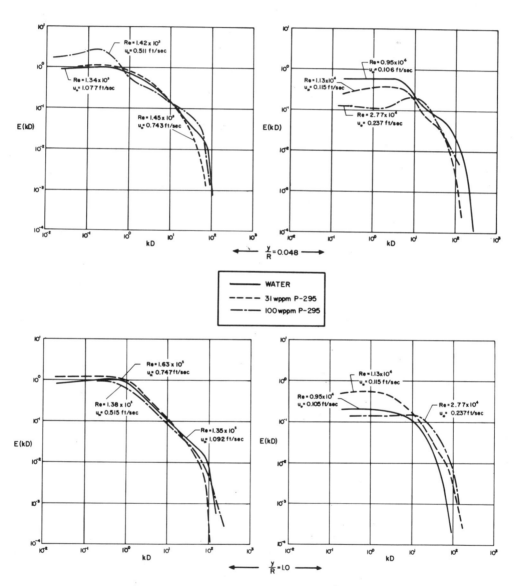

Figure 4 Dimensionless Turbulent Eenrgy Spectra.

Briefly, it can be stated that no appreciable differences exist in the spectra for water and for both P-295 solutions at any of the test conditions. In Reference 11 it was found that the turbulent energy in the CMC appeared to be shifted toward higher wave numbers as compared to water but that is not as apparent with the P-295 data. This may be partially due to the fact that the P-295 data were examined in more detail in the low wave number range and the measured absolute energy level was found to be dependent on the averaging time and sampling time of the wave analyzer in such a way that a decreased energy level at low wave numbers was indicated when the sweep rate of the wave analyzer was too great.

Changes in the macroscale and microscale for all of the spectra in Figure 4 were determined in the manner presented in the preceding section of this paper. The results are tabulated in Figure 5 relative to water. The scale value for water in each case is set equal to one and the relative scales of the P-295 spectra are given to show any changes in scale. As in the intensity profiles, the measured scale values for P-295 are found to be both increased and decreased compared to water at various conditions and there is no apparent pattern to the changes. This again suggests some sort of possible elastic effect on the turbulence field.

Surface Roughness Effects

Turbulent pipe flow experiments were conducted to examine the friction drag-reduction phenomenon for rough surfaces and to test the concept of a roughness function for friction-reducing fluids such as has been defined for Newtonian fluids (Ref. 16, 17). Three pipes were fabricated with uniform machined roughness in the form of 24, 48, and 96 threads per inch as described in a preceding section. Friction factor versus Reynolds number data were taken in all three pipes for water and a 31 wppm solution of P-295. The water friction factors were used to compute the Newtonian roughness function over a range of Re_w in each pipe according to Equation (12) for $\alpha = 0$. Using the designed roughness height the 24 and 48 threads per inch roughnesses were found to be equivalent to Nikuradse's sand grain roughness of the same size in the fully rough regime. The 96 threads per inch roughness was found to be effectively more rough than sand grain roughness and an effective roughness height of 0.0080 inches was necessary to correlate the data, lowering the value of R/K from 72 to 47. This is a 54 percent increase in the designed roughness size and cannot be definitely explained. However, this particular roughness required a double cutting operation not used with the other two and quite possibly could have been left with a burr along the crest of the thread resulting in the larger effective roughness.

MACROSCALE

		WATER	31 WPPM P-295	100 WPPM P-295
LARGE FRICTION REDUCTION	$Y/R = 1.0$	1	1.08	1.62
	$Y/R = .048$	1	1.25	.83
SMALL FRICTION REDUCTION	$Y/R = 1.0$	1	.46	.24
	$Y/R = .048$	1	1.55	.39

MICROSCALE

		WATER	31 WPPM P-295	100 WPPM P-295
LARGE FRICTION REDUCTION	$Y/R = 1.0$	1	.70	.90
	$Y/R = .048$	1	.75	1.17
SMALL FRICTION REDUCTION	$Y/R = 1.0$	1	.45	.64
	$Y/R = .048$	1	2.30	2.00

Figure 5.   Effects of P-295 on Turbulence Scale.

The water data and P-295 data are shown in Figure 6 as friction factor versus Reynolds number. The dashed lines in the lower part of the figure are fairings of the water data. The solid line is the smooth wall correlation for P-295 with the friction reduction onset shown by the break in the curve near Re_w = 9000. It can be seen that the roughest test section was hydraulically fully rough before $u*_{crit}$ was reached and remained fully rough (constant f) for P-295 for the entire turbulent range of Re_w with a reduction in friction

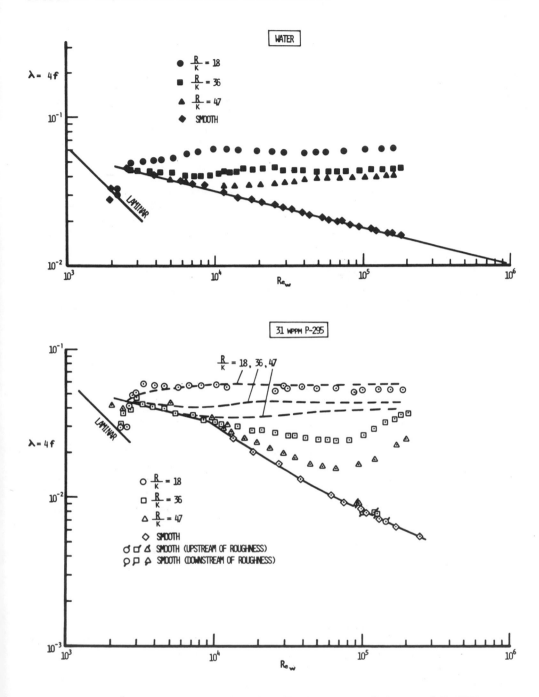

Figure 6 Rough-Pipe Friction Factors for Water and P-295.

factor of about 9 percent compared to water. The medium roughness
data show the friction factor to be less for P-295 than for water
at all Re_w above the friction reduction onset point. The P-295
data follow the smooth wall curve out to Re_w = 9000 at which point
the roughness effect appears to begin coincident with the friction
reduction onset for the smooth wall. The trend of the P-295 data
for the smallest roughness is similar to that for the medium roughness with an apparent tendency to follow the smooth wall curve for
a slight distance beyond the friction reduction onset point before
the onset of the roughness effect.

In both the medium and smallest roughness cases for P-295 the
onset of the roughness effect is delayed considerably from that
for water but when it occurs the transition is much more rapid.
Also, the fully rough regime is never reached with P-295 for these
roughness sizes and there is an absolute friction reduction relative
to water everywhere beyond the friction reduction onset point. It
appears that the P-295 friction factors might eventually get as
large as the water friction factor at higher Re_w implying that no
appreciable friction reduction would exist once the fully rough
regime is reached.

One other point should be made concerning these data. It is
well known that the very effective friction reducing polymers are
sensitive to degradation, or breaking of the molecules, by extreme
shear. It is suspected that the high shear stresses caused by
surface roughness might degrade the polymer solutions and lower the
friction-reducing effectiveness. This could cause the type of trend
seen with these data in the higher Re_w range. However, friction
factors in a smooth wall test section downstream of the roughness
sections were measured in all of these tests and there was no change
from the smooth wall values measured ahead of the roughness. The
smooth wall data are shown as the flagged symbols in Figure 6,
confirming that the rising friction factor trends at high Re_w reported here are not due to shear degradation.

The roughness function data, as calculated from Equation (12),are
given in Figure 7. The water data are shown in Figure 7(a) compared
to Nikuradse's data. The P-295 data are shown in Figure 7(b).
Equation (12) only allows the calculation of F from the data and does
not provide the functional form of F, whatever that may be. A logical
first test of the data would be to compare the calculated values of
F with F_N to see if the roughness effect is the same in both drag-
reducing and Newtonian fluids. It is obvious from the data that F
becomes larger than F_N once the critical shear stress is exceeded
and the deviation continues to increase with increasing n_K. Also,
F does not correlate simply with n_K as does F_N but shows a dependence on K.

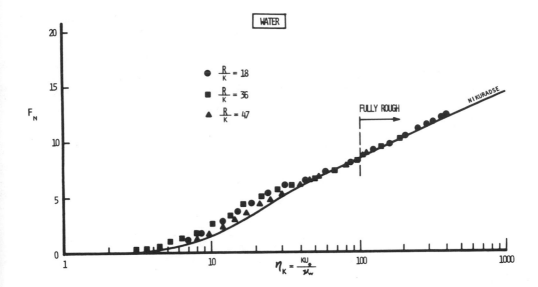

Figure 7(a) Roughness Function for Water.

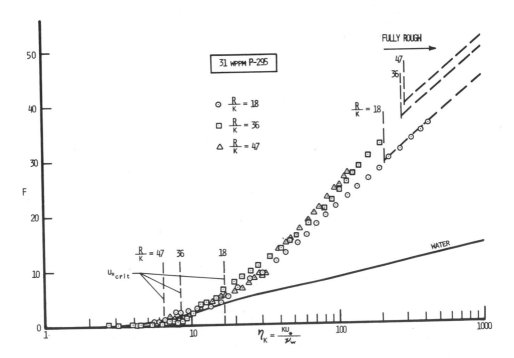

Figure 7(b) Roughness Function for P-295.

Further insight may be gained by referring to Figure 6. Since the data for the largest roughness show this pipe to be fully rough and have little or no net friction reduction then the Newtonian roughness function should predict this friction effect relative to the smooth-pipe Newtonian case. However, the roughness function for P-295 according to Equation (12) has been based on the smooth-pipe drag-reducing case which differs from the Newtonian case by the term

$$\alpha \ \log_{10} \ \frac{u_*}{u_{*crit}}$$

Then the roughness function for P-295 necessary to agree with these data can be expressed as

$$F = F_N + \alpha\log_{10} \ \frac{u_*}{u_{*crit}} \quad ; \quad u_* \geq u_{*crit} \tag{13}$$

In Reference (17) F_N is given exactly for the fully rough regime by the expression

$$F_N = A\log \ \eta_K - C \tag{14}$$

Substituting Equation (14) into Equation (13) and expanding the last term gives

$$F = A\log_{10} \ \frac{u_* K}{\nu} - C + \alpha\log_{10} \ \frac{u_* K}{\nu} - \alpha\log_{10} \ \frac{u_{*crit} K}{\nu} \tag{15}$$

or upon combining terms

$$F = (A + \alpha) \ \log_{10} \ \eta_K - \alpha\log_{10} \ \frac{u_{*crit} K}{\nu} - C \tag{16}$$

where A and C are the Newtonian constants 5.77 and 3.00 respectively. Equation (16) expresses F in a form similar to F_N for the fully rough regime but as can be seen the slope of the curve is changed by α and the intercept changes with α and is also dependent on K and u_{*crit}. This is to say that if no friction reduction occurs in the fully rough regime for any roughness size then the experimental values of F in that regime should be predicted for each roughness size by Equation (16).

The fully rough curves for each of the three roughness sizes described by Equation (16) are shown in Figure 7(b). The onset of the fully rough regime for each roughness size was calculated by determining the value of η_K for the condition $\eta_K/\eta_{sublayer} \geq 8.5$

which defines the fully rough regime for Newtonian flow. The experiments with the medium and smallest roughness sizes did not get
to high enough Reynolds numbers to reach fully rough flow. However,
the trend of these data in Figure 7(b) strongly suggests that these
pipes would have also lost all of the drag-reducing effect in the
fully rough regime.

The predicted onset of the drag-reducing effect is shown in
Figure 7(b) for each of the roughness sizes. Below the respective
value of η_K based on $u*_{crit}$ for each roughness α is effectively
zero and Equation (12) reduces to the Newtonian case with F being
equivalent to F_N. The data show the deviation from the Newtonian
curve to start when $u*_{crit}$ is reached. Thus Equation (16) adequately
defines the roughness function for P-295 above the fully rough
threshold for these data and below $u*_{crit}$ the roughness function for
the drag-reducing fluid agrees with that for Newtonian fluids.
Equation (16) could also be tested in the transition roughness
regime by changing the constants in Equation (14) to approximate the
Newtonian transition regime with logarithmic segments connecting
η_K for $u*_{crit}$ with η_K for the fully rough threshold for P-295.
Examination of the data shows that this would overestimate F in the
transition regime. The net conclusion from all of this is that
once $u*_{crit}$ is exceeded in a rough pipe roughness effects and sublayer thickening effects interact in some as yet unidentified manner
in the transition region to give a reduced drag-reduction effectiveness and in the fully rough regime to eliminate all drag reduction.
However, since both ends of the roughness function seem to be well-
defined reasonable estimates of the function between the limits
can be made.

One other look at these data is worthwhile from a practical
standpoint. If the point of interest is one of simply comparing
friction losses in rough pipes for drag-reducing and Newtonian fluids
rather than defining a roughness function per se, the net effect on
the flow may be examined by combining roughness and polymer effects
into one term and comparing this with the Newtonian case. A single
function, ΔB, which represents the shift of the law of the wall
profile due to any cause, can be defined from Equation (9),

$$\Delta B = \phi - A \log_{10} \eta - 5.5 \tag{17}$$

or, evaluating Equation (17) at the pipe centerline and using
Equation (10), ΔB can be evaluated from friction factor data,

$$\Delta B = \sqrt{2} \left(4 \log_{10} Re_w \sqrt{f} - \frac{1}{\sqrt{f}} - .394 \right) \tag{18}$$

This equation describes smooth-pipe Newtonian flow when the left-hand side is zero. Thus a comparison of experimentally determined values of ΔB with F_N will show over what range of η_K, if any, a net drag reduction will be realized in a rough pipe with a drag-reducing fluid. If the ΔB term is equal to F_N there is no drag reduction. If it is less than F_N and greater than zero the skin friction will be higher than for a smooth pipe but less than for the same rough pipe with Newtonian flow. If it is negative the skin friction will be even less than the Newtonian smooth-pipe case.

The data are presented in this manner in Figure 8. Values of ΔB calculated from the data are compared with the Newtonian roughness function and the smooth-wall drag-reducing function. Note that since the independent variable is η_K, there is a different smooth-wall drag-reducing function for each roughness size. The largest roughness data agree well with F_N at all η_K again showing that this pipe became fully rough before the polymer could become effective

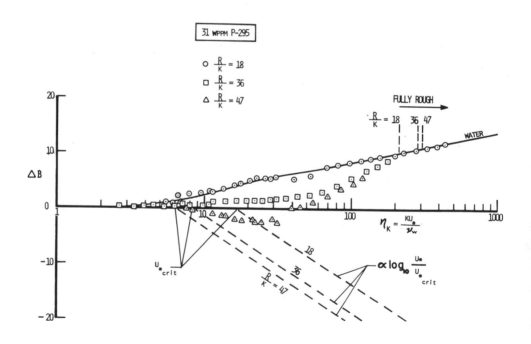

Figure 8 ΔB for Water and P-295 in Rough Pipes.

and no significant friction reduction was realized. The medium
roughness data show a net friction reduction relative to water
beyond $u*_{crit}$. The smallest roughness data show a sharp drop in
friction as $u*_{crit}$ is reached falling below the smooth-pipe Newtonian level for a moderate range of η_K and then rising rapidly
toward the Newtonian roughness level. It is even more apparent
in this figure than in Figure 7(b) that the medium and smallest
roughness data are tending toward the Newtonian friction level,
i.e., no friction reduction, as the fully rough regime is approached.

In summarizing these results with P-295 it can be said that
the only region in which the polymer additive will reduce rough-
pipe friction is in the transition roughness regime and the analysis as applied here is as yet inadequate to correlate the data in
this regime. However, the roughness function for drag-reducing
fluids is analytically described by Equation (16) in the fully
rough regime and is equivalent to the Newtonian roughness function
before the onset of drag-reduction. In between these two limits
there is a smooth transition with some drag-reduction occurring.
A case of particular interest was not covered in these experiments - that of onset of drag-reduction preceding the onset of
roughness. The smallest roughness was chosen for this case, but
the water data showed the effective roughness to be considerably
larger than the physical roughness. This made the two onset points
nearly identical. This remains an experiment of great interest
since even greater deviation from the Newtonian roughness function
than found in the present data can be expected in the transition
region. In all, the findings of these experiments are consistent
with the physical explanation of the effects of drag-reducing
additives found in earlier work.

CONCLUSIONS

1. Strong effects on turbulence intensity occur in the buffer zone
for both fluid concentrations and in the turbulent core for the more
concentrated solution. The effects are dependent on Reynolds number
and concentration but are not directly related to the drag reduction
implying a possible viscoelastic behavior.

2. Turbulence spectra are not significantly affected by the additives in either concentration. At high Reynolds numbers the effects
on microscale and macroscale for both concentrations are slight.
At low Reynolds numbers microscale and macroscale are both affected
to an extent which seems to be related to concentration and independent of friction reduction, again implying elastic effects.

3. The onset of roughness is the same for Newtonian and drag-reducing fluids, if the onset of roughness precedes the onset of drag-
reduction. Also, the drag reduction onset is the same in smooth

and rough pipes if flow is not in the fully rough regime.

4. The percentage friction reduction in rough pipes with drag-reducing fluids (relative to Newtonian friction) initially increases with Reynolds number beyond u_{*crit} reaching a maximum in the transition roughness regime and then decreasing with further increases in Reynolds number until little or no net friction reduction is realized in the fully rough regime. For small roughnesses the net drag will even be less in part of the transition regime than for Newtonian fluids at the same Reynolds numbers in smooth pipes. All of these trends are dependent on K, α, and u_{*crit} .

5. A roughness function defined for drag-reducing fluids can be used to predict friction factors below u_{*crit} and above the onset of the fully rough regime. The same function shows a smooth transition between the two limits.

6. Data are needed to determine the effects of roughness which becomes effective after the onset of drag reduction.

ACKNOWLEDGEMENTS

      This research was supported by independent research and development funds of Ling-Temco-Vought, Inc., and the National Aeronautics and Space Administration under Contract NASw-729 (Fluid Physics Branch of the Research Division, OART). The author would also like to express his appreciation for the interest and assistance in this work of Dr. J. Harkness and Dr. C. S. Wells of the Aerophysics Group, LTV Research Center.

SYMBOLS

a   viscosity power-law coefficient; 1.007 cp for 31 wppm, 1.688 cp for 100 wppm of P-295

D   pipe diameter, 0.761 inches smooth and 0.750 inches rough for these experiments

f   frequency, Hertz; also friction factor, defined to be

$$\frac{2\,\tau_w}{\rho \bar{u}^2}$$

λ pipe flow resistance coefficient, defined to be

$$\frac{2D}{\rho \bar{u}^2}\ \frac{\Delta p}{\Delta L}\ ;\ \text{also turbulence microscale}$$

L   length along pipe

n   viscosity power-law exponent; 0.99 for 31 wppm, 0.94 for 100 wppm of P-295

p   static pressure

p_t' fluctuation component of the total pressure

R   pipe radius

Re_w Reynolds number, defined to be $\dfrac{\bar{u}D}{\nu_w}$

u   steady velocity, ft/sec

u'   instantaneous longitudinal fluctuation component of velocity, ft/sec

u_{max} velocity at the centerline, ft/sec

$\bar{u}$ mean flow velocity, computed from measured flow rate and pipe diameter, ft/sec

u_* defined to be $(\tau_w/\rho)^{1/2} = (\frac{\Delta p}{\Delta L} \cdot \frac{D}{4\rho})^{1/2}$, shear velocity, ft/sec

u_{*crit} shear velocity for onset of friction reduction; 0.0968 ft/sec for 31 wppm, 0.0570 ft/sec for 100 wppm of P-295

y   distance from pipe wall

α correlation constant, defined by Equation (3); 17.2 for 31 wppm, 23.8 for 100 wppm of P-295

τ shear stress

ν kinematic viscosity, μ/ρ

μ viscosity

ρ density

ϕ defined to be u/u_*, law of the wall velocity, dimensionless

η defined to be yu_*/ν_w, law of the wall distance, dimensionless

k   wave number, defined by Equation (6)

K   roughness height

$\bar{E}$ dimensionless energy, defined by Equation (5)

η_K dimensionless roughness height, defined to be Ku_*/ν_w

F roughness function for drag-reducing fluids, defined by Equation (12)

F_N roughness function for Newtonian fluids

Λ turbulence macroscale, defined by Equation (7)

Subscripts

w   conditions at the wall

L   local conditions in flow stream

REFERENCES

1. Dodge, D. W., and Metzner, A. D., "Turbulent Flow of Non-Newtonian Systems", A.I.Ch.E. Journal, Vol. 5, pp. 189-203 (1959).

2. Ernst, W. D., "Investigation of the Turbulent Shear Flow of Dilute Aqueous CMC Solutions", A.I.Ch.E. Journal, Vol.12, pp 581, 586 (1966).

3. Shaver, R. G., and Merrill, E. W., "Turbulent Flow of Pseudo-Plastic Solutions in Straight Cylindrical Tubes", A.I.Ch.E. Journal, Vol. 5, pp 181-187 (1959).

4. Wells, C. S., "Anomalous Turbulent Flow of Non-Newtonian Fluids", A.I.A.A. Journal, Vol. 3, pp 1800-1805 (1965).

5. Fabula, A. G., "The Toms Phenomenon in the Turbulent Flow of Very Dilute Polymer Solutions", Proceedings of the Fourth International Congress on Rheology, Part 3, Ed.; E. H. Lee, pp 455-479 (1964).

6. Meyer, W. A., "A Correlation of the Frictional Characteristics for Turbulent Flow of Dilute Non-Newtonian Fluids in Pipes", A.I.Ch.E. Journal, Vol. 12, pp 522-525 (1966).

7. Granville, P. S., David Taylor Model Basin Hydromechanics Laboratory Report, 1966.

8. Wells, C. S., "Turbulent Heat Transfer in Drag-Reducing Fluids", A.I.Ch.E. Journal, Vol. 14, No. 3, pp 406-410 (1968).

9. Wells, C. S., "An Analysis of Uniform Injection of a Drag-Reducing Fluid into a Turbulent Boundary Layer", presented at the Symposium on Viscous Drag Reduction, LTV Research Center, Dallas, Texas, September 24-25, 1968.

10. Brennen, C., and Gadd, G. E., "Aging and Degradation in Dilute Polymer Solutions", Nature, Vol. 215, (1967).

11. Wells, C. S., Harkness, J., and Meyer, W. A., "Turbulence Measurements in Pipe Flow of a Drag-Reducing Non-Newtonian Fluid", A.I.A.A. Journal, Vol. 6, pp 250-257 (1968).

12. Virk, P. S., "The Toms Phenomenon - Turbulent Pipe Flow of Dilute Polymer Solutions", Massachusetts Institute of Technology, Sc.D. Thesis, Nov. 1966.

13. Johnson, B., and Barchi, R. H., "Effect of Drag-Reducing Additives on Boundary Layer Turbulence", Journal of Hydronautics, Vol. 2, No. 3, pp 168-175 (1968).

14. White, A., "Turbulence and Drag-Reduction with Polymer Additives", Research Bulletin No. 4, Hendon College of Technology, January 1967.

15. Ernst, W. D., "Turbulent Flow of an Elasticoviscous Non-Newtonian Fluid", A.I.A.A. Journal, Vol. 5, No. 5, pp 906-909 (1967).

16. Nikuradse, J., "Strömungsgesetze in rauhen Rohren", VDI - Forschungsheft 361, 1933.

17. Fenter, F. W., "The Turbulent Boundary Layer on Uniformly Rough Surfaces at Supersonic Speeds", Report No. RE-E9R-2, Vought Research Center, Chance Vought Aircraft, Inc., December 1959.

18. Wells, C. S., and Spangler, J. G., "Effects of Local Injection of a Drag-Reducing Fluid into Turbulent Pipe Flow of a Newtonian Fluid", Physics of Fluids, 10, 9, p 1890 (1967).

19. Metzner, A. D., and Astarita, G., "External Flows of Viscoelastic Materials: Fluid Property Restrictions on the Use of Velocity-Sensitive Probes", A.I.Ch.E. Journal, Vol. 13, No. 3, pp 550-555 (1967).

20. Oliver, D. R., "The Expansion/Contraction Behavior of Laminar Liquid Jets", Canadian Journal of Chemical Engineering, Vol. 44, 100 (1966).

TURBULENT SKIN FRICTION

OF DILUTE POLYMER SOLUTIONS IN ROUGH PIPES

H. Brandt, A. T. McDonald*, F. W. Boyle**

University of California, Davis

ABSTRACT

Turbulent flow of dilute aqueous CMC solutions in smooth
and in rough pipes was studied. Results are presented for
pipes of 1-inch i.d., both plain and roughened with silicon
carbide particles in 60, 100, and 120 grit sizes. Each pipe
system was tested with polymer concentrations of 0, 100, 250,
and 500 ppm of CMC by weight.

The results show that flow properties are extensively influenced by polymer addition and surface roughness. In the
transition and fully rough flow regimes, friction reduction
appears to be affected by wall conditions alone. Addition of
CMC to water appears to be more effective in smooth than in
rough pipes. For example, addition of 500 wppm of CMC reduced
drag in the smooth pipe system by 19.3 percent at a Reynolds
number of 5×10^5, whereas in the roughest pipe tested drag was
reduced only 1.4 percent.

INTRODUCTION

Polymer-modified turbulent flows have received much attention during the past decade because of their technical and
industrial importance. Recent studies have shown these flows
to be highly complicated. To utilize effectively the unique
properties of polymer solutions, fundamental research is needed
to delineate the mechanism of friction reduction in turbulent
flow, and to extend experimental results to cover new applications.

---

* Currently at Purdue University
** Currently at The U. S. Army, Aberdeen Proving Ground

Laminar viscometry is unsatisfactory to determine turbulent flow behavior of polymer solutions. In turbulent flow, dilute solutions exhibit a thickened viscous sublayer, but otherwise little departure from purely viscous behavior. This polymer effect on the sublayer has been termed an "inverse roughness" by Granville (Ref. 1), since purely viscous flow over rough surfaces will thin, and eventually will eliminate the viscous sublayer.

The behavior of rough surface flows may be explained in terms of the turbulent velocity profile. As Reynolds number is increased, the relative thickness of the viscous sublayer decreases and eventually the roughness elements protrude through the sublayer. When this occurs, the predominant source of pressure drop becomes form drag caused by the roughness elements, and the flow is termed "fully rough."

In terms of the universal turbulent flow mean velocity profile (law of the wall)

$$\frac{u}{u_*} = A \log \frac{yu_*}{\nu} + D \tag{1}$$

where the symbols are defined in the notation. As the sublayer thickens, the value of D increases. An equation for wall shearing stress derived from Equation 1 gives good agreement with experimental results for flow of Newtonian fluids.

The concept of an inverse roughness suggested that valuable engineering information might be obtained by using a rough pipe as a turbulent flow rheometer. If the effects of wall roughness and polymer additive were to superpose, two tests with different roughnesses would allow calculation of constants A and D. If the effects would not superpose, a more complicated situation would exist; in this case the rough-pipe rheometer would become an essential tool for the accurate determination of friction factors in rough surface flows.

Most surfaces in engineering practice are not hydrodynamically smooth. The requirements on smoothness become more stringent as Reynolds number increases, and as a result, the designer of a large scale system can seldom afford to provide a smooth surface. Interest in applying polymer modified turbulent flows to large scale systems has exposed the present lack of knowledge about their behavior in flow over rough surfaces.

The purpose of this paper is to report experimental data for flow of dilute aqueous CMC solutions in rough pipes. These data can be used to estimate the benefits derived from using this drag reducing fluid on rough surfaces in general.

PREVIOUS STUDIES

Lindgren and Hoot (Ref. 2) studied flow of polymer solutions in a rough duct. They chose a rectangular duct about 14 mm. square, of which two opposite sides were roughened with sand grains of 0.2 - 0.7 mm. and the remaining sides were smooth. The smooth sides contained pressure taps and permitted observation of the flow within the duct. Results were obtained also for flow in a smooth duct of similar configuration for Reynolds numbers up to 46,000.

The polymer used, polyethylene oxide WSR-301*, was injected continuously into the flowing water to give bulk concentrations of either 15 or 60 wppm**. The results show some reduction in turbulent skin friction at the higher Reynolds numbers for both the smooth and rough ducts. The authors suggest that a trend toward constant friction factor of 0.06 appears at a Reynolds number of about 30,000, but that further studies are necessary to evaluate more fully the effect of polymer concentration on friction reduction.

THE ROUGH-PIPE FLOW SYSTEM

A pipe flow system was chosen for the present study because skin friction can be obtained directly from pressure drop measurements. The test system was fabricated from 1-inch (1.01-inch actual i.d.) stainless steel tubing to permit accurate flow measurements over a Reynolds number range from 10^4 to 5×10^5. Pipe sections were roughened by applying waterproof silicon carbide sandpaper to the inside wall. A series of 11-inch sections constituted each of the sand-roughened test sections.

---

*A product of Union Carbide Corporation, sold under the trade name "Polyox" (3)

**wppm = concentration, in weight parts polymer per million parts solvent

The sections, which were cut of a single piece of tubing, were
marked and numbered before cutting so that they could be
correctly reassembled and aligned. Details of the procedure for
attaching the sandpaper may be found in Reference 4. A
schematic diagram of the apparatus is shown in Figure 1.

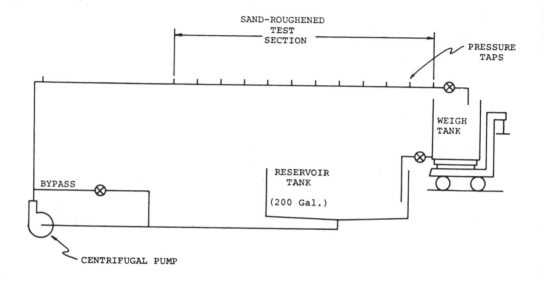

Figure 1 Schematic of Flow System

     Data were obtained with four separate test sections, con-
sisting of one industrially smooth pipe and three sand-roughened
pipes. The industrially smooth test section was smooth with the
exception of five 0.040-inch holes which were drilled and
carefully deburred for use as static pressure taps. The roughened
sections were joined by sealing couplings which contained taps
for static pressure measurements. In all test sections, an
entrance length of about 60 pipe diameters preceded the first
static pressure tap.

     Both geometry and spacing of roughness elements are impor-
tant in rough-surface flow. The abrasive particles had jagged
edges and departed greatly from a spherical shape. Close
inspection of the sandpaper itself showed close packing among
the particles. The size distribution of the particles is given
in Table 1.

Table 1 Size Distribution of Silicon Carbide Particles

Grit	100 Percent through Screen Opening	99.5 Percent through Screen Opening	Percent on a Screen of Opening		Percent through a Screen of Opening	
			Percent	Opening	Percent	Opening
60	0.0215 in.	0.0164 in.	4.4-8.4	0.0131 in.	21-25	0.0094 in.
100	0.0131	0.0094	3.0-6.0	0.0066	18-22	0.0052
120	0.0094	0.0066	10.0-16.9	0.0052	25-29	0.0039

The polymer used in this study was sodium carboxymethyl-cellulose, grade CMC - 7HSP, manufactured by the Hercules Powder Company. Complete data may be found in Reference 5.

PROCEDURE

Aqueous polymer solutions were prepared in concentrations of 100, 250 and 500 wppm. The hygroscopic nature of CMC made the moisture content an important consideration in determining the weight of polymer required to make up a given concentration. To determine the moisture content of the CMC before a series of runs, a sample was weighed, heated to about 325°F for 10 hours, and weighed again. This temperature was high enough to drive off moisture without any detectable physical change in the CMC powder. The powder lot used had a moisture content of approximately 11 percent.

The CMC was mixed with water by gradually sprinkling the fine powder over a stream of water entering the weigh tank. The particles separated rapidly in the fast moving stream and the active mixing resulted in a lump-free solution. A homogeneous solution was ensured by continuous recirculation for approximately 15 minutes.

In the roughened test sections, the influence of minor section misalignment was pronounced in the section with 120 grit sandpaper and negligible in the section with 60 grit paper. Alignment was considered satisfactory if the difference between the highest and lowest differential pressure readings across each section did not exceed ±5 percent of the average reading.

To improve the accuracy of pressure drop measurements, static pressures were measured across a minimum of two roughened pipe sections. When this pressure drop became too small to be read with mercury manometers, readings were taken across 11 sections using a water filled manometer. In this way the pressure drop per section could be measured to about 0.1 inch of water.

The cross-sectional area of a sand-roughened test section was determined from the difference in weights between an empty and a water filled section. During each run the aqueous solution temperature was measured.

After a series of runs, a few of the first measurements were repeated to check for possible shear degradation of the solution. No evidence of degradation was found in the entire investigation, nor was any long term buildup of polymer detected.

RESULTS AND DISCUSSION

Calculation of Reynolds Number

All friction factor data for dilute solutions are plotted against Reynolds numbers based on the viscosity of pure water. Due to the slight non-Newtonian nature of solutions containing friction reducers, a question arises as to which Reynolds number should be used. A non-Newtonian Reynolds number has been suggested (Ref. 6) which causes the laminar portion of the friction factor-Reynolds number curve to coincide with that for Newtonian fluids. However, the turbulent flow portion of the curves appears to be correlated only for Newtonian fluids, in which case the non-Newtonian Reynolds number reduces to the Newtonian Reynolds number. It appears that the added complexity of the non-Newtonian Reynolds number outweighs any advantages that it might offer in correlating the results of this study.

It also has been suggested (Ref. 7) that the conventional Reynolds number be used, but with an "apparent" viscosity computed from viscometric data corresponding to flow conditions in the pipe. At high shear rates the viscosity of the dilute polymer solutions used in this investigation approaches that of pure water.

A slight variation in defining viscosity has been proposed by Ernst and Meyer (Refs. 8, 9) to account for the importance of the wall region in drag reduction. Ernst assumes that a power law velocity profile is valid at the wall and that the local viscosity can be calculated from the local wall shear stress using measured viscometric data. Meyer indicated that the ratio of local apparent viscosity to the viscosity of pure water ranged only from 1.1 to 2.2 for a study covering shear rates similar to those in the present study.

For the shear rates of interest in this investigation (up to 10^6 sec^{-1}), it is not meaningful to measure viscosity directly with a viscometer due to the onset of turbulent flow. A common method of predicting viscosity at such high shear rates is to plot data measured at lower shear rates and then to extrapolate the curve to the shear rates of interest. This procedure is subject to errors in extrapolation, and its validity has not been demonstrated.

The inherent problems in dealing with the viscosity of fluids in turbulent flow are the difficulty in choosing an appropriate shear rate for comparison, and the possibility of the effect of viscoelasticity. A Reynolds number based on the viscosity of water was used for this study, because it is easily computed, precisely defined, and allows direct comparison with familiar Newtonian results.

Calculation of Tube Roughness

To check the repeatability of the experimental data and to evaluate the equivalent sand-grain roughness of the test section, preliminary runs were made with pure water. In Figure 2, the resulting friction factor data form curves of the shapes expected for sand-grain roughened surfaces. At low Reynolds numbers, data for the industrially smooth pipe blend into Prandtl's law of friction for smooth pipes (Ref. 10). At high Reynolds numbers the smooth pipe curve resembles those of Moody (Ref. 11), and the beginning of the fully rough region may be seen.

The equivalent sand-grain roughness of a test section is determined by the friction factor in the fully rough region. The roughness parameter, R/k_s, is calculated from

$$\frac{1}{\sqrt{f}} = 2 \log_{10}\left(\frac{R}{k_s}\right) + B \qquad (2)$$

which is derived from Equation 1. In the calculation, the value of f obtained from water data in the fully rough region in Figure 2 is used. The value of B for water is 1.74 (Ref. 12). Calculated values of R/k_s for the 60, 100, and 120 grit roughnesses were 11.8, 24.9, and 41.3, respectively. The smooth pipe was estimated to have an R/k_s value of 5000.

The calculated sand grain roughness size of the roughness elements is larger than their physical size. The difference between physical and apparent roughness sizes is attributed to differences in shape of the particles. The silicon carbide particles are extremely jagged, whereas photographs of the sand grains used by Nikuradse (Ref. 13) indicate a much smoother surface and a more nearly spherical shape.

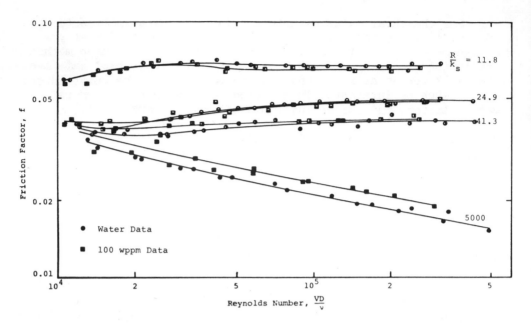

Figure 2   Friction Factor Data for Water and 100 wppm Solution

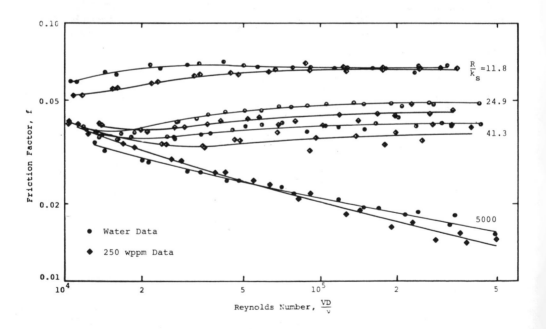

Figure 3   Friction Factor Data for Water and 250 wppm Solution

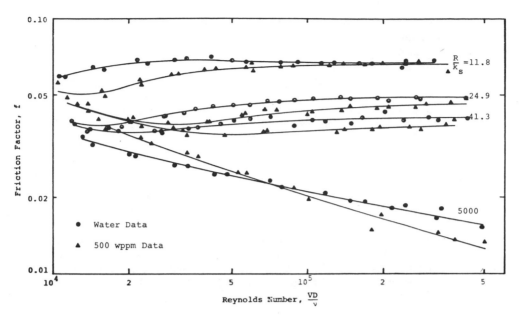

Figure 4   Friction Factor Data for Water and 500 wppm Solution

Friction Factor Data

In Figures 2 through 4, friction factor data for each polymer concentration are compared with friction factor data for water flow in all four pipes tested. These presentations show the effect of changes in pipe roughness and indicate the regions where the data approach the smooth pipe curve.

Figure 2 shows that a 100 wppm solution has less than a 4 percent effect on friction factor compared to flow of water. Drag is increased nearly 11 percent for the smooth pipe, but is affected only slightly for roughened pipes.

The data for 250 wppm, Figure 3, show about 13 percent drag reduction at high Reynolds numbers (5×10^5) for the smooth pipe. The first sign of a "crossover" between the water and polymer solution curves occurs. Drag in the smooth pipe is increased slightly for low Reynolds numbers, but the trend changes smoothly to a slight decrease at high Reynolds numbers.

For the 250 wppm solution, the drag is also reduced for rough pipes. The reduction for the 120 and 100 grit pipes

extends to higher Reynolds numbers, but there is still a pronounced effect in the 60-grit tube. In each case, the friction
factor at high Reynolds number approaches the water value.
Thus in the fully rough region, there is relatively little
effect due to polymer addition.

The 500 wppm data in Figure 4 show a more pronounced
crossover for the smooth pipe. Drag is reduced 19.3 percent
at a Reynolds number of 5×10^5, but is increased a like amount
at a Reynolds number of 1.5×10^4. This effect was also noted
in Reference 4, and has been observed by others (Ref. 14). As in
the case for 250 wppm solution flow, significant drag reduction
is present in the transition region, but the onset of the fully
rough regime is delayed.

It appears quite possible that the crossover is caused by
basing the Reynolds number on the solvent viscosity. If the
actual, higher viscosity had been used, the slope of the curve
would have become more gradual, and the curve would have blended
into the curve for water in smooth pipes.

The similarity between polymer solution and water behavior
observed in the fully rough regime supports the theory that
drag reduction is a wall phenomenon. The thickened viscous
sublayer is responsible for delaying transition to larger Reynolds
numbers. Experiments on blunt bodies have shown that form drag at
low Reynolds numbers is insensitive to the presence of polymer
solution. Since pressure drop in rough-pipe flow is due entirely
to form drag, the friction factor should be constant in fully rough
flow.

It is only in the transition regime of rough-pipe flow
that the friction factor depends on both Reynolds number and
roughness height. Once the fully rough region is reached, the
resistance formula of pure solvent, Equation 2 may be used.

Utility of Rough Pipe Rheometer

Figure 4 illustrates particularly well the effect of polymer
solutions in extending the transition region to higher Reynolds
numbers. It is evident that the onset of the fully rough region
has been delayed to Reynolds numbers higher by as much as a
factor of ten, compared to flow of pure water. Furthermore,
as the Reynolds number increases, the effect of the additive
decreases until finally it has no effect at all. These results
strongly support the concept that friction reduction is a wall
phenomenon only, and that the effect of the additive is to
thicken the viscous sublayer.

An analysis of the data shown in Figures 2 through 4 indicates that drag reducing agents produce more than a simple shift in the values of constants A and D in Equation 1. Therefore the effects of roughness and polymer additives do not superpose. Consequently more than two measurements are necessary to determine flow properties of drag-reducing solutions.

For flow of water in rough pipes, friction factor data in the fully rough region could be represented either by the simple relationship of Equation 2 or by the well known Moody chart. On the other hand, for flow of dilute aqueous solutions of CMC in rough pipes, the polymer requires that one consider additional variables. In this case, a friction factor correlation equivalent to that of Equation 2 would be impractically complex. Therefore it is recommended that Figures 2 through 4 be used directly in the determination of friction losses for flow of dilute aqueous CMC solutions in rough pipes.

CONCLUSIONS

The data and analysis presented indicate some general conclusions regarding the addition of friction reducer CMC to water.

The addition of CMC is more effective in reducing turbulent skin friction on smooth surfaces than on rough surfaces, based on percentage reduction.

The friction reducer appears to have little or no effect on flow in the fully rough regime, but the onset of this regime is considerably delayed.

Behavior in the transition regime strongly supports the presence of a thickened viscous sublayer, and tends to localize the friction reduction phenomenon as a wall effect only.

The rough-pipe flow rheometer appears to be an essential tool in determining flow properties of a polymer solution in rough-pipe flow.

ACKNOWLEDGMENT

Part of the experimental equipment was constructed with funds given by the R. C. Baker Foundation to the University of California at Davis. One of the authors, Mr. F. W. Boyle, was supported during these studies by a graduate fellowship of the R. C. Baker Foundation.

NOMENCLATURE

A   Constant in Equation 1

B   Constant in Equation 2

D   Constant in Equation 1

f   Friction factor, dimensionless, defined by $\Delta p = f \dfrac{L}{2R} \rho \dfrac{V^2}{2}$

k_s Roughness height, ft

L   Distance between pressure taps, ft

P   Static pressure, lb/ft^2

R   Pipe radius, ft

u   Time mean axial velocity, ft/sec

u_* Wall shearing velocity, ft/sec, $u_* \equiv \sqrt{\tau_0/\rho}$

V   Mass average flow velocity, ft/sec

y   Distance from conduit wall, ft

ν Kinematic viscosity, ft^2/sec

ρ Density, $lb\text{-}sec^2/ft^4$

τ_0 Wall shear stress, lb/ft^2

REFERENCES

1.   Granville, P. S., "Chairman's Remarks," ONR Symposium on the Hydrodynamics of Drag Reduction, Washington, D. C., June 2, 1966

2.   Lindgren, E. R. and Hoot, T. G., "Effects of Dilute High Molecular Weight Polymers on Turbulent Flows of Water in Very Rough Pipes," Trans. ASME, J. Appl. Mech., 35E 2, June 1968, pp. 417-418

3.   Union Carbide Corp., POLYOX Water Soluble Resins, Union Carbide Corp., New York, N. Y., 1967

4. Boyle, F. W., "Prediction of Pressure Drop in Pipe Flow
    of Water that Contains Friction Reducing Additives,"
    M.S. Thesis, University of California, Davis, June 1967

5. Hercules Powder Co., Hercules Cellulose Gum: Properties
    and Uses, Hercules Powder Co., Wilmington, Del., 1960

6. Metzner, A. B. and Reed, J. C., "Flow of Non-Newtonian
    Fluids - Correlation of Laminar, Transition and Turbu-
    lent-Flow Regions," AIChE J., 1, 4, Dec. 1955, pp. 434-
    440

7. Wilkinson, W. L., Non-Newtonian Fluids, New York: Pergamon
    Press, 1960, p. 59

8. Ernst, W. D., "Investigation of the Turbulent Shear Flow
    of Dilute Aqueous CMC Solutions," AIChE J., 12, 3, May
    1966, pp. 581-585

9. Meyer, W. A., "A Correlation of the Frictional Character-
    istics for Turbulent Flow of Dilute Viscoelastic Non-
    Newtonian Fluids in Pipes," AIChE J., 12, 3, May 1966
    pp. 522-525

10. Schlichting, H., Boundary-Layer Theory, 4e., New York:
    McGraw-Hill, 1960, p. 515

11. Ibid., p. 528

12. Ibid., p. 525

13. Nikuradse, J., "Stromungsgesetze in rauhen Rohren," For-
    schungsheft, 361, 1933. Also available as NACA TM 1292,
    1950

14. Elata, C., Lehrer, J. and Kahanovitz, A., "Turbulent Shear
    Flow of Polymer Solutions," Israel J. Technol., 4, 1,
    1965, pp. 87-95

DRAG-REDUCTION MEASUREMENTS FOR THREE POLYMERS AT 4°C

W. D. White

Naval Undersea Warfare Center

ABSTRACT

Pressure-drop measurements were made for dilute solutions of three high-molecular-weight polymers in a miniature pipe-flow apparatus. The test section was 0.023 inch in diameter and could operate at Reynolds numbers from 1,000 to 7,000, so that both laminar and turbulent flow as well as the transition region were investigated.

The results obtained with Polyox WSR 301 at 4° were nearly identical with those previously obtained at room temperature and at 37°C. Drag reductions ranged from 20% for a 0.5-ppm solution at a Reynolds number of 3,700 to 58% for an 8-ppm solution at a 6,700 Reynolds number.

At 4°C a polyacrylamide (Separan AP-30) gave results similar to Polyox, except that approximately four times as much polymer was required to produce the same percent drag reduction.

The Guar gum curves had a different shape from those of the other two polymers, and required from 10 to 40 times as much polymer as Polyox to give the same drag reduction.

The different-shaped curve is probably the result of greatly diminished mechanical degradation with Guar gum, while the higher concentration requirement is attributable to its lower molecular weight.

INTRODUCTION

A great quantity of data has been accumulated on the flow properties of dilute polymer solutions in a small pipe-flow apparatus. Most of the experiments were performed with poly (ethylene oxide) solutions at room temperature ($20°$ to $25°C$; Ref. 1) but some, using transfusion fluids as the solvent, took place at body temperature ($37°C$; Ref. 2). Over this temperature range, the drag-reducing effectiveness of the polymer at a given concentration seemed to be only a function of the viscosity of the solvent, so that nearly identical results were obtained when drag reduction was plotted as a function of the solvent Reynolds number.

Since much of the deep ocean as well as great expanses of fresh water are close to $4°C$, it seemed important to determine whether any abnormal effect on drag reduction occurred at this temperature. The pipe-flow apparatus is small enough so that the entire mechanism can be installed in an ordinary household refrigerator (Fig. 1) to maintain the test solutions at a nearly constant temperature. With the apparatus installed in the refrigerator, tests were made with three different polymers representing the main types of compounds that produce drag reduction.

Figure 1   Pipe Flow Apparatus Installed in Refrigerator

EQUIPMENT AND MATERIALS

The small pipe-flow apparatus (Fig. 2) consists of a variable-speed DC motor connected to a linear actuator that drives the plunger on a 5-cc hypodermic syringe. The test fluid is forced through the 0.023 inch-ID tubing at preset velocities from less than 10 to more than 60 ft/sec. Strain-gage transducers measure the static pressure at two locations 3 inches apart along the tube, so that the pressure drop over this distance can be determined. The fluid velocity is calculated from the time required for the syringe to move 1 inch in conjunction with the physical dimensions involved. The timer was marked in hundredths of a second, and plus or minus 1 millisecond could be estimated fairly well. The pressure transducers were calibrated and recorded on a Consolidated Electrodynamics Corp. oscillograph, with an overall pressure-drop accuracy of about ±2%.

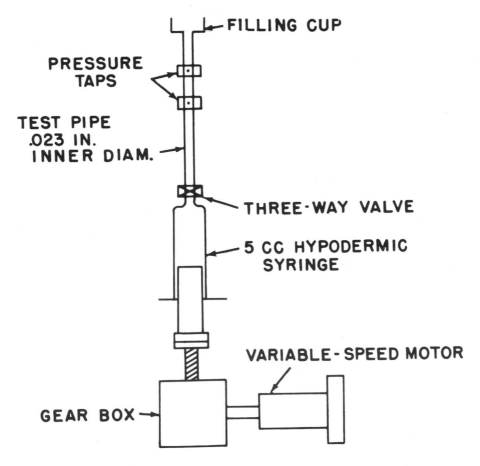

Figure 2   Schematic Diagram of Pipe-Flow Apparatus

The three polymers used in these tests were selected because
they represent the most diverse materials that have produced the
drag-reduction effect. Polyox WSR 301 (Union Carbide Chemicals
Co.) has a molecular weight of 2.5 to 4 million, and is representative of the very effective polymerization products of ethylene
oxide that form the simplest possible high-molecular-weight, water-
soluble molecule, generically called poly (ethylene oxide) to distinguish it from an oxidation product of polyethylene.

The second polymer was Separan AP-30 (Dow Chemical Co.),
which is a polyacrylamide with a molecular weight of about 1 million and a fairly simple linear configuration. The third material
was J2FP Guar Gum (The Western Co.), which is naturally occurring polysaccharide with a molecular weight of about 250,000 and
a fairly complex structure resulting from regularly spaced short
branches on the main chain of the molecule.

TEST RESULTS

Figure 3 is a plot of pressure drop between the two measuring
points as a function of fluid velocity through the test section

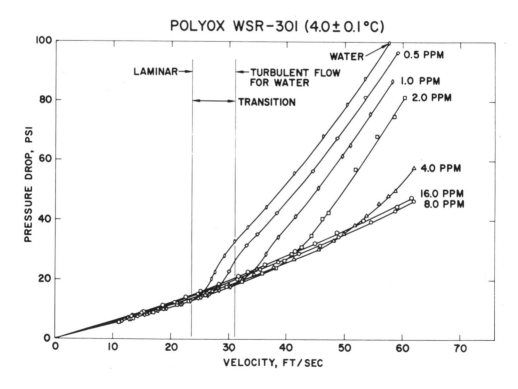

Figure 3   Pressure Drop vs. Velocity for Polyox

for water and six different concentrations of Polyox-water solution. It is easy to identify the regions of laminar, turbulent,
and transitional flow from the change in slope of the water curve
at different velocities. The curve for 0.5-ppm Polyox has a very
similar shape, but the transition to turbulent slope is definitely
shifted to a higher velocity. At all velocities above the laminar
region for water, the solution definitely gives a lower pressure
drop than water. As the concentration is increased to 1, 2, and
4 ppm, transition to a turbulent-flow slope occurs at a progressively higher velocity and the pressure drop at a given velocity
is progressively lower. At concentrations of 8 and 16 ppm, transition to a turbulent-flow slope has not occurred at the highest
velocity obtainable from the apparatus. In addition, these concentrations give the lowest values of pressure drop at the higher
velocities; however, they do give slightly higher pressure drops
at the lower velocities even down into the laminar-flow region.

Figure 4 is a different plot of this same data, with the
velocity converted to a Reynolds number based on the viscosity of

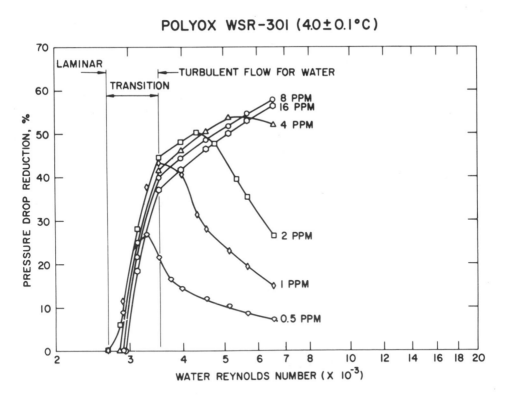

Figure 4   Pressure Drop Reduction vs. Reynolds Number for Polyox

water. The pressure drop is shown as a percent reduction from the
value of pure water at the same velocity. The curve for 0.5 ppm
shows that a drag reduction of more than 25% can be obtained with
this extremely dilute solution at velocities only slightly higher
than laminar, and that drag reductions of more than 5% are
maintained up to a Reynolds number of around 7,000. The greatest
drag reduction shown here is 58% for the 8-ppm solution at a
Reynolds number of 6,500, but it appears to be limited by the
maximum velocity of the apparatus. Undoubtedly values of 75 to
80% would be obtained at higher concentrations if the fluid velocity could be increased sufficiently. The data shown in Fig. 4 are
identical, within experimental error, to those obtained at room
temperature and 37°C (Figs. 5 and 6).

     As a check on the possible effects of the 35,000-ppm dis-
solved salts in sea water on these low concentrations of polymers,
the 2-ppm Polyox solution was repeated with filtered natural gas
water as the solvent. The curve was identical to the distilled
water results.

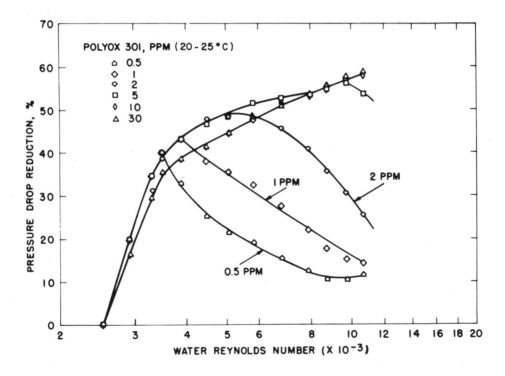

Figure 5   Pressure Drop vs. Reynolds Number for Polyox (20-25°C)

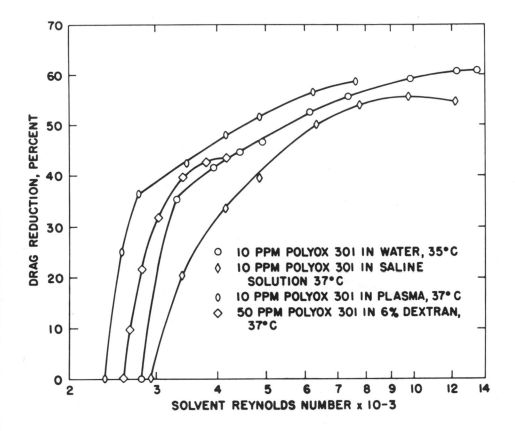

Figure 6   Effect of Reynolds Number on Drag Reduction

Figure 7 gives the results from the next series of tests,
which was made with Separan AP-30.   The curves are very similar to
those of Polyox, except that the concentrations had to be about
four times as great to give the same pressure drops.   Figure 8
shows that 32 ppm of Separan gives 57% drag reduction at a
Reynolds number of about 6,500, which is almost the same performance as 8 ppm of Polyox.   The 4-ppm Separan curve is very nearly
the same as the 1-ppm Polyox curve.

Figure 9 gives the results of the third series of tests made
with Guar gum solutions.   The curves have an entirely different
shape than the previous ones, in that they all seem to break away
from the laminar-flow slope in the transition zone and assume a
progressively lower intermediate slope as the concentration increases.   Separan and Polyox had a fairly sharp jump between two
distinct slopes at progressively higher velocities as the concentrations increased.   This difference is also seen in Fig. 10 as a
flatter curve of drag reduction as a function of Reynolds number.

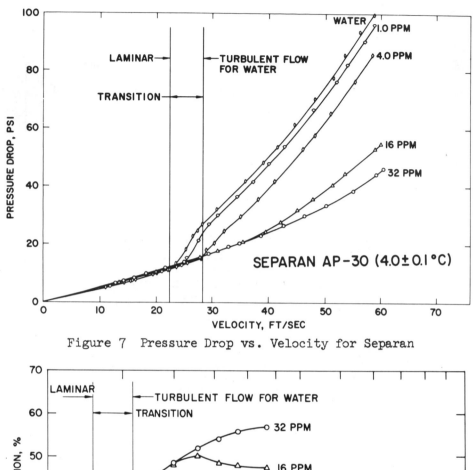

Figure 7   Pressure Drop vs. Velocity for Separan

Figure 8   Pressure Drop Reduction vs. Reynolds Number for Separan

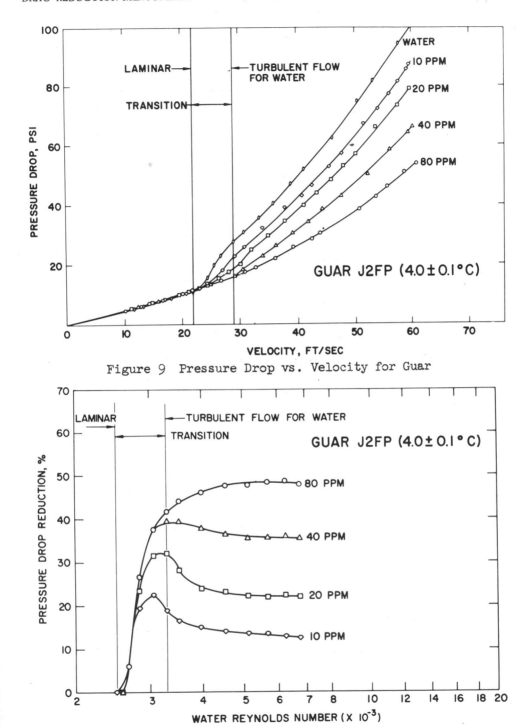

Figure 9   Pressure Drop vs. Velocity for Guar

Figure 10   Pressure Drop Reduction vs. Reynolds Number for Guar

The reason for the different behavior is probably the greater
resistance to mechanical degradation of the Guar gum, as compared
to Polyox and Separan. It is also more difficult to make a direct
comparison of effectiveness between Guar and the other two polymers
because the ratio is a function of velocity or Reynolds number.
For the range of experimental conditions covered in these tests,
from 40 to 10 times as much Guar as Polyox was required to give
the same drag reduction at the same Reynolds number.

SUMMARY

The drag-reducing effectiveness of high-molecular-weight
polymers is not a direct function of temperature, at least between
4 and 37°C. However, there is an indirect effect, in that temperature changes the viscosity of the solvent. This can lead to an
apparent difference in effectiveness if it is not taken into
account by, for instance, making the comparison at a common
Reynolds number.

Extremely dilute solutions of Polyox (0.5 ppm) have produced drag reductions of up to 25%; the phenomenon is not affected
by the presence of many thousand times as much dissolved salts as
in sea water.

Very similar performance is obtained with three widely
differing compounds; the main difference is the concentration
required to produce a given reduction, which appears to be a
function of molecular weight and a difference in the slope of some
of the performance curves. This probably results from differing
degrees of mechanical degradation of the polymer molecules when
subjected to the shear stresses in a flowing boundary layer.

REFERENCES

1. White, William D., "Pressure-Drop Reduction in a Small
    Pipe-Flow Apparatus," Proceedings of the 5th U. S. Congress
    of Applied Mechanics, Minneapolis, Minnesota, June 1966

2. Hoyt, J. W. and W. D. White, "High-Polymer Additive
    Effect on Turbulent Flow of Dextran, Saline Solution,
    and Plasma," Proceedings of the Annual Conference on
    Engineering in Medicine and Biology, San Francisco,
    California, Vol. 8, 1966

CONTRASTS IN THE SOLUTION DRAG REDUCTION CHARACTERISTICS

OF POLYMERIC SOLUTIONS AND MICELLAR SYSTEMS

J. G. Savins

Mobil Research and Development Corporation

ABSTRACT

Solution drag reduction displays such a variety of unusual
flow phenomena that it is desirable from the needs of the
experimentalist, theoretician, and engineer, to describe,
identify, and classify the features of categories of solution
drag reduction behavior observed in real fluids. This paper
develops information useful to the eventual formulation of a
structuring scheme embodying hierarchies of solution drag reduction behavior. Three categories of behavior have been discovered
in micellar-type systems. Four categories of behavior can be
identified in polymeric-type systems. Their characteristics are
discussed in detail. The morphology of micellar-type drag
reducer systems is also discussed, and estimates are presented
of morphological parameters for conditions corresponding to the
threshold shear stress where maximum drag reduction activity
occurs.

INTRODUCTION

It seems inevitable that as chemically distinct additives
are investigated, different manifestations of solution drag
reductive behavior are discovered. The identification and
classification of different categories of solution drag reduction
is useful for a number of reasons. Structuring drag reduction
phenomena could provide detailed insight into the diverse characteristics of the phenomenon as it is manifested by different
materials under different flow conditions. It might establish
a more orderly and realistic basis for collaboration between the
experimentalist, theoretician, and engineer. The resulting

183

"over-view" of the phenomena characteristic of solution drag
reduction which could result would surely facilitate the improvement of existing theories and scale-up correlations, and the
ultimate development of predictions which are more palatable
with the behavior of real drag reducer systems. Recognition of
the diverse facets of solution drag reduction would also seem
to be of pragmatic interest from the viewpoint of the needs of
engineering applications.

Efforts have already been put forth in this direction by
Patterson, et alia (Ref. 1) and Hershey and Zakin (Ref. 2). They
have described the salient features of different categories
of solution drag reduction behavior in polymeric systems. This
paper provides additional information derived from investigations
of drag reduction activity in micellar systems.

EXPERIMENTAL

Preparation of Materials

The soaps used in this study were a purified grade of sodium
oleate (Baker), USP grades of oleic acid (Baker) and sodium
stearate (MCB), and a reagent grade of myristic acid (Eastman).
Also used were reagent grades of sec-butylamine, ethylamine
hydrochloride, sodium hydroxide, potassium hydroxide, potassium
carbonate, potassium chloride, and ammonium hydroxide. Solution
preparation procedures varied depending upon the soap composition.
For example, preparation of a potassium oleate soap consisted of
admixing together 25 gallons of distilled water with the necessary
quantities of potassium hydroxide and sodium oleate until the
soap dissolved. The required amount of potassium chloride was
then introduced and mixing at a high level of shear continued for
about three hours. The soap solution was then mixed at a low
level of shear for an additional sixteen hours prior to injection
into the pipe viscometer system. The sec-butylamine oleate,
potassium myristate, and ammonium oleate solutions were prepared
in situ by neutralization with the appropriate base after which
the other ingredients were added. Typical soap compositions are
also given in Reference 3. Successively higher concentrations of
soap in a given electrolyte system were always freshly prepared.

Pipeflow Measurements

Measurements of flow rate and pressure gradient for a wide
range of laminar and non-laminar flow conditions were performed
in a previously described pipe viscometer (Refs. 4, 5).

RESULTS

Stress Controlled Drag Reduction Activity

The unusual stress controlled drag reduction activity observed in aqueous solutions of derivatives of oleic acid, an unsaturated 18 carbon atom fatty acid has been described in a previous paper (Ref. 5). One observes that drag reduction activity increases with increasing rate of flow until a critical shear stress $(\tau_w)_c$

is attained. For $\tau_w = (\tau_w)_c$, maximum drag reduction activity occurs. For $\tau_w > (\tau_w)_c$, the activity decreases steadily until the turbulent flow behavior of the soap solution becomes indistinguishable from the Newtonian turbulent flow behavior of the soap-free solution. Maximum drag reduction activity is again obtained when the flow conditions are readjusted so that the condition $\tau_w = (\tau_w)_c$ is again attained. In contrast, in flowing

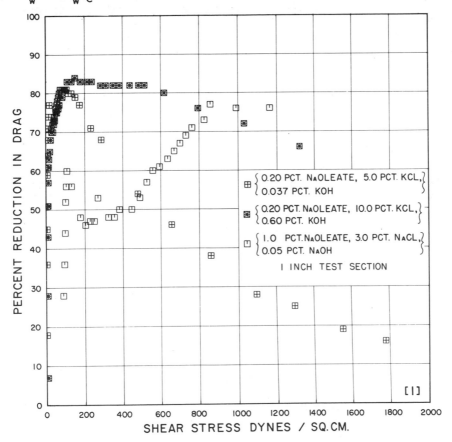

Figure 1   Drag Reduction Activity Typical of Micellar Systems

polymer solutions which are not undergoing shear degradation, a more or less constant level of drag reduction activity is reached at progressively higher flow rates. Typical supporting data on sodium oleate systems containing different supporting electrolytes are presented in Figure 1. These results illustrate the threshold shear stress effect and different characteristics of drag reduction activity.

Drag reduction activity is characteristic of a variety of other micellar systems, including those derived from certain amines and other aliphatic monocarboxylic acids containing from 12 to 18 carbon atoms (Ref. 3). For example, we also investigated the drag reduction activity of soap systems prepared from saturated fatty acids containing 14 and 18 carbon atoms, e.g., myristic acid and stearic acid. Typical results are presented in Tables I and II, respectively, for a myristate system: (0.93 per cent potassium myristate and 11.6 per cent K_2CO_3), and for a stearate system: (0.23 per cent sodium stearate, 6.18 per cent K_2CO_3, and 0.03 per cent KOH). Table III summarizes flow data pertaining to a secondary butylamine oleate system: (0.15 per cent soap, 0.06 per cent ethylamine hydrochloride, and 0.008 per cent NaOH).

TABLE I

DRAG REDUCTION IN A MICELLAR SYSTEM DERIVED FROM A 14-CARBON ATOM SATURATED FATTY ACID*ϕ

Flow Rate (GPM)	Shear Stress (dynes/cm^2) Soap Solution	Control Solution	Per Cent Reduction in Drag
15	60.9	88.4	31.2
20	84.1	146.0	42.5
30	138.0	297.0	53.5
40	190.0	491.0	61.4
50	314.0	725.0	56.8
60	578.0	997.0	42.1
70	990.0	1305.0	24.2
80	1361.0	1648.0	17.5
90	1733.0	2025.0	14.5

* $\left[0.93\% \text{ potassium myristate, } 11.6\% \text{ } K_2CO_3 \right]$

$\phi \left[1 \text{ in. tube data; flow line temp.: } 65°F \right]$

TABLE II

DRAG REDUCTION IN A MICELLAR SYSTEM DERIVED FROM
AN 18-CARBON ATOM SATURATED FATTY ACID*ϕ

Flow Rate (GPM)	Shear Stress (dynes/cm^2) Soap Solution	Control Solution	Per Cent Reduction in Drag
5	6.4	13.4	52.4
10	13.9	43.3	67.9
15	23.8	88.4	73.1
20	43.3	146.0	70.4
30	120.0	297.0	59.8
40	256.0	491.0	47.9
50	490.0	725.0	32.5
60	748.0	997.0	25.1
70	1137.0	1305.0	12.9
80	1547.0	1648.0	6.2

*[0.23% sodium stearate, 6.18% K_2CO_3, and 0.03% KOH]
ϕ[1 in. tube date; flow line temp. = 110°F]

Different flow line temperatures were used in these studies because of differences in coacervation temperatures in these systems. The coacervation point is actually a region over which the soap precipitates out of solution. The amine oleates represent an interesting class of micellar drag reducers because an additional electrolyte is not required to produce activity.

We have determined that the drag reduction characteristics of ammonium oleate systems are similar to the behavior of the previously described sodium and potassium derivatives of oleic

TABLE III

DRAG REDUCTION IN A MICELLAR SYSTEM DERIVED FROM
A SECONDARY BUTYLAMINE OLEATE* ϕ

Flow Rate (GPM)	Shear Stress (dynes/cm^2)		Per Cent Reduction in Drag
	Soap Solution	Control Solution	
20	7.9	13.6	42.0
40	21.6	45.2	53.0
60	37.3	91.5	60.0
80	57.0	150.0	63.0
100	72.7	222.0	68.0
140	106.0	398.0	74.0
180	518.0	617.0	16.0

* $\left[0.15\% \text{ sec-butylamine oleate, } 0.06\% \text{ ethylamine hydrochloride, and } 0.008\% \text{ NaOH} \right]$

$\phi \left[1.89 \text{ in. tube date; flow line temp.: } 85°F \right]$

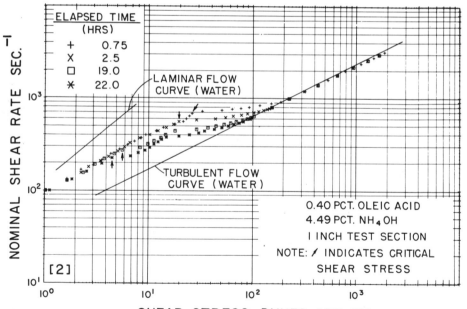

Figure 2   Flow Characteristics of an Ammonium Oleate
            Drag Reducer Solution

acid. However, compositions containing the ammonium salt are
usually chemically unstable, and it is difficult to obtain
reproducible flow data under prolonged pumping conditions.
Typical experimental data, compiled from four successive pumping
cycles and recorded at intervals of 0.75 hrs, 2.5 hrs, 19 hrs,
and 22 hrs, are recorded in Figure 2 for the system: (0.40
per cent oleic acid, 4.49 per cent NH_4OH). The solution was
circulated through the pipe viscometer system at a rate of 15
GPM between each set of flow measurements. Note the rapid
decrease in drag reduction activity between the second and third
runs. In all runs, above $\tau_w = (\tau_w)_c$, the turbulent flow data
are indistinguishable from the Newtonian behavior of the soap-
free (control) solution. This rapid, time-dependent, and
irreversible decline in drag reduction activity can be eliminated
in ammonium oleate systems by the addition of small quantities
of NH_4Cl.

Morphology of Micellar Drag Reducer Systems

As noted elsewhere (Ref. 5), there are significant morphological differences between polymeric-type and micellar-type drag
reducers. The "fine" structure of the respective flow units is
distinctly different. It is generally agreed that the morphology
of a polymer in solution resembles a loose three-dimensional
network consisting of variously extended macromolecular segments.
In contrast, it has been postulated (Ref. 6) that in a soap
system, initially spherical micelles rearrange into cylindrical
or rod-like micelles under the influence of electrolyte. These
flow units form a network of interlaced rod-like elements. The
viscoelastic properties of soap solutions have been the subject
of several investigations (Ref. 7). Hypotheses have been advanced
to explain the formation of viscoelastic properties under a
variety of conditions. We favor the mechanism discussed by
Pilpel (Ref. 7) whereby viscoelasticity arises from the formation
of large interlinking secondary micelles. Pilpel reasons that
if in soap solutions viscoelastic behavior is due to physical
entanglements of micellar units then it is immaterial whether
the units are lamellae, cylindrical micelles, or bead-like strings
of spherical micelles. At low rates the rheological equation
of state for a soap solution ought to be expressible by an expression of the form (Ref. 8),

$$\pi^{ij} + p\gamma^{ij} = CkT \int_{t'=-\infty}^{t} N(t-t')\gamma^{ij}(t')dt', \quad i,j = 1,2,3 \qquad (1)$$

where γ^{ij}, π^{ij}, and p denote, respectively, strain variable,
stress variable, and arbitrary hydrostatic pressure. Also
N(t-t')dt' denotes concentration per unit volume, of effective
function points in the network formed in a previous time
interval t', t + dt', and still existing at time t, C is a
numerical factor of order unity, k is Boltzmann's constant, and

T is absolute temperature. However, the term $\int_{t'=-\infty}^{t} N(t-t')dt'$
represents the sum of contributions from an infinite
number of independent and transient networks. Since Equation
(1) cannot be solved explicitly, Pilpel has used a simpler model
(Ref. 8) derived from the kinetic theory of rubber-like elasticity (Refs. 8, 9) to obtain information about the size and weight
of micellar soap units. According to Pilpel, the basis for the
model of a rubber-like solid is a system contrived from interlinked
units with properties which approach those of an ideal elastic
liquid as: (a) temperature and shear rate are reduced, and (b)
the time taken for structural deformation becomes small compared
to the time involved in the thermal-induced breaking and reforming
of entanglement points. Invoking this conceptually simpler
model, Pilpel has used Equations (2) and (3), viz:

$$G = kTN_o \qquad (2)$$

$$G = \frac{3RTc_o}{5M} \qquad (3)$$

and the results of low shear rate elasticity measurements on
aqueous soap gels exhibiting maximum viscoelasticity to calculate
a variety of morphological parameters*. Here G, N_o, c_o, and M
denote, respectively, shear elasticity, number of junction points
per unit volume of gel, soap concentration (gm/ml), and molecular
weight of micellar structural units.

Earlier, we speculated that the reversible stress-controlled
drag reduction phenomenon characteristic of micellar systems
might be the result of a flow induced transient network disentanglement mechanism (Ref. 5). We also indicated that for conditions
where the electrolyte concentration is varied and the soap
content is fixed, there is a simultaneous increase in apparent
viscosity over a wide range of shear rates, and enhanced drag
reduction activity. We have also found an identical response
results for conditions where the soap concentration is varied and
the electrolyte concentration is fixed. In studies of aqueous

* Equations (2) and (3) imply that N_o = 0.6m, where m is the
  number·density of micelles.

soap systems under similar chemical conditions, Pilpel (Ref. 10)
suggests the observed increases in apparent viscosity and elasticity arise from the development of network structures comprised
of micellar units. It would be of some interest to derive
estimates of morphological parameters for micellar systems under
conditions corresponding to the threshold shear stress point
where maximum drag reduction activity occurs. In the absence
of corresponding information on rheological properties under
these flow conditions, and in view of previously discussed
uncertainties related to the interpretation of viscoelastic
parameters from high shear rate jet thrust measurements (Ref. 5),
we necessarily invoke a gross assumption. In order to estimate
weight, size, and other morphological parameters for micellar
structural units we make the assumption that the parameter G
in Equations (2) and (3) can be replaced by the sharply defined
threshold or critical shear stress $(\tau_w)_c$ found in turbulent flow

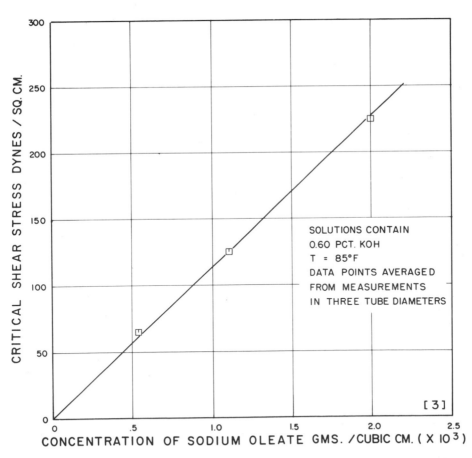

Figure 3   Critical Shear Stress Behavior: Na Oleate - KCl Systems

experiments on micellar-type drag reducers.   Thus, Equations (2)
and (3) become:

$$N_o = (\tau_w)_c /kT \tag{4}$$

$$M = 3RTc_o/5 (\tau_w)_c \tag{5}$$

on assuming that the threshold shear stress can be equated with
the material parameter referred to as the "modulus of shear
elasticity". Substituting measured values of $(\tau_w)_c$ and c_o
into Equations (4) and (5), we should be able to determine
whether the derived morphological parameters N_o and M are
consistent with the values obtained, for example, by Pilpel
(Ref. 7).   However, we do not expect these estimates to be very
precise, since the estimates of micelle size derived by Pilpel
(Ref. 7) were obtained at low shear rates on soap systems exhibiting "maximum viscoelastic behavior".

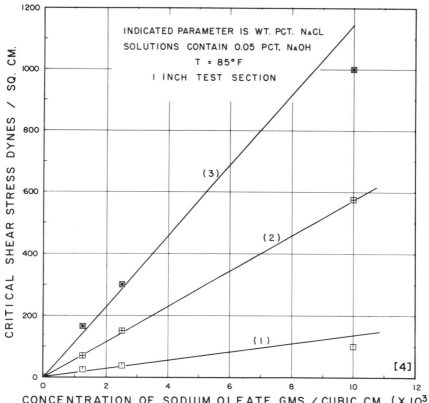

Figure 4   Critical Shear Stress Behavior:
Na Oleate - NaCl Systems

Earlier (Ref. 5), we indicated that for micellar-type drag reducers derived from sodium oleate there seems to be a relatively simple relationship between $(\tau_w)_c$ and electrolyte concentration, for fixed soap content, e.g., Figure 3 of Reference 5. Additional data, obtained for conditions of different levels of fixed electrolyte concentration, are shown in Figures 3 and 4 for micellar-type drag reducers derived from the system: sodium oleate-KCl, and the system: sodium oleate-NaCl, respectively. These data were used to obtain estimates of four relevant morphological parameters for conditions corresponding to the threshold shear stress where maximum drag reduction activity occurs. Estimates of N_o and M were obtained from Equations (4) and (5), respectively. Using these derived parameters, estimates were also obtained for micellar volume and the number of molecules per micelle. These results are summarized in columns 3-6 of Table IV. Following Pilpel (Ref. 10), the micellar volume (v) was calculated from the relation: $v = M/A\rho$, where A is Avogadro's number, and the density of the micelle has been taken to be $\rho = 0.8$ gm/cm^3, corresponding to its hydrocarbon portion. The number of molecules per micelle (N) was calculated from the relation $N = M/M_s$, where $M_s = 304$, corresponding to the molecular weight of sodium oleate.

TABLE IV
MORPHOLOGICAL PARAMETERS FOR SOAP-TYPE DRAG REDUCERS FOR
CONDITIONS OF MAXIMUM DRAG REDUCTION ACTIVITY

(1) $C_o \times 10^3$	(2) $(\tau_w)_c$	(3) $N_o \times 10^{-14}$	(4) $M \times 10^{-5}$	(5) $v \times 10^{18}$	(6) $N \times 10^{-3}$	(7) D	(8) D/L
SYSTEM: Na Oleate - 1% (wt.) NaCl							
1.25	25.0	6.09	7.56	1.56	2.40	238.0	6.80
2.50	37.5	9.14	10.0	2.07	3.20	274.0	7.82
10.0	100.0	24.3	15.1	3.12	4.90	336.0	9.60
SYSTEM: Na Oleate - 2% (wt.) NaCl							
1.25	70.0	17.0	2.70	0.55	0.88	141.0	4.02
2.50	150.0	36.5	2.52	0.52	0.82	137.0	3.91
10.0	575.0	140.0	2.63	0.54	0.86	140.0	4.00
SYSTEM: Na Oleate - 3% (wt.) NaCl							
1.25	165.0	40.2	1.14	0.23	0.37	91.4	2.61
2.50	300.0	73.1	1.26	0.26	0.41	97.0	2.77
10.0	1000.0	243.0	1.51	0.31	0.49	106.0	3.02
SYSTEM: Na Oleate - 7.5% (wt.) KCl							
0.54	65.0	15.8	1.25	0.25	0.41	95.2	2.72
1.1	125.0	30.4	1.33	0.27	0.43	98.8	2.82
2.0	225.0	54.8	1.34	0.27	0.44	98.8	2.82

In analogy with polymeric systems, one might interpret the observed correlation between viscoelastic behavior or drag reduction activity and increased soap content to be a natural consequence of an increase in apparent micelle molecular weight. However, from Figures 3 and 4 we observe the critical shear stress is approximately linearly related to soap concentration. According to Equation (5) such a result implies that the molecular weight of the micellar structural unit is constant for a given system containing a fixed electrolyte content. The data of Table IV show that, for practical purposes, M is constant for each system; only for the system sodium oleate-1% NaCl, does this behavior begin seriously to fail. Compared to results obtained with polymeric systems, these findings are somewhat unusual. However, on equating (4) and (5), a constant micelle molecular weight seems to imply that the effective concentration of network junction points is linearly related to c_o. This result is consistent with the thesis that the enhanced viscoelastic behavior and drag reduction activity observed to persist to higher shear stresses with increase in soap concentrations are due primarily to an increase in the number of available junction point crosslinks with soap content. Considering the several assumptions involved in their derivation, the values for these morphological parameters agree favorably with data on sizes of micellar units deduced from low shear rate measurements by Pilpel (Refs. 7 and 10) on similar soap gels exhibiting "maximum viscoelasticity". A possible explanation for the lower values for M, and hence the number of molecules per micelle, is that these results were derived from the threshold shear stress where maximum drag reduction activity occurs. It is likely that the existing non-laminar flow conditions have already initiated some localized disruptive effects in the aggregate network structure. This would be analogous to a reversible depolymerization, and would naturally be reflected as degradation, and therefore as lower values for the micelle molecular weight.

There seems to be negligible precise information about the configurations of micellar aggregates. There is reason to believe that at the concentrations of interest here, the micelles transform into microcrystallites and that anisotropic regions exist (Ref. 11). It has been suggested that if one assumes essentially one kind of micelle is present under these conditions, the most probable form is either the lamellar or cylindrical geometry. Let us assume, for example, the micelle configuration can be represented by a cylindrical structural unit in which the length of the structure (neglecting the ends) is two fully extended end-to-end hydrocarbon chains. The diameter (D) of the cylinder is given by:

$$D = \sqrt{\frac{2v}{n\pi l}} \qquad (6)$$

where v is the volume of the micellar structural unit, n is the number of $(-CH_2-)$ groups in each soap chain, and $1 = 1.25A°$ per $(-CH_2-)$ group. (12) For an oleic acid chain n = 14, so that for the system considered here, Equation (6) becomes,

$$D = (1.907 \times 10^3)v^{1/2} \tag{7}$$

Results of these calculations are summarized in column 7 of Table IV. Although these derived values cannot be considered exact, they seem to be of the magnitude that has been proposed by other investigators (Refs. 7-10). The D/L ratios given in column 8 are intended to show that the micellar aggregate is apparently disc-like in shape at conditions corresponding to maximum drag reduction activity. It has been postulated (Ref. 12) the geometrical changes occurring in the formation of a structural unit involve aggregation of single soap molecules into spherical micelles, followed by a flattening of the spheres into discs and finally the packing of X of them together to form a cylindrical aggregate. Thus, the disc-like (rouleaux) geometry suggested by the D/L values supports the thesis that localized disintegration of cylindrical micellar aggregates and their networks occurs before the threshold shear stress is attained.

DISCUSSION

Categories of Drag Reduction Behavior in Micellar Systems

The systems considered here are derived from an unsaturated 18 carbon atom monocarboxylic acid: oleic acid. However, as indicated earlier, these particular micellar systems were prepared directly from sodium oleate, the alkali metal soap of this fatty acid.

Type IM Behavior. Typical results for a "Type IM" drag reducing behavior observed in micellar systems are presented in Figures 5-7. The system is 0.20 per cent sodium oleate, 5 per cent KCl, and 0.037 per cent KOH. Figure 5 is the usual representation of flow data in terms of nominal shear rate and shear stress, referenced to the wall of the pipe. As discussed elsewhere (Ref. 13), this treatment should collapse laminar Poiseuille flow data onto a diameter-independent invariant flow curve. However, we observe that the majority of the data are characteristically different for each diameter. Furthermore, in contrast to the usual behavior of polymeric-type drag reducers, substantial drag reduction activity is observed at rather low velocities. For

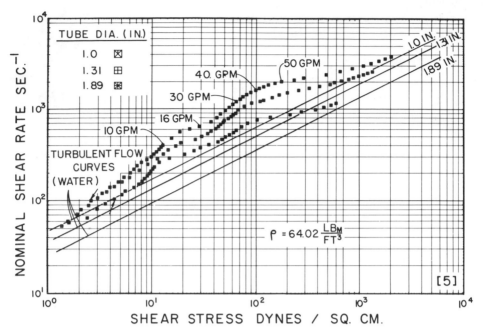

Figure 5   Flow Characteristics: Type IM Drag Reduction Behavior
              (0.20% Na Oleate, 5.0% KCl, 0.037% KOH)

example, at the point referenced by the arrows in Figure 5,
there is approximately 40 per cent drag reduction at one ft/sec
in the smallest tube, and 65 per cent drag reduction at 2 ft/sec
in the largest tube. As noted by Patterson, et alia, economic
pipe sizes permit velocities of only a few feet per second
(Ref. 1), whereas drag reduction of 30 per cent or more has
usually been difficult to obtain below 10 ft/sec with polymers
in aqueous or organic solvents. This latter result implies
that in the case of a large pipeline in order to exploit the drag
reduction effect with polymeric additives it might be necessary
to operate above an optimum or economic flow rate.

      The unusual nature of the Type IM behavior is illustrated
in more detail in Figure 6 where the (Poiseuille) apparent
viscosity, calculated directly from the pipe flow data, is
graphed versus the nominal rate of shear. Some of the flow rate
values shown in Figure 5, and pertaining to the 1 in. tube, are
also indicated. The approximate loci of the critical shear
stresses corresponding to conditions of maximum drag reduction
activity for this soap solution are also indicated by the dashed
curve. The separate curves for each diameter suggest the presence
of a "wall effect". As noted elsewhere (Ref. 5), these micellar
systems may exhibit a behavior which can be interpreted as an
Oldroyd-type "slip effect". It should be noted that the general

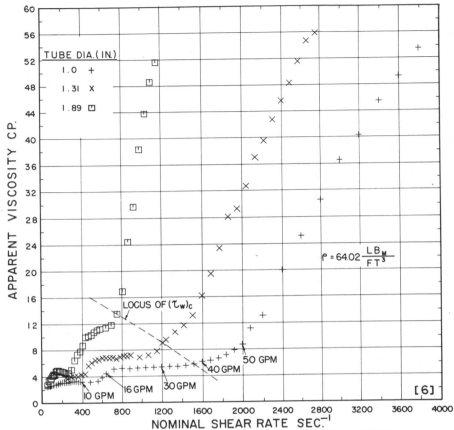

Figure 6   Gradient Dependent Viscosity: Type IM Behavior
(0.20% Na Oleate, 5.0% KCl, 0.037% KOH)

trend of the apparent viscosity function is such that the apparent
viscosity is increasing with increasing values of a parameter
which is some multiple of the rate of shear. We observe the
appearance of regions of discontinuous Newtonian-like flows. As
an example, a narrow region of approximately constant apparent
viscosity is evident between 200 sec^{-1} < $\frac{8V}{D}$ < 400 sec^{-1}.   A
broader region with similar characteristics, but higher apparent
viscosity, occurs between 700 sec^{-1} < $\frac{8V}{D}$ < 1000 sec^{-1}. Rheological
behavior of this type is characteristic of certain shear thickening
systems under viscometric flow conditions. However, it is
difficult to interpret the behavior illustrated in Figures 5
and 6. Transitional and turbulent flows of Newtonian and
rheologically complex fluids are traditionally characterized
by an increase in viscous resistance with shear rate. Additionally, these data also show a systematic increase of viscosity
with increasing tube diameter. Since it is difficult to resolve
the true nature of these drag reducing flows, it is not feasible

to use the pipe flow data to compute material parameters for
the purpose of correlating friction factors and generalized
Reynolds numbers, even in terms of the simple power law model.

From these results, we conclude that Type IM drag reduction
behavior seems to be characterized by the following combination
of phenomena: (i) multiply-connected regions of constant apparent viscosity suggesting (ii) Newtonian-like rheological behavior
under drag reducing conditions, but complicated by (iii) a
systematic diameter effect, suggesting that the flow is not
laminar, followed by (iv) increasing resistance to flow, suggesting a shear thickening response or the appearance of a transitional flow behavior under drag reducing conditions, and finally
(v) a threshold shear stress effect, and (vi) reversion to non-
drag reducing turbulent flow. The data presented in Figure 7
suggest in a very qualitative way that a transitional-type flow
is associated with the response of Type IM drag reduction behavior.
Illustrated is a comparison of pressure fluctuations recorded
while pumping the soap solution and the soap-free solution at
various flow rates. These data were recorded at a pair of wall
taps spaced 10 ft. apart in the 1 in. test section. The flow
rate markers correspond to points similarly identified in Figures
5 and 6. As points of reference, the critical shear stress
occurs at about 38 GPM in the 1 in. tube, and a flow rate of
9 GPM corresponds to a solvent Reynolds number of about 36,000.

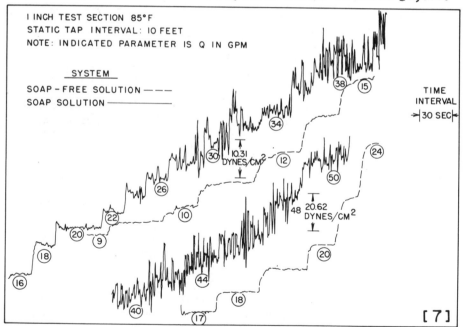

Figure 7   Pressure Drop Fluctuations: Type IM Behavior
              (0.20% Na Oleate, 5.0% KCl, 0.037% KOH)

Comparing both sets of pressure loss data, it is evident that
considerably disturbed flow conditions arise while pumping the
viscoelastic soap solution. Both the amplitude and the frequency
of the pressure loss fluctuations are grossly intensified. As
the rate is increased above 46 GPM there is a slight decrease
in the amplitude of the recorded pressure loss signals. As
indicated in Figure 5, a gradual transition to Newtonian turbulent
flow conditions occurs at these higher flow rates, while the
results shown in Figure 6 show the monotonic increase in apparent
viscosity characteristic of turbulent flow. Admittedly, it is
difficult to draw any firm conclusions about the unusual flow
conditions associated with the characteristic of Type IM behavior.

Type IIM Behavior. Figures 8 and 9 show typical results for
a "Type IIM" drag reducing behavior also observed in micellar
systems. This solution contains 1.0 per cent sodium oleate,
0.05 per cent NaOH, and 3.0 per cent NaCl. The results shown
in Figure 5 are in marked contrast to the laminar flow behavior
illustrated in Figure 8. Here is a clasic example showing that
in the absence of such aberrations as wall effects, entrance
effects, degradation, etc., data from a laminar tube flow experiment should yield an invariant "flow curve". The non-laminar
region is clearly identifiable as a suite of three curves, one
for each tube diameter, diverging from the master curve. However,
when this flow curve is compared with similar flow curves for

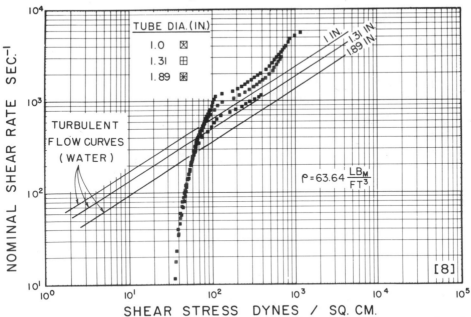

Figure 8   Flow Characteristics: Type IIM Drag Reduction Behavior
(1.0% Na Oleate, 3.0% NaCl, 0.05% NaOH)

drag reducer systems derived from polymeric additives it is apparent that unusual effects are present in the results shown in
Figure 8. Looking closely at the region within which the experimental points intersect the faired turbulent flow curves for the
soap-free solution we observe superposition of the experimental
points characterizing the flow curve for the soap solution. This
means that segments of well defined laminar flow are penetrating
the turbulent region, causing regions of reduced drag to develop.
The coordinates of the points of penetration and the corresponding
Reynolds numbers for each tube are as follows:

Tube Dia. (in).	$8V/D$ (sec^{-1})	τ_w (dynes/cm^2)	N'_{R_e}
1.0	550	82	3177
1.31	400	68	2359
1.19	280	64	3200

Since the flow conditions only approximated the simple power
law model over two decades of nominal shear rate, it was necessary
to generalize the Dodge-Metzner method by defining power law-
type parameters as follows (Ref. 14):

$$n = \frac{d \ln \tau_w}{d \ln F(\tau_w)} \qquad (8)$$

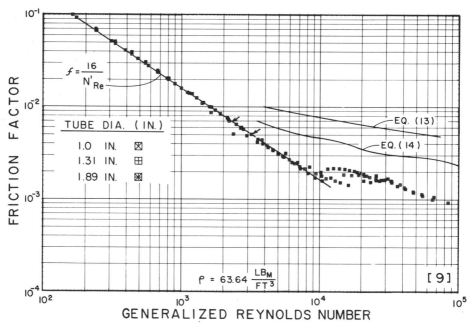

Figure 9   Friction Factor Correlation: Type IIM Behavior
(1.0% Na Oleate, 3.0% NaCl, 0.05% NaOH)

$$K = \frac{\tau_w}{[4F(\tau_w)]^n} \tag{9}$$

$$F(\tau_w) \equiv \frac{Q}{\pi R^3} = \frac{1}{\tau_w^3} \int_{0,\phi}^{\tau_w} \tau^2 f(\tau) d\tau \tag{10}$$

The n ,K) values for the range of laminar flow conditions were
computed from the laminar portion of the tube data using these
relations in a generalized scale-up procedure described elsewhere
(Ref. 14). It was necessary to extrapolate the upper region
of laminar flow in the scale-up to obtain (n ,K) values for
the range of shear stresses corresponding to the non-laminar
flow conditions. The generalized power law parameters were then
used to compute the corresponding Dodge-Metzner generalized
Reynolds numbers and friction factors from the relations

$$N'_{R_e} = \frac{D^n V^{2-n} \rho}{g_c K(8)^{n-1}} \tag{11}$$

$$f = \frac{2\tau_w}{\rho V^2} \tag{12}$$

The complete derived (N'_{R_e}, f) data are graphed in Figure 9.
The penetration range is indicated by arrows. As additional
reference correlations, we have included the smooth tube relations
of Nikuradse (Ref. 15) for the Newtonian fluid, Equation (Ref. 13),
and that of Dodge-Metzner (Ref. 16) for the generalized power
law behavior of this particular micellar system, Equation (14):

$$\frac{1}{\sqrt{f_N}} = 4.0 \log_{10}\left[R_e \sqrt{f_N}\right] - 0.40 \tag{13}$$

$$\frac{1}{\sqrt{f_{DM}}} = \frac{4.0}{(n)^{0.75}} \log_{10}\left[N'_{R_e}(f_{DM})^{1-\frac{n}{2}}\right] - \frac{0.40}{(n)^{1.2}} \tag{14}$$

Several features of the experimental friction factor correlation are worth noting. Comparing the (N'_{R_e}, f) correlation with the results given in Figure 9, it is apparent that, over a wide range of flow conditions, considerable drag reduction activity occurs but negligible regions of non-laminar flow conditions exist. It appears that a pronounced stabilization of a laminar flow exists out to $N'_{R_e} \approx 10^4$. This stability phenomenon is also characteristic of certain polymeric-type drag reducer solutions. Similar order-of-magnitude increases in the transition Reynolds number have also been reported by Metzner and Park (Ref. 17), among others. In the terminal region of laminar flow indicated at $N'_{R_e} \approx 10^4$, the results obtained from the 1.89 in. tube experiment seem to suggest that a transition region has finally been penetrated. Except for the poorly defined conditions between $10^4 < N'_{R_e} < 2 \times 10^4$, there isn't much evidence of the "diameter effect" which characterizes the turbulent flow behavior of certain systems, e.g., Figure 12 of this paper, the data of Toms (Ref. 18) as recomputed by Savins (Ref. 19), and the results given in (Ref. 2). Summarizing, Type IIM drag reduction behavior is characterized by the following combination of characteristics: (i) initial region of well defined laminar flow, (ii) region of extended laminar flow, (iii) transition region with drag reduction, (iv) region of developed drag reducing turbulent flow, and (v) absence of a "diameter effect".

It is worth noting that the experimental friction factor at $N'_{R_e} \approx 65{,}000$ is $f_{OBSV} \approx 10^{-3}$, compared to predicted values of $f_{DM} \approx 2.8 \times 10^{-3}$ from Equation (14) and $f_N \approx 5 \times 10^{-3}$ from Equation (13). Since $f_{DM} < f_N$ it might appear that a drag reduction effect is predicted from the Dodge-Metzner correlation. However, as noted previously (Ref. 4), it can be quite misleading to interpret this lowering of the friction factor as evidence of drag reduction per se. To avoid this complication, we also rely on the flow diagram, e.g., Figures 2, 5, 8 for the drag reducer of interest, with an overlay of the corresponding diameter-dependent flow curves for the additive-free solution. With this method one can quickly detect the presence of drag reduction and determine the prevailing flow conditions. It should be noted that Hershey and Zakin (Ref. 2) have also recognized this complication. Their procedure involves a correlation in which friction factors are graphed against solvent Reynolds number.

Type IIIM Behavior. Typical results for a "Type IIIM"
behavior observed in the micellar system: 0.20 per cent
sodium oleate, 10 per cent KCl, and 0.60 per cent KOH, are
presented in Figures 10 and 11. This different drag reduction
behavior displays the following combination of characteristics:
(i) an initial region of well defined laminar flow, followed by
(ii) a region of extended laminar flow and (iii) an absence of a
well defined transition region, together with (iv) a pronounced
"diameter effect", and (v) a threshold shear stress effect, and
(vi) reversion to normal or non-drag reducing turbulent flow. In
contrast to the preceding results, the shear stress-nominal shear
rate diagram, Figure 10 shows a limited region of laminar flow,
complicated by a gradual transition to non-laminar flow conditions.
A power law fit of the data up to a shear stress of about 10 dynes/
cm^2 yields for the first power law parameter, n = 0.387 and for
the second power law parameter, K' = 2.291 x 10^{-3} lb_F sec^n/ft^2.
Obviously, the laminar flow behavior is of the shear thinning
type. These derived (N'_{R_e},f) correlations, Figure 11, should
probably be interpreted with even more restraint considering that
the power law parameters used in the Reynolds number calculations
were determined under conditions where the laminar shear stresses
are as much as two to three orders of magnitude smaller than the
non-laminar shear stresses. It follows that the non-laminar drag
reducing behavior which seems to characterize the correlation
above N'_{R_e} ≈ 3200 may only be a rough approximation to the actual
flow behavior. Nevertheless, certain other gross features of the
correlation can be sorted out. Perhaps the most obvious feature
is a pronounced diameter effect. Secondly, is the appearance
of multiple-connected transition-like drag reducing flow behavior;
the transition effect is very noticeable in the data from the
largest tube. Additionally, we observe the appearance of a threshold shear stress effect at N'_{R_e} ≈ 58,000. The contrast in
drag reduction activity between polymeric-type and micellar-type
systems is more apparent when we consider, for example, the
application of the friction factor ratio introduced by Metzner and
Park (Ref. 17) to correlate the turbulent flow characteristics
of certain polymeric-type drag reducer fluids,

$$F = (f_{pV} - f)/(f_{pV} - f_1) = \phi \; [N'_{R_e}, n, (p_{11} - p_{22})/\tau_{12}]$$

(15)

to these micellar systems. The parameter F normalizes turbulent
flow data, and is useful in rating the drag reduction activity of
additives as a function of concentration, elasticity, etc. In
the case of fluid exhibiting purely viscous turbulent flow behavior,

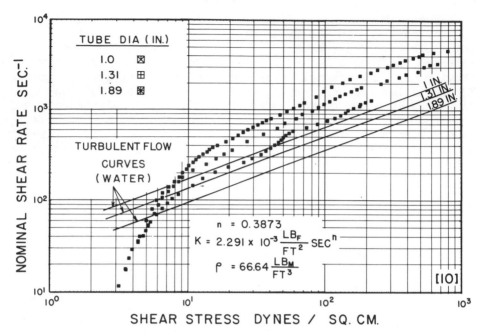

Figure 10   Flow Characteristics: Type IIIM Drag Reduction Behavior
            (0.20% Na Oleate, 10.0% KCl, 0.60% KOH)

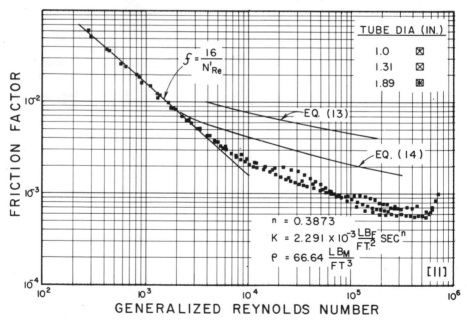

Figure 11   Friction Factor Correlation: Type IIIM Behavior
            (0.20% Na Oleate, 10.0% KCl, 0.60% KOH)

$f = f_{\rho_V}$ so that $F = 0$. Complete stabilization of laminar flow
leads to $F = 1$ since $f = f_1$. In the case of micellar systems
$f \rightarrow f_N$, where f_N is the friction factor characteristic of the
Newtonian fluid, as $\tau_w \geq (\tau_w)_c$. With increasing N'_{R_e}, the
function given by Equation (15) will pass through a maximum,
possibly on the order of unity, for a finite range of stabilized laminar flow. The function will decrease as the threshold condition $\tau_w = (\tau_w)_c$ is approached. For $\tau_w > (\tau_w)_c$,
there is a further decrease in the function until the condition
$f = f_{pV}$ is reached at which $F = 0$. However since $f \rightarrow f_N$ and

$f_N > f_{pV}$, it follows that with further increase in N'_{R_e} the
function will take on negative values as Newtonian-like turbulent
flow behavior is approached.

Categories of Drag Reduction Behavior in Polymeric Systems

Type IP Behavior. Patterson, et alia (Ref. 1) observed that
polymer solution drag reduction seems to occur from one of two
effects; namely, an extension of laminar behavior or the reduction of drag in developed turbulent flow. More precisely, Hershey
and Zakin (Ref. 2) note that a drag reduction behavior, which we
hereafter refer to as "Type IP", observed in a 2% solution of LMMH
grade poly(isobutylene) in cyclohexane, i.e., their Figure 6, is
characterized by the following combination of characteristics: (i)
an extended laminar region followed by (ii) a normal or non-drag
reducing transition, and (iii) by a normal or non-drag reducing
turbulent flow. According to Hershey and Zakin, several examples
in Shaver's data (20), e.g., see Figure 7 in Reference 2, seem
to confirm the existence of this behavior. They suggest the
mechanism responsible for Type IP behavior is a stabilization
effect arising from the presence of polymer molecules in the
flow field. This explanation is qualitatively similar to the
theory proposed by Saffman (Ref. 21), and discussed by Savins
(Ref. 4).

Type IIP Behavior. Tom's data (Ref. 18) on a 0.025% solution of poly(methylmethacrylate) in monochlorobenzene, Savin's
data (Ref. 4) on 0.0179% and 0.143% aqueous solutions of partially
hydrolyzed polyacrylamide, i.e., the "Vinyl 1" solution shown in
Figure 1 of Reference 4, and the Hershey-Zakin data (Ref. 2) on
a 0.10% solution of poly(isobutylene) grade L80 in cyclohexane, i.e.,

their Figure 2, are examples of what Hershey and Zakin describe
as a different drag reduction behavior, and we categorize here
as "Type IIP" behavior. Dilute "Newtonian-like" polymeric solutions very often exhibit a Type IIP behavior which seems to be
characterized by: (i) an initial region of normal turbulent flow,
followed by (ii) the appearance of a critical Reynolds number
heralding the onset of drag reducing turbulent flow. Virk (Ref.
22), and Fabula, et alia (Ref. 23), among others, claim this is
a "threshold shear stress" effect. In Reference 24, Hershey and
Zakin discuss a threshold shear rate effect where the rate of
shear is calculated by postulating a laminar sublayer. Thus
their explanation for Type IIP behavior would appear to differ
from other explanations by a factor of viscosity. Hershey (Ref.
25) notes there seems to be insufficient data to prove or dis-
prove one explanation over another simply because the range of
viscosity for any given system is comparatively small.

   Type IIIP Behavior. Hershey and Zakin (Ref. 2) distinguish
still another drag reduction behavior, which we categorize as "Type
IIIP", in which much of the drag reduction apparently occurs within
the laminar or transition region. Hershey and Zakin claim that in
much of Shaver's data (Ref. 20), the critical Reynolds number,
based on solvent viscosity, occurs in the laminar or transition
region, e.g., Figure 10 in Reference 2, pertaining to Shaver's data
on a 0.50 per cent solution of CMC 70S. Indeed, when Shaver's
data are replotted using the Reynolds number computed originally
in Reference 20, it is evident that a laminar-like region is
extended to a Reynolds number of approximately 10,000, followed
by a narrow drag reducing region between Reynolds numbers of 10,000
and 20,000. Type IIIP behavior therefore seems to be characterized
by the following combination of characteristics: (i) region of
well defined laminar flow, followed by (ii) region of extended
laminar flow, but characterized by (iii) absence of a well-defined
transition region. According to Hershey and Zakin (Ref. 2),
some of the data of Dodge (Ref. 26) and Park (Ref. 27) exhibit
Type III behavior.

   Type IVP Behavior. In addition to Types IP, IIP, and IIIP polymer solution drag reduction behavior, it now appears that a "Type
IVP" can also be described. Figure 12 shows data of Savins (Ref. 4)
on a 0.286% solution of hydroxyethyl-cellulose, i.e., the "Cellulose
II" solution data shown in Figure 11 of Reference 4. The superposition of data points below a generalized Reynolds number of 2500
confirms that a well defined laminar flow exists in this region.
The onset of transition flow in this moderately shear thinning
fluid, i.e., first power law parameter is $n' = 0.8627$, is sharply
defined at $N'_{R_e} = 2500$ for the smaller tubes. The departure
from laminar flow is more gradual for the 1.89 in. tube, but

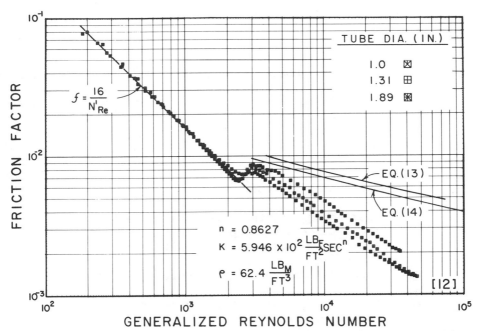

Figure 12   Friction Factor Correlation: Type IVP Drag Reduction
Behavior (0.286% Hydroxylethylcellulose Solution)

this behavior corresponds reasonably well with that usually
observed with Newtonian fluids. A stong dependence on tube
diameter is also evident. Therefore, Type IVP drag reducing
behavior consists of the following combination of characteristics:
(i) an initial region of well defined laminar flow, (ii) absence
of an extended laminar region, (iii) transition Reynolds number
characteristic of normal Newtonian behavior, followed by (iv)
a region of developed drag reducing flow with (v) strong diameter
effect.

Structuring Solution Drag Reduction Phenomena

The foregoing discussion indicates that solution drag
reduction displays a remarkable variety of rheologically complex
flow phenomena. The three identifiable categories of drag reduction behavior observed in micellar-type systems: IM, IIM, and
IIIM, have not been previously discussed in the literature.
Of the four identifiable categories of drag reduction behavior
observed in polymeric-type systems, Types IP, IIP, and IIIP have
been discussed by Patterson, et alia (Ref. 1) and Hershey and Zakin
(Ref 2). The characteristics of Type IVP behavior apparently
have not been discussed elsewhere. A preliminary structuring
scheme for classifying solution drag reduction could be developed
from the characteristics summarized in Table V. It is very

TABLE V CATEGORIES OF SOLUTION DRAG REDUCTION BEHAVIOR

Micellar-Systems

TYPE		Characteristics*	Examples
IM	(i)	multiply-connected regions of constant apparent viscosity.	The system: 0.20% sodium oleate, 5% KCl, 0.37% KOH (this study and Ref. (5).
	(ii)	Newtonian-like behavior under drag reducing conditions.	
	(iii)	systematic diameter effect.	
	(iv)	increasing resistance to flow suggesting shear-thickening response or transitional flow under drag reducing conditions.	
	(v)	threshold shear stress effect.	
	(vi)	reversion to non-drag reducing or normal turbulent flow.	
IIM	(i)	initial region of well defined laminar flow.	The system: 1% sodium oleate, 3% NaCl, 0.05% NaOH (this study and Ref. (3).
	(ii)	region of extended laminar flow.	
	(iii)	transition region with drag reduction.	
	(iv)	region of developed drag reducing turbulent flow.	
	(v)	absence of a diameter effect.	
IIIM	(i)	initial region of well defined laminar flow.	The system: 0.20% sodium oleate, 10% KCl, 0.60% KOH (this study and Ref. (5).
	(ii)	region of extended laminar flow.	
	(iii)	absence of well defined transition region.	
	(iv)	pronounced diameter effect.	
	(v)	threshold shear stress effect.	
	(vi)	reversion to non-drag reducing or normal turbulent flow.	

* In the order of their appearance.

TABLE V CATEGORIES OF SOLUTION DRAG REDUCTION BEHAVIOR (cont'd)

Polymeric Systems

TYPE		Characteristics	Examples
IP	(i)	extended laminar region.	Refs. (1,20).
	(ii)	normal or non-drag reducing transition.	
	(iii)	normal or non-drag reducing turbulent flow.	
IIP	(i)	initial region of normal or non-drag reducing turbulent flow.	Refs. (2,4,18).
	(ii)	critical Reynolds number heralding onset of drag reducing turbulent flow.	
IIIP	(i)	region of well defined laminar flow.	Refs. (2,20,26,27).
	(ii)	region of extended laminar flow.	
	(iii)	absence of a well defined transition region.	
IVP	(i)	initial region of well defined laminar flow.	Ref. (4).
	(ii)	absence of an extended laminar region.	
	(iii)	transition Reynolds number characteristic of normal Newtonian behavior.	
	(iv)	region of developed drag reducing turbulent flow.	
	(v)	pronounced diameter effect.	

unlikely that the seven distinctive hierarchies presented here represent a complete description of solution drag reduction phenomena. This outline does serve to illustrate that certain unique features and categories of behavior are currently identifiable in known fluid systems. Obviously diverse combinations of unusual flow phenomena are more common in real fluids than previously suspected. Hopefully, investigators will interpret the results of efforts to structure solution drag reduction phenomena as prima facie evidence that certain existing theories proposed to explain or describe the "phenomenon of drag reduction" have limited usefulness when solution drag reduction per

se is considered. At this point it seems prudent to avoid
generalizations about mechanisms since theories necessarily
lead to predictions of rheological behavior under drag reducing
conditions and the predictions should approximate the behavior
of real drag reducer fluids. Also we would hope the reader would
be encouraged by the fascinating array of phenomena evidenced
in a very few examples of drag reducer systems to conclude that
grossly different, and possibly bizarre, hierarchies of drag
reducer behavior await discovery.

ACKNOWLEDGMENT

The author wishes to thank Mobil Research and Development
Corporation for permission to publish this information.

REFERENCES

1.   Patterson, G. K., Zakin, J. L., and Rodriguez, J. M., "Drag
      Reduction," I.E.C. Fundamentals (in press).

2.   Hershey, H. C. and Zakin, J. L., "Existence of Two Types of
      Drag Reduction in Pipe Flow of Dilute Polymer Solutions,"
      Ibid, 6, 3 , 381 (1967).

3.   Savins, J. G., "Method of Decreasing Friction Loss in
      Turbulent Liquids," U. S. Patent No. 3,361,213 (1968).

4.   Savins, J. G., "Drag Reduction Characteristics of Solutions
      of Macromolecules in Turbulent Pipe Flow," Soc. Petr. Engr.
      Jnl., 4, 3 , 203 (1964); Trans. A. I. M. E., 231 11, 203
      (1964).

5.   Savins, J. G., "A Stress Controlled Drag Reduction Phenomenon,"
      Rheo. Acta, 6, 4 , 323 (1967).

6.   Booij, H. L., Association Colloids, Ch. 14, 681-722. In:
      H. R. Kruyt, Editor, Colloid Science II (London) (1949).

7.   Pilpel, N., "Viscoelasticity in Aqueous Soap Solutions,
      Part 4," Trans. Faraday Soc., 62, 526 , 2941 (1966).

8.   Lodge, A. S., Elastic Liquids, Academic Press, New York (1964).

9.   Ferry, J. D., Viscoelastic Properties of Polymers, John
      Wiley, New York (1961).

10. Pilpel, N., "Viscoelasticity in Aqueous Soap Solutions, Part 3," Trans. Faraday Soc., 62, 1015 (1966).

11. McBain, M. E. L. and Hutchinson, E., Solubilization and Related Phenomena, Academic Press Inc., New York (1955).

12. Pilpel, N., "On Gel Formulation in Soaps," Jnl. Colloid Sci., 9, 285 (1954).

13. Savins, J. G., Fluid Rheological Measurements, 408-463, In: F. D. Snell and C. L. Hilton, Editors, Encyclopedia of Industrial Chemical Analysis, III, John Wiley, New York (1966).

14. Savins, J. G. and Cox, D. B., "Pumpability of Rheologically Complex Oils Below the Pour Point," Fuel, XLII, 363 (1963).

15. Nikuradse, J., "The Laws Governing the Turbulent Flow in Smooth Pipes," Research Paper No. 356, Supplement to "Research in Engineering Field," Forsch. auf dem Geb. des Ingen. Ed. B, 3 (Sept-Oct.) (1932).

16. Dodge, D. W. and Metzner, A. B., "Turbulent Flow of Non-Newtonian Systems," A. I. Ch. E. Jnl., 5, 189 (1959).

17. Metzner, A. B. and Park, M. G., "Turbulent Flow Characteristics of Viscoelastic Fluids," Jnl. Fluid Mech., 20, 291 (1964).

18. Toms, B. A., "Some Observations on the Flow of Linear Polymer Solutions Through Straight Tubes at Large Reynolds Numbers," Proc. First International Congress on Rheology, 135, (1949).

19. Savins, J. G., "Some Comments on Pumping Requirements for Non-Newtonian Fluids," Jnl. Inst. Petr., 47, 329 (1961).

20. Shaver, R. G., "Turbulent Flow of Pseudoplastic Fluids in Straight Cylindrical Tubes," PhD Thesis, MIT (1957).

21. Saffman, P. G., "On the Stability of Laminar Flow of a Dusty Gas," Jnl. Fluid Mech., 13, 120 (1962).

22. Virk, P. S., "The Toms Phenomenon-Turbulent Pipe Flow of Dilute Polymer Solutions," D. S. Thesis, MIT (1966).

23. Fabula, A. G., Lumley, J. L., and Taylor, W. D., "A Molecular Viscoelasticity Interpretation of the Wall Shear Stress Threshold in the Toms Effect," AD 620143 (1965).

24. Hershey, H. C. and Zakin, J. L., "A Study of the Turbulent
     Drag Reduction of Solutions of High Polymers in Organic
     Solvents," Preprint 21B, A. I. Ch. E. Meeting, Philadelphia,
     Pa., Dec. 7, 1965.

25. Hershey, H. C., personal communication.

26. Dodge, D. W., "Turbulent Flow of Non-Newtonian Fluids in
     Smooth Round Tubes," PhD Thesis, Univ. of Delaware (1958).

27. Park, M., "Turbulent Flow and Normal Stresses of Visco-
     elastic Fluids," MS Thesis, Univ. of Delaware (1964).

EXPLORATORY DRAG REDUCTION STUDIES IN

NON-POLAR SOAP SYSTEMS

I. Radin, J. L. Zakin, and G. K. Patterson

University of Missouri - Rolla

ABSTRACT

The effects of concentration, flow rate, and tube diameter
on drag reduction in non-polar soap solutions were studied.
Aluminum dioleate in toluene solutions were used in pressure
drop measurements at concentrations of 0.2, 0.5, 0.75 and 1.0
per cent. Pressure drop measurements were made in tube
diameters ranging from 0.01 to 2.0 inches. A few such measurements were also made with an aluminum palmitate soap in toluene.

The results of these measurements differed from those
observed in aqueous systems. Higher concentrations (0.75 per
cent) were required before drag reduction occurred. No critical
upper shear stress was observed. While little mechanical degradation was observed after an initial holding period, the solutions degraded on aging.

Thus, while aqueous soap systems have appeared to be at
equilibrium and have shown reversible shear effects, the changes
in viscosity with time for these non-polar systems indicate that
they were not at equilibrium. It is believed that the differences in the nature of the soap structure in solution for the
two types of systems cause the observed differences in the
turbulent flow behavior.

INTRODUCTION

Despite early reports of drag reduction in aluminum soap
solutions by Mysels (Ref. 1) and by Agosten, et al. (Ref. 2),
most drag reduction investigations have been made in polymer

solutions. Recently, Savins (Refs. 3, 4) and White (Ref. 5) have made studies of drag reduction in aqueous soap solutions.

The present investigation was aimed at studying the effect of concentration, flow rate and tube diameter on drag reduction in hydrocarbon solvent-soap solutions. Aluminum dioleate in toluene solutions were studied at concentrations of 0.2, 0.5, 0.75 and 1.0 per cent. Pressure drop measurements were made in tube diameters ranging from 0.01 to 2.0 inches. A few measurements were made with an aluminum palmitate soap in toluene.

LITERATURE REVIEW

The term drag reduction in conduit flow was defined by Savins (Ref. 6) as the ratio of the pressure drop of a solution to the pressure drop of the pure solvent at the same flow rate:

$$Dr = \left. \frac{\Delta P_{solution}}{\Delta P_{solvent}} \right|_{constant\ flow\ rate} \tag{1}$$

If the drag ratio is less than unity the solution is said to be drag reducing. Polymer, soap and solid suspension additives have been observed to be drag reducing in both polar and non-polar solvents (Ref. 7).

Rather than attempt to review the complete field of drag reduction the reader is referred to a paper by Patterson, Zakin, and Rodriguez (Ref. 7), which gives a general coverage of the field and a bibliography. Only the few papers on soap systems will be covered.

During the Second World War, in the course of designing and testing flame throwers, the flow properties of gasoline thickened with aluminum soaps, the early constituents of napalm, were studied. Due to wartime requirements for haste, precision and sophistication were not stressed, but the results are interesting. Agoston, et al. (Ref. 2) observed drag reduction starting at about 50 fps in a 1/8-inch diameter pipe. The concentration of the solution was not given. In more concentrated, jelly-like solutions they noted a definite viscoelastic effect with extremely long relaxation times. When pumping was stopped, pressure gradients persisted for several minutes.

Osterhout and Hall (Ref. 8) have data showing that No. 2 diesel oil gelled with an unnamed soap at an unspecified concentration gave drag reductions of 40 to 50 per cent at about 35 fps in 2- and 2 1/2-inch diameter pipes.

Savins (Ref. 3) observed drag reduction up to 80 per cent with a 0.2 per cent solution of sodium oleate in water containing an electrolyte. His data were taken in a 1-inch diameter pipe. In order to obtain drag reduction he needed to add an electrolyte (in most cases KCl) to his solution. Maximum drag reduction occurred with from 5 to 10 per cent KCl added to the sodium oleate solution. In this range of electrolyte concentrations the maximum reduction in drag was approximately constant. He explained that in his aqueous solutions initially spherical micelles were rearranged into cylindircal micelles due to the influence of the electrolyte. The cylindrical micelles form a network of interlaced rod-like elements.

Savins also observed two other interesting effects. At a critical shear stress the solution suddenly lost its drag reducing ability and began a steep return to purely viscous pressure drop behavior. This critical shear stress seemed to depend on the amount of electrolyte present. With 3 1/2 per cent KCl the critical shear stress was about 25 dynes/cm^2 and with 7 1/2 per cent KCl it was about 225 dynes/cm^2. (It has been shown both theoretically (Ref. 9) and experimentally (Refs. 10, 11) that the addition of salts to an aqueous soap solution will both lower the critical micelle concentration and raise the micelle molecular weight. The determining factor is the ionic strength of the solution for the case of micelles with a low charge density. This is consistent with the data of Savins at different electrolyte concentrations.) He also observed that once the critical shear stress was exceeded and drag reduction was lost, the flow rate could be lowered to a point below the critical shear stress and drag reduction would reoccur. After approximately 88 hours of continuous shearing, no permanent degradation was noted. This is very different from typical polymer degradation where shearing will break chemical bonds and permanently lower the molecular weight. Savins suggested that perhaps the effect was due to a temporary network disentanglement induced by turbulent vortices. Savins also has other data (Ref. 4) showing the critical shear stress effect in a variety of aqueous soap systems derived from mono-carboxylic acids containing from 12 to 18 carbon atoms, neutralized with sodium or potassium hydroxide, ammonium hydroxide, or sec-butylamine. Using the capillary thrust technique, Savins did not detect any normal stress differences in the shear rate range of 2 x 10^3 to 1.25 x 10^5 sec^{-1} in an aqueous solution containing 0.2 per cent sodium oleate and 10.0 per cent KCl and 0.6 per cent KOH.

White (Ref. 5) obtained results similar to Savins' with an equimolar system of cetyltrimethylammonium bromide (CTAB) and 1-naphthol in water. The total concentration was 550 weight ppm.

He studied flow in pipes of 0.090, 0.272, and 0.500 inches in
diameter. White was able to obtain drag reduction up to 70
per cent in the 0.500-inch pipe. If a wall shear stress of
0.1 lbs/ft^2 (50 dynes/cm^2) were exceeded, independent of tube
diameter, the friction factor began to return to the friction
factor of pure water. White also did not note any permanent
shear degradation over a period of several days.

EXPERIMENTAL

Turbulent flow pressure drops were measured in a large
circulatory pumping system (tube diameters of 1/2, 1, and 2
inches) and in a small pumping system (tube diameters from 0.01
to 0.1 inches), described earlier (Refs. 12-15). The latter
system was also used to characterize the laminar flow behavior
of the solutions studied.

Attempts were made to characterize the solutions by normal
stress, low shear rate viscosity, and light scattering measurements. The normal stress measurements were made with a jet
thrust apparatus similar to that described by Green (Ref. 16)
and by Patterson, Hershey, Green, and Zakin (Ref. 17). Modifications to it are described by Radin (Ref. 14). The low shear
rate viscosities were measured by Cannon Ubbelohde gravity
flow viscometers, and the light scattering measurements were
made with a Brice-Pheonix photometer.

Soaps used in solution were Alumagel (Witco Chemical Co.,
Chicago, Ill.), and aluminum disoap whose fatty component is
primarily oleic acid, and aluminum palmitate (Metasoap Div.
of Nopco Chemical Co., Newark, N. J.). The toluene solvent
used for the flow experiments was nitration grade (G. H. Robins,
St. Louis, Mo.) and that used for light scattering and low
shear rate viscosity measurements was analytical grade (Mallinckrodt
Chemical Co., St. Louis, Missouri).

RESULTS

Figures 1, 2, and 3 are plots of friction factor versus
solvent Reynolds number measured in the small unit for 0.50,
0.75 and 1.0 per cent solutions of aluminum dioleate in toluene.
The solid lines represent the conventional solvent friction factor
equations. By using solvent Reynolds number rather than solution
Reynolds number, it is immediately clear that when a solution's
friction factor falls below the solid line it is a drag reducing
solution.

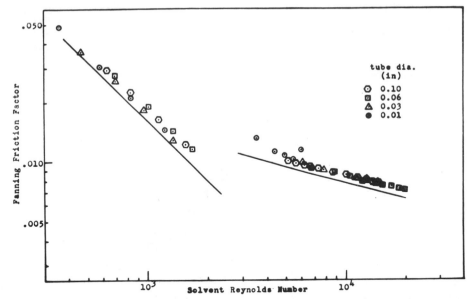

Figure 1   Friction Factor Data for 0.5% Aluminum
Dioleate in Toluene

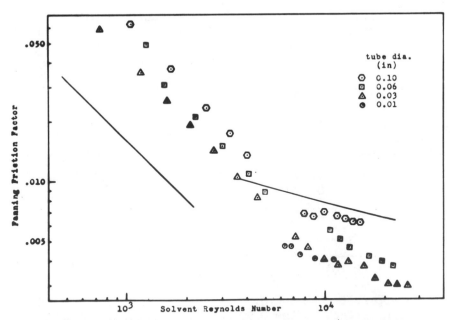

Figure 2   Friction Factor Data for 0.75% Aluminum
Dioleate in Toluene

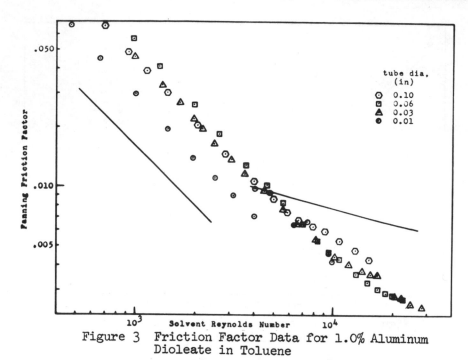

Figure 3   Friction Factor Data for 1.0% Aluminum
Dioleate in Toluene

The table below shows rheological constants in power law
equation for the solutions as determined from laminar flow data
in the small unit. A large viscosity increase is evident
between 0.5 per cent and 0.75 per cent solutions.

Rheological Constants of Solutions

Al-dioleate Conc. wt. %	K'*	n'*	η_{app} at $8V/D = 10^4$ sec^{-1} poise
0.20	0.0057	1.003	0.00565
0.50	0.00704	0.985	0.00587
0.75	0.0631	0.835	0.0138
1.00	0.0346	0.898	0.0157

*where $\tau_w = K' (8V/D)^{n'}$ in dynes/cm^2.

It is apparent that the 0.50 per cent solution was not drag
reducing. The effect of the 0.50 per cent solution's slight
increase in viscosity over the pure toluene can be noted in
the way the points lie above the pure solvent lines. The results
for the 0.20 per cent solution were very similar to those of
the 0.50 per cent and will not be shown.

The 0.75 per cent solution, however, gave good drag reduction. This was accompanied by a large increase in apparent viscosity as can be seen in the data for the laminar region. In the 1.0 per cent solution the trends were similar with an overall gain in drag reduction.

A discrepancy in the data is noted in the laminar region of the 1.0 per cent solution. The data for the 0.1-inch tube lies closer to the laminar line than does the data for 0.06-inch tube although the solution is shear thinning. This is probably caused by the fact that both the 0.1-inch and 0.01-inch tubes were run about ten days after the 0.06-inch and 0.03-inch tubes and, as will be shown below, these solutions were later found to degrade slightly with time.

Because the 1.0 per cent solution gave the greatest drag reduction, a larger sample was prepared and run in the large system. Figure 4 shows these results for 1/2-, 1-, and 2-inch diameter pipes. The maximum reduction in pressure drop over the pure toluene was just over 70 per cent and occurred at the highest flow rate in the 1/2-inch pipe. Data taken two weeks later, after at least 10 hours of additional pumping, showed no appreciable loss in drag reduction.

In the Reynolds number range covered, drag reduction was observed only in the smallest tubes at the highest flow rates for a 1.0 per cent solution of aluminum palmitate in toluene. The minimum drag ratio was 0.90 in the 0.01-inch tube.

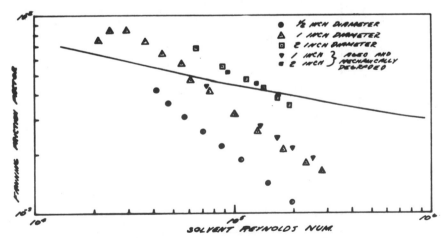

Figure 4   Friction Factor Data for 1% Aluminum
Dioleate in Toluene

First normal stress differences at the wall $(P_{11}-P_{22})_w$ in
the 1.0 per cent solution for the shear rate range 2×10^3 to
3×10^4 sec^{-1} are shown in Figure 5. Contrary to the results
of Savins (Ref. 3), significant values were exhibited by this
soap solution. They were about half the level found by Patterson,
et al. (Ref. 17) for 1.0 per cent polyisobutylene (Vistanex
L-80, Enjay Chemical Co.) in cyclohexane.

Since drag reduction and high viscosity appeared suddenly
at 0.75 per cent soap, solutions in this concentration range
were examined to detect any sudden agglomerate formation or
sudden agglomerate size change. The turbidity τ_c of the aluminum
dioleate-toluene solution was calculated at various concentrations by measuring the intensity of the light scattered normal
to a beam of light of known intensity. An abrupt increase in
turbidity for rising concentration would indicate a critical
micelle concentration or agglomerate size increase. No critical
micelle concentration was observed for starting concentrations
(before dilution) of 1.43 per cent, 1.22 per cent, and 1.02

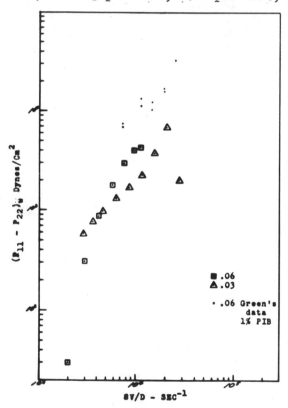

Figure 5   Normal Stress 1% Aluminum Dioleate in Toluene

per cent. The dissymmetry (I_{45}/I_{135}) for the 1.43 per cent
solution was rather high. This was probably caused by the
high viscosity of the solution which made dust removal by
centrifuging difficult. Lower dissymmetry values were obtained
for the 1.22 per cent starting concentration. This could have
been caused by a more effective dust removal in the lower
viscosity solution or by a lower agglomerate weight as a result
of the lower starting concentration. Such an effect has been
seen by Sheffer (Ref. 18).

To ensure a dust free solvent, reagent grade toluene, which
was relatively free of water, was used in the light scattering
measurements. It has been noted in the literature (Ref. 18, 19)
that the hydrogen bonds between soap molecules in non-polar
systems might break to preferentially form ionic bonds with any
water molecules present. In order to check the effect of additional water, an excess of water was added to the 1.02 per cent
solution. When the solution was centrifuged the excess water was
removed. The results still showed no critical micelle concentration, but at any concentration the turbidity was still lower than
obtained by dilution of the other two solutions. Since the
starting concentration of the soap in the water saturated toluene
was again lower (1.02 per cent), it is not known whether the
decrease in turbidity was caused by break up of soap particles
due to the water or by starting concentration effects.

In order to detect any subtle differences, more rigidly
controlled standard procedures than used here would be required.
For example, the effects of starting concentration, aging, and
length of time in the centrifuge, which caused the sample to
be heated, would have to be considered.

Figure 6 is a plot of solution concentration divided by
the difference between turbidities for the solution τ_c and the
solvent τ_o versus the concentration for the three solutions
mentioned above. Since all three curves are nearly horizontal
and variations can be explained by small errors in the measurements, it was assumed that all three solutions were ideal,
that is, they should plot on Figure 6 as straight horizontal
lines.

From a measurement of dn/dc (the change in the refractive
index of the solution with concentration) and from the average
values of $c/(\tau_c - \tau_o)$ of Figure 6, the weight average molecular
weights were calculated to be 10,400, 8,400, and 7,100 for the
bottom, middle, and top curves, respectively.

Also plotted on Figure 6 is the average value of $c/(\tau_c - \tau_o)$ versus the starting concentration of the solution. When the straight line which is drawn through these points is extrapolated to zero starting concentration a molecular weight of about 4,000 is calculated from the intercept. This corresponds to a grouping of about seven molecules. It is interesting to speculate that a micelle of this soap has a weight of about 4,000 which occurs at concentrations much lower than those used here. This rough estimate neglects the influence of solution water content on molecular weight.

The solutions used in the friction factor measurements were mixed at the concentrations that were run. Sheffer (Ref. 18) showed that for his soaps in benzene the bonds in the dry soap were retained in the solution (as opposed to individual soap molecules agglomerating in the solvent). Estimates of the relative molecular weights of these solutions were made from intrinsic viscosity measurements (Intrinsic viscosity is defined by $\lim \eta_{sp}/c$ as c approaches zero. $\eta_{sp} = (\eta_{soln} - \eta_{solv})/\eta_{solv}$). Although the more concentrated solutions were non-Newtonian at high shear rates, the shear rates in the Cannon-Ubbelohde viscometer were low enough so that this effect was not significant for qualitative comparisons. At low concentrations, the fluids approached Newtonian behavior.

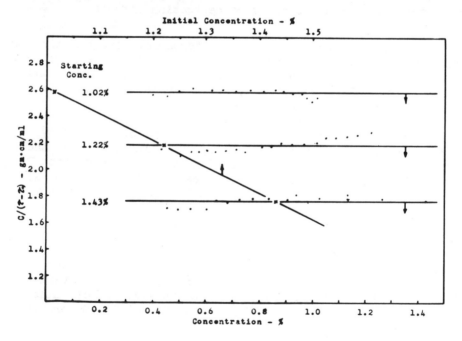

Figure 6

Figure 7 is a plot of reduced viscosity, η_{sp}/c, versus concentration for the fresh (undegraded) solutions. This plot shows the effect of various starting concentrations on the reduced viscosity at any concentration. The 1.0 per cent solution was run first and rechecked after the others were run to make sure that aging effects were not significant during a single day's run. At any concentration the 1.0 per cent initial solution had the highest reduced viscosity and the 0.2 per cent had the lowest reduced viscosity. The 0.75 per cent solution, for some inexplicable reason, did not go immediately into solution.

It is difficult to make any estimate of intrinsic viscosity from the data as the reduced viscosity begins to decrease rapidly at low concentrations. This same trend, but less marked, is apparent in some of Sheffer's data.

In nearly all cases the viscosity dropped slightly when rechecking each point indicating some mechanical degradation. The first flow time was used in calculations as this time more nearly represented the actual fresh undegraded viscosity at the new concentration. In those cases where the viscometer flow

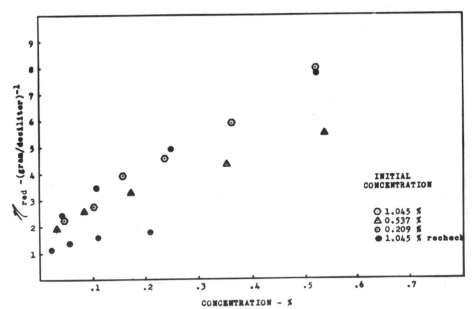

Figure 7   Aluminum Dioleate in Toluene
36 - 48 Hours Old
(not mech. degraded)

time did not drop in successive readings, an average of the
points was taken. For these comparisons the degradation had no
significant effect on the results.

The solutions were then aged for 12 days and the measurements repeated. Figure 8 shows the results of these measurements.
The reduced viscosity decreased greatly at all concentrations
for every initial concentration. The viscometer flow times
did not decrease on the second reading nearly as regularly as
they did with the fresh solutions, particularly at the lower
starting concentrations. This implies that these aged solutions were not as sensitive to mechanical degradation as the
fresh solutions.

Each 12 day old sample was then run through a 6-inch long
0.03-inch diameter tube. The pressure drop across the tube was
held constant at 300 psi. This gave a wall shear stress of
about 2.6×10^4 dynes/cm^2. Each sample was completely run
through the tube three times just prior to being run in the
viscometer. Besides the shearing action inside the tube, there
was much turbulence and foaming inside of the collection bottle
when the discharge jet struck the previously discharged fluid.
The effect of mechanical degradation was slight as compared with
the twelve days aging and it is possible that the additional
one day's aging may be partially responsible for the viscosity
decrease.

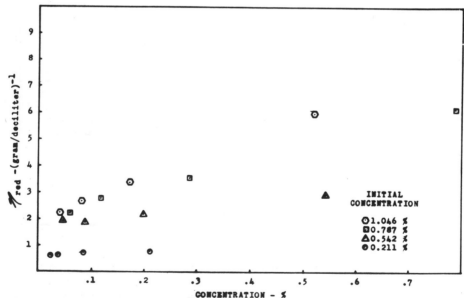

Figure 8   Aluminum Dioleate in Toluene
12 Days Old
(not mech. degraded)

These results show that the starting concentration does affect the soap particle weight and/or shape in these solutions. It is also clear that the particles definitely undergo a time dependent change of weight and/or shape. Since it has been found elsewhere (Refs. 18, 19) that impurities affect the properties of soaps in non-polar solvents, it is also probable that impurities affect the rate of aging.

DISCUSSION

Since the friction factor plots for these drag reducing soap solutions do look similar to those for polymer solutions, these data were used to test the applicability of the Rodriguez, Zakin, and Patterson correlation (Ref. 20), which applies to dilute polymer solutions. (As used here, "dilute" solutions are those which show a transition to normal friction factors in turbulent flow before showing drag reduction.) It takes the form of (f/f_{pv}) versus $(V\tau_1/D^{0.2})$. τ_1 is the polymer molecular relaxation time from the Zimm theory (Ref. 21). For a given soap solution concentration, this was regarded as a constant. When plotted in this manner, the soap solution results showed an erratic diameter effect.

A more general approach to correlating drag reduction results formulated by Seyer and Metzner (Ref. 22) was also tested. Their approach resulted in the following equation for friction factor of the von Karman form with some added terms accounting for non-Newtonian and viscoelastic behavior:

$$\sqrt{2}/f = A(1 - \epsilon_1)^2 \ln (N_{Re}, \sqrt{f}) + (1 - \epsilon_1)^2 (B(\tau) - A \ln^2\sqrt{2}) - G$$

where A is the slope of the logarithmic velocity profile, ϵ_1 is the viscous sublayer thickness divided by pipe radius, B is a function of τ (the Deborah number), and G is a constant.

At various values of τ, the Deborah number (calculated here as $P_{11} - P_{22})/2\tau_w$), values of $B(\tau)$ were calculated using the above equation for flow of the 1.0% soap solution. The table below shows that B is about the same function of τ for this solution as found by Seyer and Metzner.

Values of Seyer-Metzner Function, $B(\tau)$, for Soap Solution Data

f	D inches	V fps	$(N_{Re})_{solv}$	D_r	τ	$B(\tau)$	$B(\tau)_{S-M}$
0.00358	0.510	7.60	47,300	0.677	7.6	16.3	17

Values of Seyer-Metzner Function, $B(\tau)$, for Soap Solution Data
(Cont)

f	D inches	V fps	(N_{Re}) solv	D_r	τ	$B(\tau)$	$B(\tau)_{S-M}$
0.00315	1.002	8.14	99,500	0.699	7.6	14.0	17
0.00351	2.002	7.75	189,400	0.889	7.7	9.7	17
0.00186	0.510	17.17	106,900	0.419	11.7	23.7	22
0.00177	1.002	18.71	228,500	0.466	12.5	20.3	23
0.00113	0.510	31.31	194,900	0.288	17.5	31.4	29
0.00274	0.065	27.88	22,300	0.435	27.3	29.4	32
0.00260	0.065	29.40	23,500	0.417	28.4	29.6	32

In some cases the calculation procedure for $B(\tau)$ did not converge. These were generally, however, for low Reynolds numbers near transition where ϵ_1 became large.

From viscometer results it appears that every concentration studied for drag reduction had a different agglomerate weight as each solution was prepared at the concentration at which it was run. In the gravity flow viscosity measurements where reagent grade toluene was used, the greatest change occurred between the 0.2 and 0.5 per cent solutions. There was no rapid change in agglomerate weight between the 0.5 and 0.75 per cent solutions. Drag reduction occurred when the concentration was raised above 0.5 per cent which is the same range in which the pressure capillary flow data showed a rapid increase in viscosity.

This difference may be caused by differences in the water content of the toluene. The toluene used in the drag reduction and pressure capillary flow measurements was an industrial grade which had been stored in drums for several months and was probably water saturated (0.05 per cent), while the toluene used for the viscosity measurements was reagent grade with not more than 0.02 per cent water. Water causes a decrease in molecular weight as the polar ends of the soap molecules tend to bond to the water molecules. Thus, the soap effectively takes the water molecules out of the solution. In the case of the reagent grade toluene most of the water was apparently taken out by 0.2 to 0.3 per cent soap and any additional soap added after that could remain as a very high molecular weight agglomerate. With the industrial grade toluene's higher water content, more soap, presumably about 0.5 per cent, was required to remove the water from the solution. Thus, at about 0.75 per cent the

sudden increase in viscosity was accompanied by drag reduction
in the capillary flow unit when using the industrial grade toluene.

It has been shown that the addition of an electrolyte to an
aqueous soap system increases the micelle molecular weight
(Refs. 10, 11). Not only was Savins (Ref. 3) able to reach a
higher shear stress before losing his drag reducing effect
with increasing electrolyte concentration, but his solutions
also showed slightly greater maximum drag reducing ability.
This could be an indication of increasing molecular weight in
his system. Savins did not report the effect on K' or n'
(Ref. 4) of adding electrolyte.

The soap structures in aqueous and hydrocarbon solvents are
quite different. In a hydrocarbon solution the carboxyl ends
turn inward away from the solvent and the soap molecules are
primarily held together by hydrogen bonds between the hydroxyl
groups. In an aqueous solution the hydrophobic hydrocarbon
ends turn inward away from the solvent. The soap molecules are
then held together by a balance between the weak van der Waal
forces acting between the hydrocarbon ends, which are close
together, and the repulsive forces of the charged polar ends
which are further apart. Adding a salt has a tendency to shield
the charged polar ends and reduce their repulsion force. Therefore, the soap molecules are more strongly held together.
Because of this the critical micelle concentration will go down
and the micelle molecular weight will go up with an increase in
electrolyte concentration.

This might explain the sudden loss in drag reduction that
Savins (Ref. 3) and White (Ref. 5) noted. At some critical
shear stress the micelles were literally being torn apart faster
than they could reform. Once the shear stress fell below this
critical point, the micelles reagglomerated. White has data
showing the same effect as Savins but in various sized tubes,
showing that the loss in drag reduction is definitely related
to shear stress.

A major point of difference between the aqueous data and
these results is that the critical shear stress sensitivity
observed in the aqueous solutions was not observed in the hydrocarbon drag reducing solutions. In our data, even though
wall shear stresses of over 5000 dynes/cm^2 were reached, as
compared to critical shear stresses of 500 and 50 dynes/cm^2 for
Savins and White, respectively, a loss in drag reduction was
never observed. This is in accord with the above description in
which the forces holding micelles together in aqueous solvents
are weaker than those in hydrocarbon solvents.

Mysels (Ref. 23), in his definition of a micelle, points out that micelles exist in dynamic equilibrium. In view of the reversible effects observed by Savins and White, the probable structure of a soap micelle in an aqueous solvent, the fact that when micelles are dissociated by heating the effect is reversible (Ref. 24), and the increase in micelle molecular weight on the addition of a salt, it would seem that in aqueous systems the soap dissolves as a monomer and then agglomerates into micelles. In these solutions, one would expect a dynamic equilibrium to be reached if no chemical degradation occurs and, therefore, no dependence on starting concentration. In hydrocarbon solvents, however, starting concentration effects, irreversible molecular weight loss on heating (Ref. 18), and molecular weight dependence on soap preparation technique (Ref. 18) point to no dynamic equilibrium and to structure formation in the dry soap rather than in the solution. In these solvents the soaps act somewhat like polymers, which have a fixed molecular weight and are not in dynamic equilibrium and hence degrade irreversibly.

CONCLUSIONS

Drag reduction was observed at concentrations of 0.75 per cent and above for aluminum dioleate in toluene. Capillary viscometry data showed an abrupt rise in viscosity between 0.5 and 0.75 per cent. No critical shear stress, above which drag reducing flow returns to purely viscous flow, as has been observed for soaps in aqueous solvents, was noted in this hydro-carbon system. No critical micelle concentration, as is found in aqueous soap solutions, was detected by light scattering measurements in these hydrocarbon solutions. The first normal stress difference at the wall for a 1.0 per cent aluminum dioleate-toluene solution was about half that obtained by Patterson, et al. for 1.0 per cent PIB L-80 (mol. weight about 720,000) in cyclohexane at equal wall shear rates. Viscometry data showed that the aluminum dioleate-toluene system was time dependent. Fresh solutions were sensitive to mechanical shear. It was also noted that the viscosity of the solution depended on the initial concentration at which the soap was dissolved. After an initial holding period, extended pumping of the 1.0 per cent aluminum dioleate-toluene solution caused no significant mechanical degradation.

ACKNOWLEDGMENT

This work was partially supported by the National Aeronautics and Space Administration (NGR-26-003-003). The assistance of Mr. U. M. Oko in making the light scattering measurements is gratefully acknowledged.

NOMENCLATURE

A	slope of logarithmic velocity profile
$B(\tau)$	function of Deborah number in Seyer-Metzner equation
c	concentration of soap
D	pipe or tube diameter
D_r	drag ratio, solution to solvent
f	friction factor as observed
f_{pv}	friction factor as calculated for a purely viscous fluid
G	constant in Seyer-Metzner equation
I_{45}, I_{135}	disymmetry for 45° and 135° light scattering, respectively
K'	consistency index
n'	power law exponent
n	refractive index
N_{Re}'	generalized Reynolds number, $D^{n'} V^{2-n'} \rho / K' 8^{n'-1}$
$(N_{Re})_{solv.}$	Reynolds number based on solvent viscosity
$(P_{11}-P_{22})_w$	first normal stress difference
V	bulk mean velocity
ΔP	pressure drop per unit length
η_{app}	apparent wall viscosity
η_{sp}	specific viscosity
ϵ_1	thickness of viscous sublayer divided by pipe radius
τ	solution relaxation time divided by flow time as used by Seyer and Metzner
τ_1	first mode relaxation time from Zimm theory
τ_c	solution turbidity
τ_o	solvent turbidity
τ_w	wall shear stress

REFERENCES

1.   Mysels, J. G., U. S. Patent 2,492,173 (1949).

2.   Agoston, G. A., et al., "Flow of Gasoline Thickened by
     Napalm", Ind. Eng. Chem., 46, 1017 (1954).

3.   Savins, J. G., "A Stress Controlled Drag Reduction Phenomenon",
     Rheological Acta, 6, 323 (1967).

4.   Savins, J. G., "Method of Decreasing Friction Losses in
     Turbulent Flow", U. S. Patent 3,361,213 (1968), also Private
     Communication (May 29, 1968).

5.   White, A., "Flow Characteristics of Complex Soap Systems",
     Nature, 214, 585 (1967).

6.   Savins, J. G., "Some Comments on Pumping Requirements For
     Non-Newtonian Fluids", J. Inst. Petr., 47, 329 (1961).

7.   Patterson, G. K., Zakin, J. L., and Rodriguez, J. M.,
     "Drag Reduction: Polymer Solutions, Soap Solutions and
     Solid Particle Suspensions in Pipe Flow", Ind. Eng. Chem.,
     (in press).

8.   Ousterhout, R. S., Hall, C. D., Jr., "Reduction of Friction
     Loss in Fracturing Operation", J. Petr. Tech., 13, 217 (1960).

9.   Hobbs, M. E., "The Effect of Salts on the Critical Concen-
     tration, Size and Stability of Soap Micelles", J. Phys. &
     Colloid Chem., 55, 675 (1951).

10. Corrin, M. L., and Harkins, W. D., "The Effect of Salts on
     the Critical Concentration for the Formation of Micelles
     in Colloidal Electrolytes", J. Am. Chem. Soc., 69, 683 (1947).

11. Debye, P., "Light Scattering in Soap Solutions", J. Phys. &
     Colloid Chem., 53, 1 (1949).

12. Hershey, H. C., Ph.D. Thesis, "Drag Reduction in Newtonian
     Polymer Solutions", University of Missouri - Rolla, 1965.

13. Rodriguez, J. M., M.S. Thesis, "Correlation of Drag Reducing
     Data in Dilute Polymer Solutions", University of Missouri -
     Rolla, 1966.

14. Radin, I., M.S. Thesis, "Drag Reduction in Hydrocarbon Soap
     Solutions", University of Missouri - Rolla, 1968.

15. Hershey, H. C., and Zakin, J. L., "The Existence of Two Types of Drag Reduction in Pipe Flow of Dilute Polymer Solutions", Ind. Eng. Chem. Fund., 6, 381 (1967).

16. Green, C. D., M.S. Thesis, "An Apparatus to Measure Capillary Jet Thrusts in the Evaluation of Normal Stresses in Fluids", University of Missouri - Rolla, 1965.

17. Patterson, G. K., et al., "The Effect of Degradation by Pumping on Normal Stresses in Polyisobutylene", Trans. Soc. Rheol., 10:2, 489 (1966).

18. Sheffer, H., "Aluminum Soaps as High Polymers", Can. J. Research, 26B, 481 (1948).

19. Arkin, L., and Singleterry, C. R., "The Effect of Water on the Size and Shape of Soap Micelles in Benzene Solution", J. Colloid Sci., 4, 537 (1949).

20. Rodriguez, J. M., Zakin, J. L., and Patterson, G. K., "Correlation of Drag Reduction with Modified Deborah Number", Soc. Petr. Eng. J, 7, 325 (1967).

21. Zimm, B. H., Roe, G. M., and Epstein, L. F., "The Solution of a Characteristic Value Problem with the Theory of Chain Molecules", J. Chem. Phys., 24, 279 (1956).

22. Seyer, F. A., and Metzner, A. G., "Turbulent Phenomena in Drag Reducing Solutions", presented A. I. Ch. E. Meeting, New York, Nov. 26-30, 1967.

23. Mysels, K. G., Introduction to Colloid Chemistry, Interscience Publishers, Inc., New York, 1959.

24. Jirgensons, B., and Straumanis, M. E., A Short Textbook of Colloid Chemistry, the MacMillan Company, New York, 1962.

VELOCITY PROFILES DURING DRAG REDUCTION

G. K. Patterson and G. L. Florez[*]

University of Missouri - Rolla

ABSTRACT

A short review of previous attempts to measure velocity profiles in drag reduced flow of polymer solutions is followed by a
description of hot-film anemometer techniques developed during
this work to make such measurements. The large radial variations
in sensor response which have been observed for impact tube measurements were not evident in these measurements. Hot-film measured
profiles were an average of 2 percent in error when integrated to
obtain the bulk mean velocity for solvents and for drag reducing
polymer and soap solutions.

Velocity profiles for the drag reduced flow of more concentrated polymer solutions had a much higher ratio of maximum (axial)
velocity to bulk mean velocity than for more dilute solutions at
the same level of drag reduction. This result is similar to that
obtained by Seyer and Metzner in their streak photography measurements. When plotted as u^+ versus y^+, the profiles indicated
thickened viscous sublayers, as have some of the least erroneous
impact tube measurements.

The soap solution indicated completely different behavior,
even though it showed about the same levels of drag reduction.
The profiles were much blunter in the turbulent core with rapid
velocity decreases farther from the wall than normal. The $u^+ - y^+$
plots were inconclusive because measurements did not extend close
enough to the wall to indicate transition to viscous behavior.

[*]Currently at Refineria Ecopetrol Laboratorio,
 Barrancabermeja, Columbia, South America

LITERATURE REVIEW

Because of the relatively large experimental effort expended recently in studying the unusual effect called "drag reduction", which occurs in the turbulent flow of some polymer solutions, soap solutions, and solid suspensions (Refs. 1-20), many attempts have been made to measure the resulting velocity profiles (Refs. 12, 16, 21-25). Most of this work has been done in pipe flow, although drag reduction has been measured for the flow around certain bodies for which a turbulent boundary layer was formed (Refs. 26-28). Most of the previous velocity profile measurements were made with an impact tube, which registers a pressure difference between the impact tube and the pipe wall. For normal (non-drag reducing) fluids the pressure difference corresponds very closely to the "velocity head" or stagnation pressure $\rho \bar{u}^2/2g$, but for drag reducing polymer solutions and soap solutions the pressure difference is the sum of the velocity head effect and a normal stress difference effect (Ref. 24) caused by the viscoelasticity of the fluid. The output pressures of both impact tube and wall tap are affected. Velocity profiles for suspension flow with drag reduction have not been reported.

The normal stress contributions to the impact tube and static wall tap output pressures cause incorrect velocity profiles to be obtained from the data - always giving low bulk mean velocities when integrated over the pipe area. The magnitude of error involved depends on the magnitude of the normal stress effect and, therefore, on the type, effective molecular weight, and concentration of polymer or soap. Ernst (Ref. 16) and Wells (Ref.23), for instance, have reported relatively small errors (less than 7 percent) for velocity profile measurements in dilute guar gum solutions with drag reduction. Pruitt and Crawford (Ref. 21) on the other hand, have reported impact measured velocity profiles with such large errors that the apparent velocity head was negative near the wall. Astarita and Nomicos (Ref. 24) provided examples from their own investigation of this problem with impact measured profiles in error as much as 29 percent for Dow ET597 solutions. None of the studies of velocity profiles in the turbulent pipe flow of viscoelastic solutions mentioned above involved a calibration procedure for the impact tube. Since it is reasonably certain that the normal stress effect varies considerably over the radial profile (Ref.24), a calibration of velocity versus the pressure difference between impact tube and pipe wall at a given position (say the pipe axis) would be in error at any other point. Since the normal stress difference is a shear rate dependent quantity, the calibration would also be affected by wall shear rate. Therefore, a calibration procedure for the impact tube appears impractical.

Recently, Seyer and Metzner (Ref. 29) have reported velocity profile measurements in the turbulent pipe flow of Dow ET597 in water solutions for drag reducing conditions. The profiles were measured by a tracer technique wherein small gas bubbles were photographed intermittantly and their streak lengths on the film used as measures of velocity. Since the movement of the bubbles relative to the fluid was very slow, the average velocity measured by averaging many streak lengths at a given point was a correct measure. Their velocity profiles checked the measured bulk mean velocity to within 3 percent.

Elata, et al. (Ref. 22) have suggested an empirical equation for the correlation of velocity profiles for the turbulent flow of viscoelastic fluids. The equation, which is a modified "law of the wall" with a correction term involving the product of the solution relaxation time and the wall shear rate (a type of Deborah number), is as follows:

$$\frac{\bar{u}}{u^*} = \frac{1}{k} \ \ln \ \frac{y \, \rho \, u^*}{\mu} + a \, \ln\left[\frac{\rho \, \Theta (u^*)^2}{\mu}\right] + 5.5$$

For $\Theta = 0$, this equation reduces to the purely viscous law of the wall equation. The equation does not account for non-Newtonian effects unless an apparent wall viscosity is used. Seyer and Metzner (Ref. 29) proposed a more general equation wherein the viscoelastic term, $a\ln(\rho \, \Theta (u^*)^2/\mu)$, was replaced by a general function, $B(\rho \, \Theta (u^*)^2/\mu)$, which they evaluated empirically for Dow ET597 solutions.

The object of the work reported here was to develop hot-film anemometry techniques for the measurement of velocity profiles during the drag reduced flow of viscoelastic polymer and soap solutions and to make comparative measurements with and without drag reduction under various conditions. Since the heat transfer rate from the hot-film to the fluid should be primarily velocity dependent, even though this variation might be of a different nature for a viscoelastic fluid than for an ordinary fluid, calibrations of velocity versus heat transfer rate should be of practical use. The heat transfer rate is probably affected somewhat by the velocity gradient and by the level of turbulence, but these effects seem to be small (see the Discussion).

Smith, et al. (Ref. 25) observed possible radial variation in cylindrical hot-film sensitivity in attempted velocity profile measurements in fresh 0.1 percent polyethylene oxide in water solutions. This effect seemed to disappear with some degradation of the polymer. Since their conclusions were based on comparisons with impact tube data in the same drag reducing solutions, however, any conclusions would seem to be in doubt. They also observed an

instability in probe sensitivity in fresh solutions which disappeared
with degradation of the polymer.

EXPERIMENTAL

The velocity profile measurements were made in a liquid pumping
apparatus which has been described in detail by Hershey and Zakin
(Ref. 5) and by Patterson and Zakin (Ref. 31). All the measurements
were made in a 1.0-inch I.D. hydraulically smooth pipe with a 200
diameter entrance length. Flow rate was monitored by a 1-3/4-inch
turbine meter which was calibrated by weighing the efflux from the
pipe for a measured time after each velocity profile measurement.
The turbine meter read-out was a digital counter.

The fluid was continuously filtered by a 72-square inch, 250
mesh screen (50 micron openings) to remove small dirt and lint
particles which cause changes in hot-film anemometer calibrations
when they collect on its surface. Since small temperature changes
also affect anemometer calibration seriously, a temperature control
system capable of controlling to within $0.02°C$ for short periods
was used.

The pressure loss in the pipe was measured by one of two manometers connected to wall taps at the 100 and 200 diameter points of
the smooth pipe: a mercury U-tube manometer and process fluid
manometer.

The impact tube used had an outside diameter of 0.036 inches and
an inside diameter of 0.018 inches at its tip. The impact tube
tip was three inches upstream of the support tube. The assembly
was mounted in a machined cross designed to cause a minimum of
disturbance at the pipe wall. The tip was positioned by an electrical
resistance method which indicated contact with the pipe wall. The
position was precise to within 0.0005 inches.

The hot-film anemometer used was a Disa model 55A01 with a
power booster. The probe used was a Thermo-Systems model 1212-60,
a cylindrical film probe with a 0.006-inch diameter and 0.080-inch
length. The cylinder was pyrex glass covered with a platinum film
which was quartz coated. The probe was positioned within the pipe
by using a reflection technique. Upon reducing the apparent distance between the probe and its reflection on the tube wall by one-
half (as seen through a telescope with a reticle) the actual distance moved corresponded to the final distance from the pipe wall.
Correction for the effect of concavity of the pipe wall on image
separation was insignificant.

The impact tube measurements were made by measuring the difference in pressure between the impact tube tip and a wall tap. The
wall tap was a few inches upstream of the impact tube tip, so a
pressure gradient correction was made. The pressure loss in the
smooth pipe was measured immediately after each velocity profile
measurement. The impact tube was used as a primary instrument with
no corrections.

The hot-film anemometer was calibrated at the axis of the pipe
for both purely viscous and viscoelastic fluids. For the viscoelastic fluids flowing at drag reducing conditions, the calibrations
were corrected iteratively by using the measured velocity profiles.
The procedure was as follows:

(1)   The axis velocity for calibration was assumed to be the
      same as for a purely viscous fluid. $\bar{u}_c/U$ values from
      Knudsen and Katz (Ref. 32) were used. U was known from
      flow rate measurements.

(2)   The velocity profiles were determined from this approximate
      calibration by a graphical procedure in the case of drag
      reducing solutions or by curve fitting in the case of
      solvents. The solutions did not yield calibration curves
      which could be fitted by the modified King's Law, $\bar{e}^2 =
      A + B(\bar{u})^n$.

(3)   The profiles were integrated to obtain new values of
      $\bar{u}_c/U$ to correct the calibration curve.

(4)   This procedure was repeated until internally consistent
      calibration and profiles were obtained.

In order to obtain the most precise time-averaged anemometer
output voltage measurements, a digital voltmeter with variable time
constant was used. A time constant of about three seconds provided
the best results in most cases.

Since calibration changes frequently occurred during use of the
hot-film probe, calibration measurements were made both before and
after each velocity profile measurement. If significant changes
occurred, the profile was rejected. The pipe pressure loss was
measured immediately after each hot-film anemometer velocity profile measurement, as in the case of the impact tube measurements.

The solutions used for these measurements were 0.2 percent
and 0.4 percent Vistanex L-200 (Humble Oil and Refining Co., Baton
Rouge, La.) (polyisobutylene or PIB) in cyclohexane and 1.0 percent
aluminum dioleate (Witco Chemical Co., Inc., Chicago, Ill.) (soap)
in toluene with approximate viscosities (Ref. 33) of 1.35 cp, 2.7 cp,
and 1.46 cp, respectively. These viscosities are for the shear

TABLE I

Solution Properties

Solute	Solvent	Concentration wt. %	K'^a	n'^a
Vistanex L-200 (PIB)	Cyclohexane	0.2	0.0135	~1.00
Vistanex L-200 (PIB)	Cyclohexane (36)	0.4	0.0830	0.884
Al -dioleate	Toluene (7)	1.0	0.035	0.92

---

[a]Constants in Rabinowitsch-Mooney equation, $\tau_w = K'(8U/D)^{n'}$, dynes/cm^2.

rate range of 10^4-10^5 sec^{-1} and were measured after several hours
of pumping. Constants for the power law equation as fit to data
for solutions similar to these are given in Table I.

DISCUSSION

Typical velocity profiles measured in the turbulent flow of
cyclohexane and toluene are shown in Figure 1. The average deviation
of ten solvent velocity profiles measured by the impact tube was
1.7 percent. Since the Reynolds number range was not large, the
solvent velocity profile shapes do not vary greatly.

The magnitude of error in the impact tube measurements caused
by the normal stress effect is shown by a typical velocity profile
result for the 1.0 percent soap solution as compared to a profile
for toluene of nearly the same Reynolds number in Figure 2. The
average velocity calculated from the measured soap solution profile was 11.3 percent below the correct value. The greatest deviation observed was a -33.3 percent error for an impact tube
profile measurement in the 0.4 percent Vistanex solution at a
Reynolds number of 27,000. For the polymer solutions the error
increased with flow rate and with drag reduction, but for the soap
solutions the error was about constant at all conditions studied.
No attempt was made to determine corrections which might be used
for impact tube measurements in such solutions.

Hot-film anemometry techniques for velocity profile measurements
were developed in the solvents. For the measurements made, the
mean deviation of the integrated bulk mean velocities from the
correct values was 2.3 percent. The same mean deviation for the
solution measurements during drag reduction was 1.9 percent. The

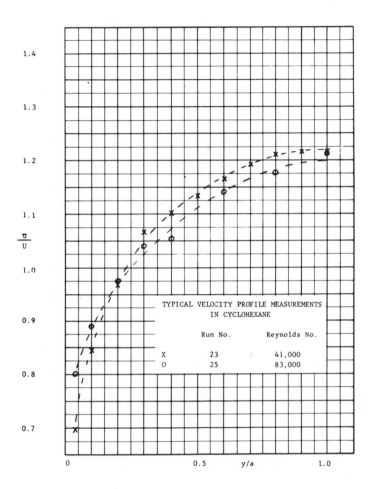

Figure 1   Typical Velocity Profile Measurements in Cyclohexane

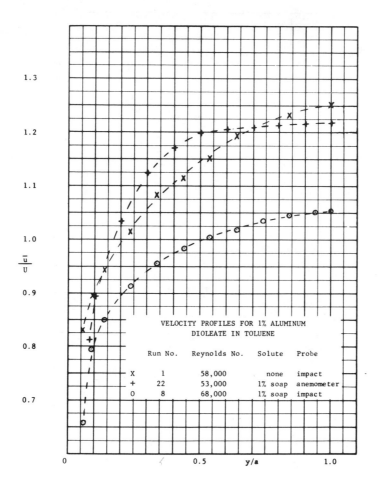

Figure 2   Velocity Profiles for 1% Aluminum Dioleate in Toluene

presence of the solutes did not seem to adversely affect the capability of the anemometer to check the bulk mean velocities. This does not mean, of course, that the solution velocity profiles necessarily have the correct shape, but is a strong indication that radial sensitivity variations are not large.

Table II shows the deviation of the flow rate calculated by integrating each measured velocity profile from the flow rate measured by timed weighing. Examination of these deviations shows a bias toward low integrated flow rates. The iterative technique used to determine the centerline probe calibrations provides profiles with zero error in total flow rate if there is no variation in probe sensitivity from the pipe axis to the wall. These deviations, therefore, represent minor errors in velocity profile shape - low velocities near the wall for negative deviation and high velocities near the wall for positive deviation. It is impossible with present knowledge to speculate on corrections to the velocity profile shapes.

TABLE II

Flow Rate Deviations in Profile Measurements

Run No.	Solvent	Solute	Reynolds No.	Drag Ratio	Bulk Mean Velocity fps	Profile Deviation %
21	toluene	Soap	36,000	0.70	8.32	-1.7
22	toluene	Soap	53,000	0.58	12.50	1.1
23	cyclo-hexane	None	41,000	1.00	6.01	-1.9
24	cyclo-hexane	None	61,000	1.00	9.05	-2.4
25	cyclo-hexane	None	83,000	1.00	12.34	-2.7
26	cyclo-hexane	0.2% PIB	27,000	0.94	6.01	-2.6
27	cyclo-hexane	0.2% PIB	40,000	0.76	9.02	-2.1
28	cyclo-hexane	0.2% PIB	55,000	0.72	12.41	-1.5
29	cyclo-hexane	0.4% PIB	13,500	0.94	6.01	-3.1
30	cyclo-hexane	0.4% PIB	20,000	0.76	9.03	-1.3
31	cyclo-hexane	0.4% PIB	27,000	0.76	12.31	2.1

A soap solution velocity profile measured by hot-film anemometry
is also shown in Figure 2. It is about the same Reynolds number
for comparison with the solvent profile. The soap solution profile is much flatter than normal (normal - as for solvents) in the
central region of the pipe. This behavior is unlike that of the
0.2 percent Vistanex solution profiles shown in Figure 3. The
polymer solution has higher than normal velocity near the pipe
axis at the low Reynolds number, but gradually approaches and
drops below normal. At the higher Reynolds number the polymer
solution velocity at the pipe axis is actually below that of the
solvent and becomes higher than solvent velocity only very near the
wall. At intermediate flow rates a situation exists in which the
polymer solution velocities are higher than normal both at the
axis and near the wall and lower than normal at an intermediate
region.

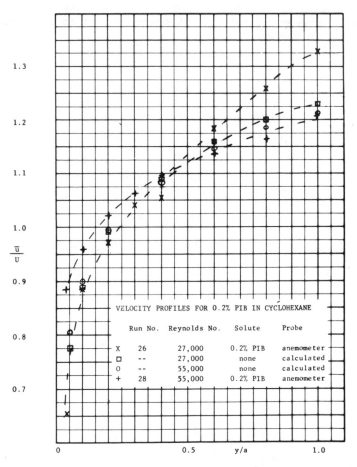

VELOCITY PROFILES FOR 0.2% PIB IN CYCLOHEXANE

Run No.	Reynolds No.	Solute	Probe
X 26	27,000	0.2% PIB	anemometer
□ --	27,000	none	calculated
O --	55,000	none	calculated
+ 28	55,000	0.2% PIB	anemometer

Figure 3   Velocity Profiles for 0.2% PIB in Cyclohexane

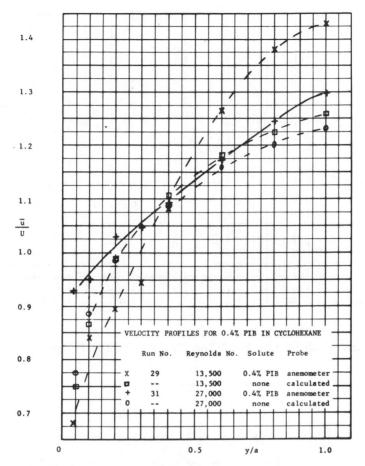

Figure 4   Velocity Profiles for 0.4% PIB in Cyclohexane

The 0.4 percent Vistanex solution as shown in Figure 4 merely magnifies the observations of the 0.2 percent solution. At the lower flow rate the $\bar{u}_c/U$ ratio is 1.43, as compared to a normal value of 1.26.

The u^+ - y^+ plot of the 0.2 percent Vistanex data in Figure 5 shows the strong tendency toward viscous boundary layer thickening reported by Wells (Ref. 23), Ernst (Ref. 16), and predicted by Elata, et al. (Ref. 22). The 0.4 percent solution showed such behavior even more strongly in Figure 6, but also manifested a very strong "wake" region in the turbulent core (Ref. 35). It is difficult to judge whether this large hump near the center is the result of intermittant turbulence as postulated by Seyer and Metzner

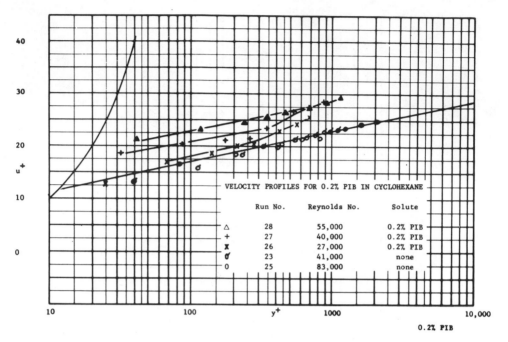

Figure 5   Velocity Profiles for 0.2% PIB in Cyclohexane

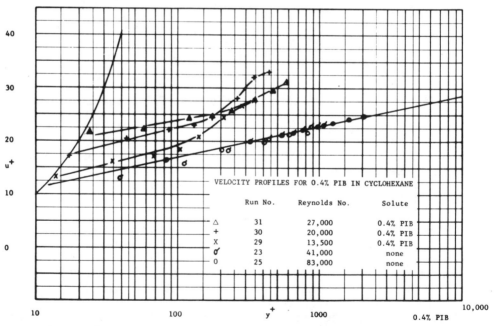

Figure 6   Velocity Profiles for 0.4% PIB in Cyclohexane

(Ref. 29) or of the great decrease in momentum transfer rate (caused by the viscoelasticity of the solution) even during constant turbulence. The Seyer and Metzner profiles, shown as u^+ versus y^+ in Figure 7, are very similar to those reported here for the polymer solutions. Turbulence intensity measurements in similar solutions (Ref. 36) have indicated a low intensity region (as compared with purely viscous solvents and oil) with high intensity regions at higher and at lower Reynolds numbers. Drag reduction at about the same levels as attained here existed during those measurements. The Reynolds number range for these profiles is in the lower than normal turbulence intensity region. Whether there is an interaction between turbulence intensity and intermittancy in this region will not be known until intermittancy measurements are made.

The Elata (Ref. 22) equation was used with the two highest flow rate profiles of both the 0.2 percent and the 0.4 percent Vistanex solutions to estimate their values of a and Θ assuming no shear rate effect over the ranges of 5,000 - 15,000 and 3,000 - 9,000 respectively. The values of Θ were 0.00022 and 0.0024 seconds for the 0.2 percent and 0.4 percent solutions, respectively. It is interesting to note that a value of Θ calculated from normal stress

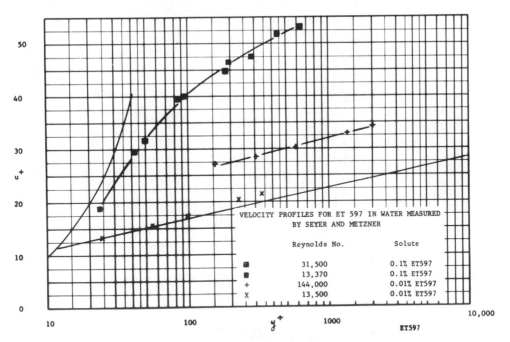

Figure 7   Velocity Profiles for ET 597 in Water
Measured by Seyer and Metzner

difference measurements at a shear rate of 4900 sec^{-1} for degraded
0.4 percent Vistanex in cyclohexane (Ref. 34) was 0.0040 seconds -
a good order of magnitude check.

    The soap solution velocity profiles show a completely different
kind of behavior than the polymer solution profiles when plotted
as u$^+$ versus y$^+$ as in Figure 8. The two profiles shown behave alike
in that they do not indicate thickened viscous boundary layers,
but some sort of transition to the purely viscous type of behavior
near the wall. Obviously data closer to the wall must be obtained
in order to fully understand the behavior of the soap solution,
which has no linear portion which would correspond to the Elata
equation. It appears from the velocity profile data that the mechanism of drag reduction for soap solutions is different from the
mechanism for polymer solutions. This is supported by turbulence
intensity data reported by Rodriguez, Patterson, and Zakin (Ref. 36)
which compares polymer and soap solution turbulent behavior.

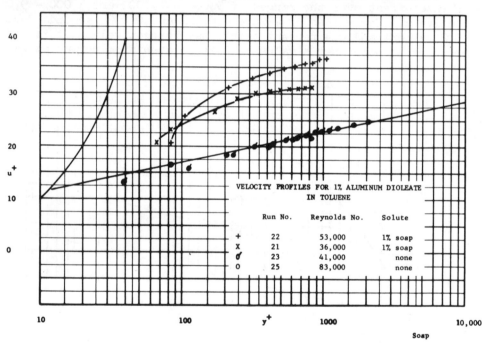

Figure 8   Velocity Profiles for 1% Aluminum Dioleate in Toluene

NOMENCLATURE

a   pipe radius

B   function of shear rate in Seyer-Metzner relation

D	tube diameter
k	mixing length constant
K'	consistency index
n'	behavior index
u*	friction velocity, $\sqrt{g_c \tau_w / \rho}$
$\bar{u}$	local average velocity
$\bar{u}_c$	pipe axis average velocity
U	bulk mean velocity
y	distance from pipe wall
a	Elata constant
μ	viscosity
ρ	density
Θ	relaxation or characteristic time
τ_w	wall shear stress

REFERENCES

1. Savins, J. G., "Drag Reduction Characteristics of Solutions of Macromolecules in Turbulent Flow", Soc. Petr. Eng. J., 4, 203 (1964).

2. Osterhout, R. S., and C. D. Hall, "Reduction of Friction Loss in Fracturing Operations", J. Petr. Tech., 13, 217 (1961).

3. Lord, D. L., B. W. Hulsey, and L. L. Melton, "General Turbulent Pipe Flow Scale-up Correlation for Rheologically Complex Fluids", preprint 1680, presented SPE Symp. on Rheologically Complex Fluids, Houston, December 1966.

4. Zandi, Iraj, "Decreased Head Losses in Raw Water Conduits", J. Am. Water Works Assoc., 59, 213 (1967).

5. Hershey, H. C., and J. L. Zakin, "Existence of Two Types of Drag Reduction in Pipe Flow of Dilute Polymer Solutions", Ind. Eng. Chem. Fund., 6, 381 (1967).

6. Savins, J. G., "A Stress-Controlled Drag Reduction Phenomenon", preprint 1724, presented SPE Symp. on Rheologically Complex Fluids, Houston, December 1966, also Rheol. Acta, 6, 323 (1967).

7. Radin, I., "A Study of Drag Reduction in Hydrocarbon Soap Solution", M.S. Thesis, University of Missouri - Rolla, 1968.

8. Bobkowicz, A. J., and W. H. Gauvin, "Turbulent Flow Characteristics of Model Fiber Suspensions", Can. J. Chem. Eng., 43, 87 (1965).

9. Vanoni, V. A., and G. N. Nomicos, "Resistance Properties of Sediment Laden Streams", Trans. ASCE, 125, 1140 (1960).

10. Ripkin, J. F., and M. Pilch, "Non-Newtonian Pipe Friction Studies with Various Dilute Polymer Water Solutions", St. Anthony Falls Hyd. Lab. Project Report 71 to David Taylor Model Basin, Nonr 710 (49), June 1964.

11. Virk, P. S., E. W. Merrill, H. S. Mickley, and K. A. Smith, "The Critical Wall Shear Stress for Reduction of Turbulent Drag in Pipe Flows by Polyethylene Oxides in Dilute Solution", in Modern Developments in the Mechanics of Continua, Ed. by S. Eskinazi, Academic Press, 1966.

12. Shaver, R. G., and E. W. Merrill, "Turbulent Flow of Pseudoplastic Polymer Solutions in Straight Cylindrical Tubes", A.I. Ch.E. J., 5, 181 (1959).

13. Meter, D. M., "Tube Flow of Non-Newtonian Polymer Solutions: Part II, Turbulent Flow", A.I.Ch.E. J., 10, 881 (1964).

14. Ram, A., E. Finkelstein, and C. Elata, "Reduction of Friction in Oil Pipelines by Polymer Additives", Ind. Eng, Chem. Proc. Design and Dev., 6, 309 (1967).

15. Elata, C., and T. Tirosh, "Frictional Drag Reduction", Israel J. Tech., 3, 1 (1965).

16. Ernst, W. D., "Investigation of the Turbulent Shear Flow of Dilute Aqueous CMC Solutions", A.I.Ch.E. J., 12, 581 (1966).

17. Rodriguez, J. M., J. L. Zakin, and G. K. Patterson, "Correlation of Drag Reduction with Modified Deborah Number for Dilute Polymer Solutions", Soc. Pet. Eng. J., 7, 325 (1967).

18. Fabula, A. G., J. L. Lumley, and W. D. Taylor, "Some Interpretations of the Toms Effect", in Modern Developments in the Mechanics of Continua, Ed. by S. Eskinazi, Academic Press, 1966.

19. Seyer, F. A., and A. B. Metzner, "Turbulent Flow Properties of Viscoelastic Fluids", Can. J. Chem. Eng., 45, 121 (1967).

20. Wells, C. S., Jr., and J. G. Spangler, "Effects of Local In-
    jection of a Drag Reducing Fluid into Turbulent Pipe Flow of
    a Newtonian Fluid", presented 4th Winter Meeting Soc. Rheol.,
    Santa Barbara, February 1967, also Phys. of Fluids, 10, 1890
    (1967).

21. Pruitt, G. T., and H. R. Crawford, "Investigation for the Use
    of Additives for the Reduction of Pressure Losses", Final Re-
    port of Western Company, Contr. No. DA-23-072-AMC-209 (T),
    1965 also AD613345.

22. Elata, C., J. Lehrer, and A. Kahanovitz, "Turbulent Shear Flow
    of Polymer Solutions", Israel J. Tech., 4, 84 (1966).

23. Wells, C. S., "Anamolous Turbulent Flow of Non-Newtonian Fluids",
    A.I.A.A. J., 3, 1800 (1965).

24. Astarita, G., and L. Nicodemo, "Velocity Distributions and
    Normal Stresses in Viscoelastic Turbulent Pipe Flow", A.I.Ch.E.
    J., 12, 478 (1966).

25. Smith, K. A., E. W. Merrill, H. S. Mickley, and P. S. Virk,
    "Anomalous Pitot Tube and Hot Film Measurements in Dilute Poly-
    mer Solutions", Chem. Eng. Sci., 22, 619 (1967).

26. Lang, T. G., and H. V. L. Patrick, "Drag of Blunt Bodies in
    Polymer Solutions", ASME, Winter Annual Meeting and Energy
    Systems Exposition, New York, November 1966.

27. Dove, H. L., "The Effect on Resistance of Polymer Additives
    Injected into the Boundary Layer of a Frigate Model", 11th
    Intern. Towing Tank Conf., Japan, October 1966.

28. Love, R. H., "The Effect of Ejected Polymer Solutions on the
    Resistance and Wake of a Flat Plate in a Water Flow", Hydro-
    nautics, Inc., Tech. Report No. 353-2, June 1965.

29. Seyer, F. A., and A. B. Metzner, "Turbulence Phenomena in
    Drag Reducing Systems", presented 60th Annual A.I.Ch.E. Meeting,
    New York, Nov. 1967.

30. Clapp, R. M., "Turbulent Heat Transfer in Pseudoplastic Non-
    Newtonian Fluids", Intern. Dev. in Heat Transfer, III, ASME,
    New York, 1961, p. 652.

31. Patterson, G. K., and J. L. Zakin, "Hot-Film Anemometry Measure-
    ments of Turbulence in Pipe Flow: Organic Solvents", A.I.Ch.E.
    J., 13, 513 (1967).

32. Knudsen, J. G., and D. L. Katz, Fluid Dynamics and Heat Transfer, McGraw-Hill, New York, 1958, p. 149.

33. Florez, G. L., "Velocity Profiles in Viscoelastic Drag Reducing Solutions", M.S. Thesis, University of Missouri-Rolla, Rolla, Missouri, 1967.

34. Patterson, G. K., and J. L. Zakin, "Prediction of Drag Reduction Using a Viscoelastic Model", A.I.Ch.E. J., 14, 434 (1968).

35. Coles, D., "The Law of the Wake in the Turbulent Boundary Layer", J. Fluid Mech., 1, 191 (1956).

36. Rodriguez, J. L., G. K. Patterson, and J. L. Zakin, "Turbulence Intensities in Drag Reducing Solutions", submitted to Ind. Eng. Chem. Fund.

DRAG REDUCTION ON A ROTATING DISK USING A POLYMER ADDITIVE

C. Gorman Gilbert* and John F. Ripken

St. Anthony Falls Hydraulic Laboratory
University of Minnesota

ABSTRACT

The characteristics of frictional drag on a disk rotating in an enclosure filled with water containing various concentrations of guar gum have been investigated.

Measurement of driving torque provided a sensitive means of evaluating the frictional drag reduction relative to water. Reductions ranged up to 60 percent for a smooth disk. Tests with a rough disk showed the expected increase in friction with roughness, but tests with the guar solutions showed approximately the same order of frictional benefits on both the smooth and rough surfaces.

Pitot velocity profile studies of the spiraling boundary layer near the edge of the disk showed significant shifts in the chamber core flow with the addition of guar. While profiles were similar in shape, increasing additive concentration diminished the thickness of the boundary layer. Secondary studies established that the influence of the guar on the Pitot coefficient was negligible.

Studies were made of the durability of the guar under disk shear by operating the disk continuously for extended periods and observing the increase in torque as a function of time. Limited tests indicated that the drag increased gradually for some time before reaching a stable plateau of residual benefits.

*Currently at Naval Ship Engineering Center

INTRODUCTION

This paper summarizes the results of a thesis study (Ref. 1) to better define the frictional drag reduction which can be obtained when a disk rotating in a finite chamber or enclosure filled with water is treated with various additive concentrations of guar gum.

Guar gum solutions were selected for these tests because a considerable fund of information was available on their general characteristics. This information included the fact that the solutions are good drag reducers, are fairly durable under high shear, and are relatively immune to serious instrumental distortions in Pitot velocity evaluations.

The boundary layer of a rotating disk was selected for these drag reduction studies because of certain unique features and potentials of disk systems. These systems are unique in that their boundary layers normally include the possibility of concurrent laminar, transitional, and turbulent conditions in the modest space which exists between the hub and the edge of the rotating disk. Moreover, these boundary layers may achieve relatively high shear rates and Reynolds numbers in a laboratory facility having relative physical simplicity and modest energy input. In the case of the enclosed disk, there are additional advantages in that the boundary layer is quite accessible and observable, environmental conditions are quite controllable, and only small quantities of additive are necessary for tests. Although disk studies have only an indirect relation to naval hull drag reduction problems, enclosed rotating disks are a common component of many forms of conventional hydraulic machinery and disk friction losses are significant to machine efficiencies. The reduction of these losses by polymer lubrication is an intriguing application possibility.

Boundary layers on enclosed rotating disks have had considerable study in the past. The most pertinent and extensive studies in water are those conducted by Daily and Nece (Ref. 2) at MIT. The only known previous studies using rotating disks with polymer water solutions are those by Hoyt and Fabula (Ref. 3) at the former Naval Ordnance Test Station, Pasadena. The latter studies were confined to torque evaluations with a large tank or unconfined disk and did not include detailed studies of the boundary layer. The present study provides an extension of and a tie between these two earlier studies.

In examining the boundary layers of a rotating disk for insight into the mechanism of dilute polymer solutions, it must be recognized that these boundary layers differ dimensionally in character from those common to pipe flows or flat plates. Fluid elements adjacent to the surface of a rotating disk experience not only the shearing forces of the tangential motion, but are also subject to the radially outward pressure forces of a forced vortex system. In consequence, fluid confined in a cylindrical chamber with a rotating disk boundary at one end and a stationary disk boundary at the other end will experience forces which vary with both the y distance from the face of the disk and the radial distance, r, from the center of rotation. The end result is that near the disks the boundary layer motion is primarily a two-dimensional spiral which is outward-flowing on the rotating disk and inward-flowing on the fixed disk. Between these boundary layers may exist a cylindrical core flow primarily tangential in direction. Superimposed on this core flow is a modest axial flow which moves from the rotating disk toward the fixed disk near the outer wall of the cylinder and in the reverse direction near the cylinder axis.

Daily and Nece (Ref. 2) distinguished four separate regimes in disk flows of this type depending on the axial spacing, s, between disks and the disk Reynolds number (Re $= \omega a^2/\nu$, where ω is the angular velocity, a is the disk radius, and ν is the fluid kinematic viscosity). For low values of Re and s/a, the two boundary layers are laminar and merge together. For larger values of s/a, the two boundary layers are discretely separated by a core flow. At other combinations of Re and s/a, merged and separated turbulent boundary layers may occur. In the study described herein the parameter s/a has been arbitrarily confined to the single value of 0.217 and boundary layer probing has been confined to a region near the rotating disk at an r/a position of 0.765. For these test conditions, the subject boundary layer proved to be of the discrete spiraling turbulent character phasing to a tangential core flow with increasing y values. The tests indicated that, in general, all of the disk was not covered by a turbulent boundary layer but was laminar for an appreciable radial distance outward from the axis.

In the material which follows, the physical test apparatus is described, the drag reduction as measured by torque is evaluated, and the directions and magnitudes of the boundary layer velocity probings are graphically summarized for various speeds and additive concentrations. While most of the tests relate to a smooth boundary, comparative tests with a rough boundary were included to augment the very limited information available on polymer flows with rough boundaries. Additional duration tests were included to evaluate the rate at which the polymer degraded under sustained shearing exposure.

TEST APPARATUS

The experimental apparatus consisted of a machined and polished aluminum disk of 1/4 inch thickness and 19-5/8-inch diameter, rotating

within a plexiglas cylinder of 19-3/4-inch inside diameter. The
end walls of the enclosing cylinder were spaced 2-1/8 inches from the
faces of the disk (s/a = 0.217) as shown in Figure 1. One fixed
end wall of plexiglas served for visual observations and support
for the instrument probes. The opposite wall was of aluminum and
served to transfer heat from the chambered test fluid to an external
controlled circulation of coolant water which held test temperatures
to a measured range of 45°F to 55°F.

The disk was rotated by a 10 HP electric motor providing selected
speeds in a range from 600 to 1,800 rpm. Speeds were measured to
the nearest 10 rpm by a photoelectric tachometer and torque was
measured by a reaction dynamometer to the nearest 0.023 foot-pound.
A tare torque measurement permitted suitable torque deductions for
shaft, seal, and bearings.

Most of the tests were conducted with the smooth disk, but in
one series, roughness material was cemented to one face of the disk.
The roughness consisted of "Scotch Tred," made by Minnesota Mining
and Manufacturing Co. The uniform roughness had a measured peak
to valley height of 0.018 inch.

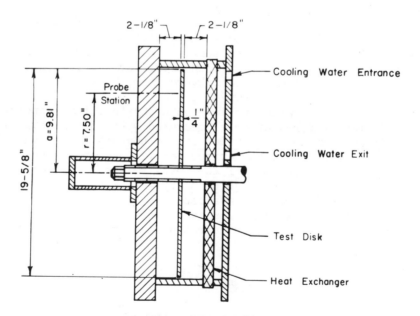

Figure 1   Test Chamber

Measurements of the magnitude and direction of the velocity of the disk boundary layer flow were made at a test station located 7-1/2 inches radially outward from the shaft axis ($r/a = 0.765$). These measurements were made at a y distance from the face of the disk varying from 0.037 to 1.200 inches using separate directional and Pitot-static probes. Determinations of direction were made first followed by magnitude measurements with the aligned Pitot-static probe.

The Pitot-static probe was separately calibrated in the submerged jet issuing from a flow nozzle attached to a head tank. The speed of the test jet was inferred from the measured gravitational head in the tank. The calibrations, which were conducted with both water and guar solutions, are discussed later.

The relative drag reducing characteristics of the guar solutions were evaluated by expelling a test sample through an 0.054-inch diameter capillary tube of 1,000 diameters length under measured pressure conditions. The apparatus and test procedures are described more fully in Reference 4.

The guar gum employed in these tests was Westco J2-FP as manufactured by the Western Company.

RESULTS

Torque Measurements

Measurements of the torque on the disk were obtained for water and six guar gum concentrations using the smooth disk. The guar gum solutions ranged in age from 1 to 3 days. These results, along with torque measurements for water and a solution of 125 ppm using the rough disk, are plotted in Figure 2 using a Reynolds number based on the viscosity of water. For simplicity only the mean line values for the data are shown. Relative values of the torque are represented by a coefficient used by Daily and Nece (Ref. 2) which is

$$C_m = \frac{2M}{\rho \omega^2 a^5}$$

In this, M is the torque, due to two faces of the disk, and ρ is the density. In Figure 2 the rough disk data have been adjusted to account for the actual presence of the roughness on only one side of the disk.

The smooth disk results are comparable to the results that Hoyt and Fabula (Ref. 3) obtained using an unconfined disk. The data describe a fanlike pattern of lines. For the lower concentrations

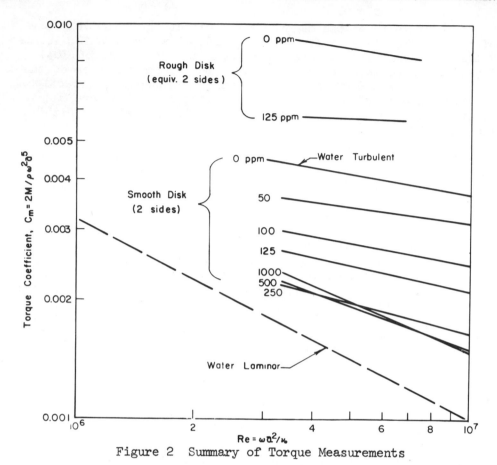

Figure 2   Summary of Torque Measurements

the lines are approximately parallel to the turbulent water line, but for the higher concentrations the data are about parallel to the laminar water line, which has been extended so as to appear in Figure 2. Hoyt and Fabula found that for concentrations below 311 ppm the data approximated the turbulent water data in slope, while for concentrations above 621 the lines were roughly parallel to the laminar water data. These limits seem consistent with the results shown in Figure 2.

The change in slope of the torque data occurs through a range of concentrations that includes the optimum drag reducing concentration. In Figure 2 this concentration is seen to depend on the Reynolds number and varies from 250 ppm to 1,000 ppm. For the Reynolds number corresponding to the velocity tests--about 4×10^6-- the optimum concentration is about 500 ppm. This optimum value agrees with that yielding a minimum boundary layer as shown in the results of the velocity magnitude tests to be described later. For a Reynolds number of 10^7 the drag reductions obtained in the smooth disk experiments are shown in Table 1.

TABLE 1

Concentration (ppm)	Reduction (%)
0	----
50	14.8
100	33.2
125	42.8
250	54.9
500	58.7
1,000	59.4

Figure 2 also shows the rough disk torque measurements. In this case the increased vibrations of the experimental apparatus severely limited the range of Reynolds numbers tested. It is obvious that although the total drag is increased by the roughness, the relative drag reduction is apparently little affected by the addition of roughness to the disk.

Shear Degradation Measurements

Shear degradation tests were conducted for a solution of 500 ppm using the smooth disk and for 100 ppm using both the smooth disk and the rough disk. The results of these tests appear in Figure 3 in terms of the torque coefficient, C_m, and show what apparently is a termination of shear degradation after a given time period. For the smooth disk, this time period is about 30 hours for 500 ppm and about 11 hours for 100 ppm. The rough disk data for 100 ppm showed a greater initial rate of degradation than for the smooth disk, followed by a decrease in the rate of degradation similar to the smooth disk data. However, the testing time period in this case was not long enough to reach a termination of the shear degradation.

The degradation tests indicate a possibly valuable aspect of guar gum solutions in that many degraded molecules can produce a stable drag reduction which is comparable to the initial drag reduction of a lesser concentration of undegraded molecules. For instance, in Figure 3 the 500 ppm solution after 30 hours still has the drag reducing capability of a fresh solution of 75 ppm, as shown in Figure 2, at the same Re. Similarly, the 100 ppm solution after 11 hours compares to a fresh solution of 50 ppm.

Velocity Directional Measurements

Figure 4 shows a mean line summary of the directional data obtained with the smooth disk for guar solutions ranging from 1 to 2 days in age. The data are plotted with angular values

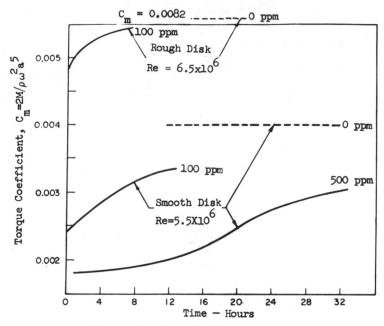

Figure 3   Degradation Measurements

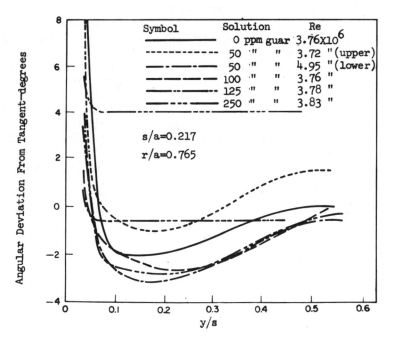

Figure 4   Summary of Directional Tests

referenced to the tangential direction as zero and with values increasing as the radial direction is approached. For the guar gum solutions, the data of this figure show what appear to be the varying effects of transition from laminar to turbulent flow somewhere radially inward of the directional probe. Both the 50 ppm and the 250 ppm solutions yielded data that fell on two separate curves, separated in the core region by 2° for 50 ppm and 4-1/2° for 250 ppm. Tests with 500 ppm and 1,000 ppm both resulted in a complete scatter of data. From these results, it appears that an increase in the concentration of guar gum resulted in increased instability in the flow. Two exceptions to this trend are the 100 ppm and 125 ppm solutions. In each of these cases, the data fell on one curve, indicating either that the instabilities were not present for these solutions or that the instabilities were of sufficiently long time periods so as not to be detected during the tests.

The instabilities seem to be a result of the transition from laminar to turbulent flow on the disk with the region of transition moving radially outward with increasing concentration. During periods of instability, the directional probe could have been sensing either values directly in the transition region or values associated with spiral vortices shed from the transition region. The role of the transition region in the creation of the instabilities was indirectly confirmed by testing the 50 ppm solution at a higher Reynolds number. The increased Reynolds number brought the transition region closer to the center of the disk, and the new data fell on only the lower curve that had previously been obtained for 50 ppm.

The second result inferred from the directional data is a decrease in the thickness of the radial outflow region with increases in concentration. This effect corresponds to the decrease in boundary layer thickness which is also noted later in the velocity profiles of Figure 5.

Velocity Magnitude Measurements

Prior to the measurement of the velocity magnitudes near the disk, the Pitot-static probe was calibrated in the submerged jet from the gravity-fed nozzle. In this calibration the differential pressure coefficient, C_p ($C_p = [h_s - h_0]/V^2/2g$), for the probe was determined for water and for 500 ppm and 1000 ppm of guar gum solutions aged up to 2 weeks. The calibration demonstrated that the effect of 1-day-old guar solutions on the values of C_p was quite small. For 500 ppm the C_p was decreased by 2.8 percent, while for 1,000 ppm, the decrease was 9.4 percent. These effects are much less than those obtained by Wetzel and Tsai (Ref. 5) for an impact probe in Polyox solutions.

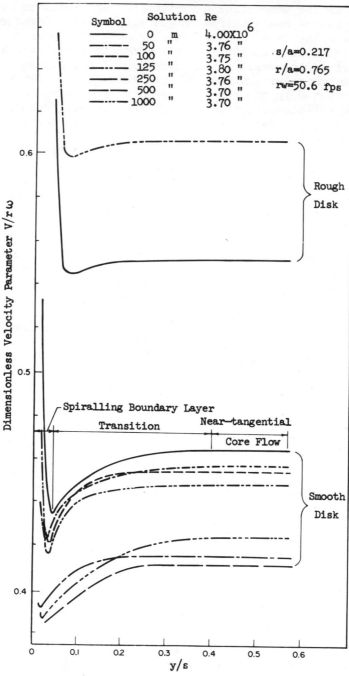

Figure 5   Profiles of Velocity Magnitude

The results of the Pitot-static probe calibration changed
with the passage of time for a given solution. Calibration tests
performed on successive days showed increases in the C_p values
until the values of C_p for water were reached. Samples of the
solution taken during this time, however, revealed little change
in drag reducing ability when tested in the capillary tube rheometer.
From these results, it might be inferred that elastic contributions
to drag reduction with guar solutions older than 1 day are not
appreciable and that the elasticity effects decrease with time.
Similar time variance has been reported by Brennen and Gadd (Ref. 6).

The velocity magnitude measurements were performed using both
the smooth disk and the rough disk and guar solutions ranging in
age from 2 to 5 days. The results of these tests are presented
in Figure 5 in terms of a dimensionless velocity parameter. For the
smooth disk the velocity profiles show two trends. For concentrations below the optimum drag reducing concentration, increases in
concentration yield reductions both in the boundary layer thickness
(see Figure 5 for the boundary layer thickness as defined herein)
and in the velocity of the core flow. Figure 5 shows that these
trends include all concentrations except for the 1,000 ppm solution,
indicating that the optimum concentration was less than 1,000 ppm,
as noted earlier. The decreases in the boundary layer are observed
in Figure 5 by noting that the dip in the velocity profile moves
toward the disk as the guar gum concentration increases.

Conversely, the rough disk produced an increase in the core
velocity as the guar gum was added. For the concentration (125 ppm)
tested with the rough disk, the value of the velocity parameter
was 0.61, as opposed to 0.55 for water.

CONCLUSIONS

A smooth disk rotating in a water-filled confined chamber will
experience a torque drag reduction of up to 60 percent when guar
gum concentrations are increased. The drag reduction is a function
of the guar concentration and a Reynolds number. The torque reduction and optimum concentration (500 ppm) were comparable in values to
those obtained by Hoyt and Fabula with unconfined chambers.

When treated with guar additive, a rough disk experiences
relative torque reduction benefits quite comparable to those
experienced by a smooth disk.

When exposed to continuous disk shear, a guar solution evidences
a decrease in torque benefits leading eventually to a stable terminal torque benefit. The rate of decrease and the terminal value
are a function of the guar concentration and the disk roughness.

Measurements in the boundary layer of a smooth disk indicate
that increasing torque benefits are in general accompanied by a
decreasing boundary layer thickness, a diminishing angle of spiral
in the boundary layer, and a decreasing tangential velocity in the
chamber core flow.

The stability of flow in a turbulent boundary layer existing
near the edge of the disk depends on the location of the laminar-
turbulent transition zone which exists somewhere radially inward
on the disk. This location appears to move radially outward as
the concentration of guar additive is increased.

The effect of guar additives on the coefficient of a Pitot-
static tube is quite minor. For guar solutions that have been aged
a few days, this effect on the probe vanishes; but the drag reduction
is almost unchanged.

ACKNOWLEDGEMENT

The financial support of the Office of Naval Research, Fluid
Mechanics Branch, as a part of Contract N00014-67-A-0013-0003 is
gratefully acknowledged.

REFERENCES

1. Gilbert, C. G., "The Effect of Long-Chain Polymer Additives on
the Flow Around an Enclosed Rotating Disk," M.S. Thesis,
University of Minnesota, 1968 (available on interlibrary
loan from the Walter Library, University of Minnesota,
Minneapolis, Minnesota)

2. Daily, J. W. and R. E. Nece, "Roughness and Chamber Effects on
Induced Flow and Frictional Resistance of Enclosed Rotational
Disks," Massachusetts Institute of Technology, Technical
Report No. 27, May 1958

3. Hoyt, J. W. and A. G. Fabula, "The Effect of Additives on Fluid
Friction," NAVWEPS Report 8636, NOTS Technical Publication
3670, December 1964

4. Ripken, J. F. and M. Pilch, "Non-Newtonian Pipe Friction Studies
with Various Dilute Polymer Water Solutions," University of
Minnesota, St. Anthony Falls Hydraulic Laboratory, Project
Report No. 71, June 1964

5. Wetzel, J. M. and F. Y. Tsai, "Impact Tube Measurements in Dilute
Polymer Solutions," Am. Inst. of Chem. Engrs. Jour., Vol. 14,
No. 4, July 1968

6.   Brennan, C. and G. E. Gadd, "Aging and Degradation in Dilute
     Polymer Solutions," <u>Nature</u>, Volume 215, Sept. 23, 1967

EFFECT OF WALL SHEAR STRESS ON DRAG REDUCTION

OF VISCOELASTIC SOLUTIONS

N. F. Whitsitt, L. J. Harrington, H. R. Crawford

The Western Company, Research Division

ABSTRACT

To determine the effect of boundary layer thickness and velocity on the drag reduction characteristics of polymer solutions, flow tests were carried out over a wide range of polymer concentrations in flow sections ranging from 0.18 inch to 6.0 inches in diameter. Two water-soluble polymers were used in the study — Separan AP-30 (Dow Chemical Company), a highly efficient drag reducer, and J2-FP (The Western Company), a guar-type, lower molecular weight, moderately efficient drag reducer.

It was found that the critical shear stress, at the inception of drag reduction, was independent of flow-section diameter (or boundary layer thickness). This critical shear stress was strongly dependent on polymer concentration for the highly efficient additive (AP-30). For the moderately efficient J2-FP, only a very slight dependence of critical shear stress on additive concentration was found.

For a given concentration of a specific polymer, the drag reduction was found to be a unique function of wall shear stress.

The high molecular weight polymer solutions were found to exhibit shear degradation at the higher shear rates, while the lower molecular weight polymer solutions did not.

INTRODUCTION

Several attempts have been made to correlate the friction-reducing abilities of visoelastic fluids and to account for so-called diameter effects.

Most correlations of diameter effects have had to rely on
flow data in only a very limited range of pipe sizes. Too,
several experiments subjected the dilute polymer solutions to
the high-shear environment of a pump upstream of a calibrated
flow section. It has been found to be quite difficult to compare
data from such various sources, primarily because of polymer age
and batch differences (resulting in differing drag-reduction
characteristics) and also the varying amounts of shear degradation
that the dilute solutions have experienced before entering the
flow section.

This study undertook experimental evaluation of the drag-
reduction characteristics of two polymers: Separan AP-30 (a high-
molecular-weight copolymer produced by Dow Chemical Company)
which exhibits very good friction-reducing properties at low concentrations, and Western's J2-FP (a guar gum) which exhibits good
friction-reduction properties at concentrations about one order
of magnitude greater than that required for Separan AP-30.

The tests with Separan AP-30 were conducted at concentrations
of 10, 50, 100, and 250 wppm in flow sections of 0.18, 0.416, and
1.624 inches in diameter. For the 100 and 250 wppm solutions, data
were also obtained in a test section with an inside diameter of
6.0 inches. This 6-inch facility was built with the support of
the Federal Water Pollution Control Administration.

The tests with J2-FP were conducted for solution concentrations of 10, 50, 250, and 1,250 wppm in test sections of 0.18, 0.416,
and 1.624 inches in diameter. In addition, data were made available
for 1,000 wppm J2-FP solution evaluated in the 6-inch test section.

Special care was taken to ensure that all dilute polymer
solutions were exposed to minimum shear prior to entrance into
the test section. Both the 0.18-inch and the 0.416-inch test
sections were air driven. The dilute polymer solutions were
never exposed to the degrading shear environment of a pump. All
solutions passed through the test section were discarded. The
1.624-inch system was gravity driven from two 200-gallon reservoirs
which developed a maximum of about 5 feet of head pressure.

In the 6-inch fluid flow test facility, the dilute solutions
were prepared "on-the-fly" from a concentrated solution reservoir.
The concentrated solution was metered through a calibrated,
positive-displacement pump and injected (in the desired proportions)
into the primary water flow. The dilute solution was allowed
to flow into a surcharge reservoir where, after mixing, it passed
into the 6-inch flow test section.

DISCUSSION OF TEST RESULTS

The reduced flow data for all polymers, concentrations, and flow-section diameters is presented in Reference 1 and will not be duplicated herein. Results of the entire investigation, however, are typified by the data obtained for the 100 and 250 wppm solutions of AP-30 and the 250 and 1,250 wppm solutions of J2-FP shown in Figures 1 through 4 respectively.

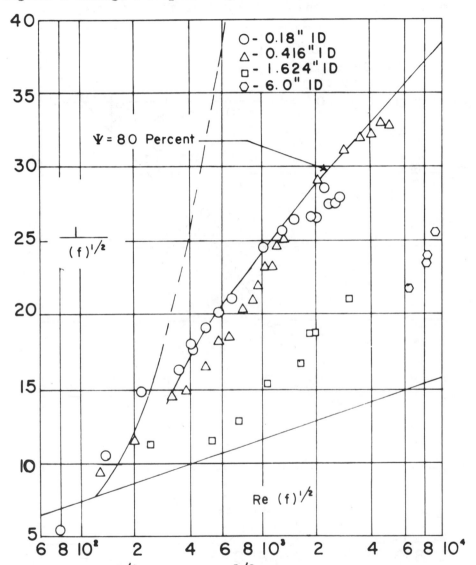

Figure 1 $1/(f)^{1/2}$ versus $Re(f)^{1/2}$ for 100 wppm AP-30 Solution in Various Tubing Sizes

The $1/f^{1/2}$ versus Re $f^{1/2}$ plot indicates that, for a given concentration, the slope of the lines through the drag-reducing data is independent of diameter, but increases as the concentration increases. This slope approaches a maximum value, however, as the drag reduction reaches the observed maximum of about 80 to 85 percent.

It should also be noted that, at high values of Reynolds number (more correctly shear stress) or Re $f^{1/2}$, the slope

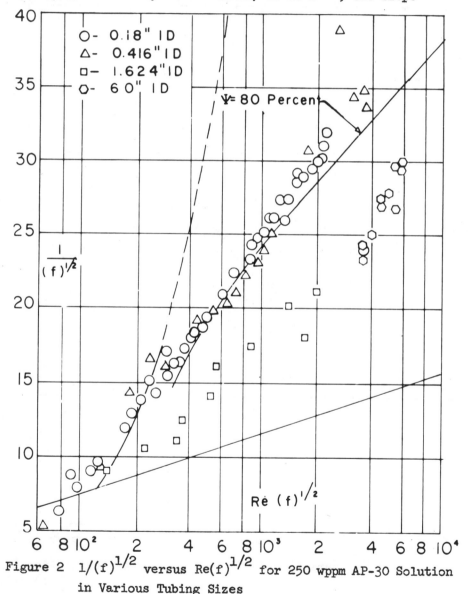

Figure 2 $1/(f)^{1/2}$ versus $Re(f)^{1/2}$ for 250 wppm AP-30 Solution in Various Tubing Sizes

decreases for AP-30 solutions but does not decrease for the J2-FP
solutions. In analyzing these data, it appears that the increased
shear in the flow environment causes an irreversible mechanical
cleavage of the polymer molecules, making its drag-reducing ability
less effective. For example, in the data for AP-30, a highly
efficient but shear-sensitive polymer, the shearing-out effects
are clearly seen (Figs. 1,2). On the other hand, J2-FP is a less
efficient but more shear-stable polymer which does not exhibit
this shearing-out phenomenon (Figs. 3,4).

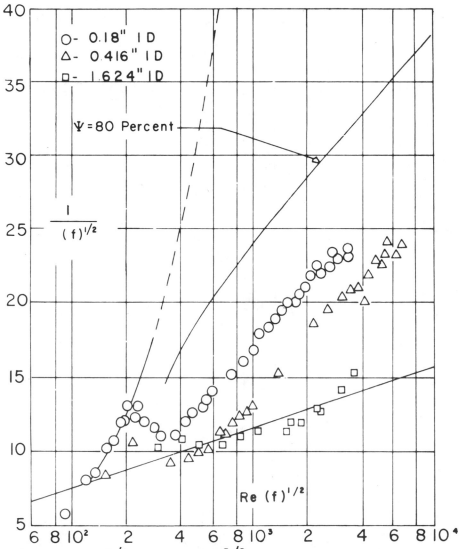

Figure 3 $1/(f)^{1/2}$ versus $Re(f)^{1/2}$ for 250 wppm J2-F P Solution
in Various Tubing Sizes

Following the method suggested by Meyer (Ref. 2), the deviation of the value of the B term from the constant of 5.5 (which holds for Newtonian fluids) was computed as a function of wall shear stress. This computation is essentially the same as Meyer's correlations with the friction velocity (u^{++}).

Only the 10 wppm of AP-30 and the 50 wppm and 250 wppm J2-FP showed the relationship of B and τ_o to possibly be independent of diameter for a given **concentration**. These data also indicate

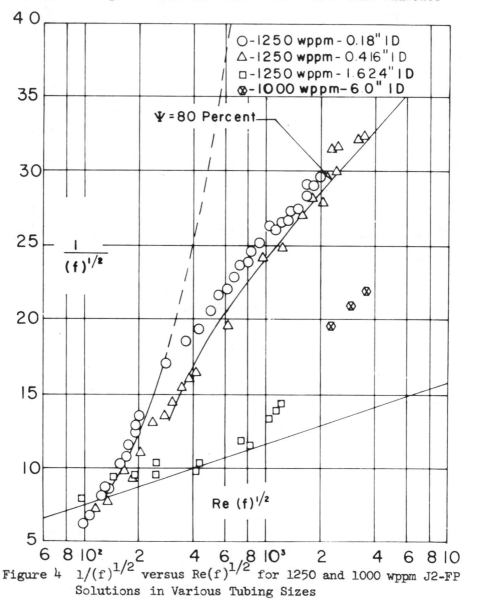

Figure 4 $1/(f)^{1/2}$ versus $Re(f)^{1/2}$ for 1250 and 1000 wppm J2-FP Solutions in Various Tubing Sizes

that the critical shear stress, above which the friction-reduction
phenomenon begins to become evident, is not a unique value independent of both diameter and polymer concentration, at least for
the AP-30 solution.

Considering that J2-FP is generally a less viscoelastic, less
effective drag-reducer than AP-30 at equivalent concentrations,
some interesting suggestions regarding the nature of friction-
reducing flow can be made. For example, from Meyer's observations
as well as these data, it seems reasonable to assume that in very
dilute solutions (or possibly more correctly, at low to moderate
friction-reducing levels) the action of the polymer is to damp the
turbulence in the transition region and thus effectively increase
the thickness of the laminar sublayer. As the additive concentration is increased (together with the drag-reduction increase
to the minimum level), it appears that an increase in the laminar
sublayer thickness alone does not fully explain the friction-
reducing phenomena. The data suggest that one of two things may
occur.

1. The laminar sublayer may increase in thickness to such an
    extent that the universal velocity profile may be applicable
    over only a very small area of the flow section. As a result,
    any theoretical analysis developed around the fact that the
    universal velocity profile is the predominant factor would
    probably provide uncorrelatable results.

2. The flow character at or near the maximum friction-reduction
    level may be a great deal different from that postulated
    for the moderate friction-reduction levels of dilute polymer
    solutions. As a result, the high or more effective additive
    concentrations may tend to not only thicken the laminar
    sublayer, but also have some effect on the universal mixing
    coefficient.

In addition, it is easily seen that, for a given concentration, the B term is not independent of diameter when the drag
reduction approaches 80 percent. For example, if B and τ_o are
related by a single function, independent of diameter, then a
corresponding family of lines (one for each pipe diameter) can be
represented on the corresponding $1/f^{1/2}$ versus Re $(f^{1/2})$ plot.
The family of lines will have the same slope, but the value of
Re $(f^{1/2})$ at their intercept with the Newtonian line will decrease
as the pipe diameter decreases; therefore, if the polymer solution
flow in the 0.416-inch test section exhibits 80 to 85 percent
draw reduction and B versus τ_o is related by a single function,
this would infer that more than 80 to 85 percent drag reduction
would be obtained in the 0.18-inch test section — which is not

the case observed in this study. First, as the maximum drag-reduction level of 80 to 85 percent is reached, the relationship between B and τ_0 does not appear to be independent of diameter. And second, these data show that the maximum obtainable drag reduction is from 80 to 85 percent and independent of flow-section diameter (or turbulent boundary layer thickness) at Reynolds numbers greater than about 5,000.

At the maximum drag-reduction level, the flow seems more laminar than turbulent. A few of the actual velocity profile measurements (Ref. 3) on the highly drag-reducing flows illustrate a velocity profile in which the turbulent eddy losses are suppressed in all except a small center region of the pipe flow. In this core region, it appears that the eddy losses are "about the same" to "somewhat greater than" the purely viscous losses.

Some of the previous investigators have indicated that, for a given polymer, there appeared to be a critical wall shear stress, independent of concentration, above which any concentra-

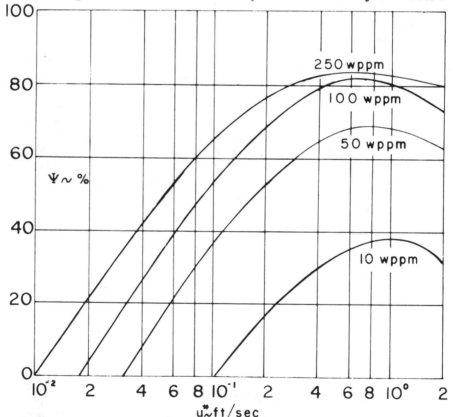

Figure 5   Friction Reduction of AP-30 Solutions versus Friction Velocity and Concentration

tion of a given polymer would exhibit the friction-reducing phenomena. Accordingly, below this critical shear stress no friction
reduction should occur. For the AP-30, we found that the critical
shear stress was a function of concentration. This is readily seen
in Figure 5, where the critical friction velocity (or the square
root of shear stress) decreases by a factor of 10 as the concentration is increased by a factor of 25.

As shown in Figure 6, our data for J2-FP indicate a very
slight change (with concentration) of the critical shear stress.
Indeed, it is possible that the critical shear stress for the low
molecular weight polymers, such as guar and CMC, is essentially
independent of concentration.

Overall it appears that the correlation techniques presently
available are insufficiently general to explain the flow behavior
of the friction-reducing polymer solutions over the wide variation
in concentrations and pipe diameters studied in this program. As
a result, a slightly more empirical approach was selected for data

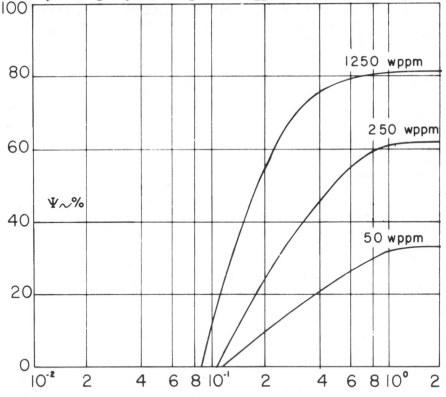

Figure 6   Friction Reduction of J2-FP Solutions versus Friction
Velocity and Concentration

interpretation. This correlation of the complete range of data
obtained in this study is discussed in the following section of
this paper.

DATA CORRELATION

In correlating the wide range of concentration and pipe
diameter data obtained in this study, it was considered important
to develop correlations or trends that would apply to as wide a
range of data as possible. The most successful and apparently
most general correlation approach found for these data was developed
from the observation that the friction-reducing ability of these
solutions was related to:

> Polymer type
> Polymer concentration
> Shear stress level.

Most polymers exhibit different friction-reducing ability
at various concentrations in the water solvent. Generally
speaking, the higher the molecular weight of polymer, the
lower the concentration required in a water solvent to produce
maximum friction reduction (80 to 85 percent). In addition,
it was shown by Pruitt and Crawford (Ref. 4) that the segmental
constitution of the polymer has a major influence on its friction-
reducing ability. That is, for a given molecular weight, the
larger the length-to-diameter ratio of the polymer molecule, the
greater is its friction-reducing ability. These authors also indicated that the critical shear stress was concentration dependent
for some polymers.

From the friction-reducing data, it is apparent that, for a
given polymer concentration, friction reduction is greater for
the smaller tubing diameter than for larger diameters at a given
Reynolds number. On the other hand, at the higher concentrations
and small pipe diameters (Fig. 2), the 0.18-inch and 0.416-inch
pipe diameter data almost overlay on a maximum friction-reduction
line of between 80 and 85 percent.

Now, for a given Reynolds number, the shear stress in a small
pipe will be larger than that in a large pipe. This suggests that
the shear stress to which the fluid is being subjected may influence
the friction-reducing ability of a given polymer solution. As a
result, the friction-reduction factor dependence on wall shear
stress or, more conveniently, the friction velocity, was investigated.

The measured drag reduction, ψ, at all pipe diameters for
given polymer concentrations in a water solution is shown versus

friction velocity (effectively, wall shear stress) in Figures 5
and 6 for AP-30 and J2-FP respectively. Within experimental
accuracy of ±15 percent, a relationship independent of diameter
can be developed for each polymer and concentration. That is, for
a given polymer and concentration, such as a 250 wppm AP-30 solution,
the friction reduction that will be obtained is a unique function
of wall shear stress. For example, it can be determined by graphic
relationship (Fig. 5). This should also be true for an exterior
flow, such as that around a torpedo with a polymer solution injected
into its boundary layer.

In comparing Figure 5 (for AP-30) with Figure 6 (for J2-FP),
several interesting observations can be made. For instance, there
appears to be a well-defined shear stress (for a given polymer
and concentration) at which inception of the friction-reduction
occurs. After the critical shear stress is exceeded, the friction
reduction increases at a decreasing rate until a maximum friction-
reduction level is reached.

The critical friction velocity (or wall shear stress) for
the inception of friction reduction appears to decrease markedly
as a polymer concentration increases for the AP-30 solutions;
however, this does not seem to be the case of J2-FP solutions
where the critical shear stress exhibits only a very slight
decrease with increasing concentration.

For a given polymer, the friction reduction increases with
concentration until it reaches the 80 to 85 percent level. After
reaching this level, an increase in concentration will not increase
the drag reduction above this level; however, an increase in
polymer concentration will cause the inception of drag reduction
to occur at lower shear stress levels, at least for the more
effective friction-reducing solutions such as AP-30. Consequently,
higher friction reduction can be produced at lower shear stress
levels.

As the shear stress increases, the friction reduction increases
to the maximum level and then begins to decrease for the AP-30
solutions, but apparently remains constant for the J2-FP solutions.
This decrease is attributed to a "shearing out" of the polymer.
Shearing out is believed to be an actual degradation or breaking
up of the polymer molecules caused by the shearing action within
the fluid. It is interesting to note in Figure 5 (where the 80-
percent friction-reduction level has just been reached) that the
degradation begins to occur at a friction velocity of about 1 foot
per second for the 10, 50, and 100 wppm AP-30 solutions. The 250
wppm AP-30 solution is actually of greater additive concentration
than is required to produce maximum friction reduction at this

shear stress level. This high polymer concentration appears to
delay the loss in percentage drag reduction until a higher shear
stress.

One other interesting point to note is that none of the J2-FP
data was taken at a shear rate sufficiently high to produce a
degradation of friction-reducing ability of the polymer. This
fact, illustrated in Figure 6, was to be expected, since exhaustive
tests (Ref. 5) have shown J2-FP to be virtually insensitive to
shear degradation while AP-30 is known to be moderately sensitive.

In obtaining the graphical correlations presented in Figures
5 and 6 for AP-30 and J2-FP, only one minor portion of the data
did not fit the correlation. The troublesome data were those
which deviated smoothly from the laminar friction factor line for
Reynolds numbers less than about 5,000. For these data, it is
seen that the viscoelastic characteristic of the fluid has delayed
transition to a Reynolds number greater than 3,000. As a result,
if the data between Reynolds numbers of 3,000 and 5,000 are included,
the friction reduction changes from 100 percent (i.e., flow is
still laminar) to the 80- to 85-percent level at a Reynolds
number above about 5,000. Rationalizing that this transition region
was only a small part of the turbulent flow region, the data below
a Reynolds number of about 5,000 were excluded.

The correlating curves for the J2-FP solutions look similar
to those for the AP-30 solutions; however, at a given concentration, the degree of friction reduction is less and the critical
shear stress (or friction velocity) at which friction reduction
starts to occur is much higher than for the equivalent concentration of the AP-30 solution.

Data correlations (Figs. 5,6), in the presented form, do
not appear to offer the presumed advantages of nondimensionality;
however, there is a unique rheological relationship between wall
shear stress and wall shear rate, and the data in Figures 5 and
6 could just as easily be presented as a unique function of the
wall shear rate.

It has been suggested (Refs. 6,7) that the correlation of
turbulent friction reduction can be made in terms of the Deborah
number. The Deborah number is defined as a ratio of the relaxation time of the solution to a representative time of the process.
If it is assumed that the time of the process can be represented
by the inverse of the shear rate, it then appears that the data
may be correlated and normalized (with respect to the inception
of friction reduction) if presented in terms of Deborah number
instead of the friction velocity. The difficulty arises, however,

in predicting or measuring the relaxation times of the solution.
If, following the suggestion of Reference 7, it is assumed that
the inception of friction reduction occurs at a unique value of
Deborah number, then the following relationship is valid:

$$\theta s = \frac{k_1}{\left(\dfrac{8V}{D}\right)_c}$$

(1)

Also, since for a given concentration of a specific polymer, there
is a unique relationship between shear rate $(8V/D)$ and shear
stress, the following relation would hold:

$$\theta s = \frac{k_2}{(\tau_o)_c} = \frac{k_3}{u_c^{+}} \cdot$$

(2)

From equation (2) and Figure 5 it can be seen that, for a high
molecular-weight, highly effective friction-reducing polymer, the
relaxation time of the solution apparently increases with polymer
concentration. In addition, from Figure 6, it would appear that
for a relatively low molecular-weight, less effective polymer,
the relaxation time of the solution apparently remains constant
or increases very slightly with increasing polymer concentration
in the solution.

It can be seen that, as presented, the Deborah number offers
no means of normalizing the magnitude of friction reduction
obtained. It appears that another parameter is needed to correlate
the level of friction reduction obtained as the function of
polymer type and concentration. This parameter is probably the
Weissenberg number. Thus, as suggested by Metzner, White, and
Denn (Ref. 8) as well as other investigators, turbulent friction-
reducing flow may be related to the three functional groups:
Reynolds number, Deborah number, and Weissenberg number. It
then may be found that the magnitude of the observed friction
reduction can be correlated with the Weissenberg number, which
essentially is the ratio of the elastic force to the viscous
force.

CONCLUSIONS

The drag reduction for a given concentration of a specific
aqueous polymer solution is a unique function of wall shear
stress (or friction velocity). This relationship was found to

be independent of boundary layer thickness (or flow-section
diameter) and included all the turbulent friction-loss data (above
a Reynolds number of 5,000) obtained in this study. This unique
relationship was found to hold over flow-section diameters ranging
from 0.18 inch to 6.0 inches. This relationship also proved
valid for polymer solutions exhibiting widely varying drag-reducing
efficiencies. The only exception to this relationship seems to
be for Reynolds numbers below about 5,000 for solutions which
have a critical wall shear stress lower than the laminar wall
shear stress would be at the transition region.

The critical shear stress (or friction velocity) at which drag
reduction begins is clearly a function of concentration for the
high molecular-weight polymer (AP-30). The critical shear stress
decreased by a factor of about 100 as the concentration of Separan
AP-30 was increased from 10 to 250 wppm.

The critical shear stress also appears to be a function of
concentration for the lower molecular weight polymers (e.g., guar
gum and carboxlmethyl cellulose), although this dependence is much
less pronounced.

ACKNOWLEDGMENT

We wish to express our appreciation to NSRDC, Hydromechanics
Laboratory, who sponsored the work under Contract No. Nonr-4306(00),
for allowing us to present this material.

NOMENCLATURE

B   Parameter related to laminar sublayer thickness and
                equal to constant (5.5) for Newtonian flow

f $\dfrac{\tau}{\dfrac{1/2\, \rho\, v^2}{2}\, g_c}$ = friction factor

g_c 32.2 lbm-ft/lb$_f$ - sec^2 - gravitational constant

k_1 Constant of proportionality

k_2 Constant of proportionality

k_3 Constant of proportionality

Re $\qquad$ $\rho\,VD/\mu_a$ = Reynolds number

u^{+} $\qquad$ $\sqrt{\dfrac{\tau_o\,g_c}{\rho}}$ = friction velocity

wppm $\qquad$ Weight parts per million

$\left(\dfrac{8V}{D}\right)$ $\qquad$ Shear rate

θ s $\qquad$ Relaxation time of an aqueous polymer solution

μ^a $\qquad$ Apparent absolute viscosity as determined from rheograms for aqueous polymer solutions

ρ $\qquad$ Fluid density

τ $\qquad$ **Shear stress**

ψ $\qquad$ $\left(\dfrac{f_t - f_a}{f_t - f_1}\right)_{Re}$ = friction-reduction factor

$(\ )_a$ $\qquad$ Apparent

$(\ )_c$ $\qquad$ Critical conditions at inception of friction reduction

$(\ )_1$ $\qquad$ Evaluated at laminar flow conditions

$(\ )_o$ $\qquad$ Evaluated at wall conditions

$(\ )_t$ $\qquad$ Evaluated at Newtonian turbulent flow conditions

$(\ )_{Re}$ $\qquad$ Evaluated at constant Reynolds number

REFERENCES

1. Whitsitt, N. F., L. J. Harrington, and H. R. Crawford, "Effect of Wall Shear Stress on Drag Reduction of Viscoelastic Fluids," Report No. DTMB-3, The Western Company, Richardson, Texas, prepared for NSRDC, Hydromechanics Laboratory under Contract No. Nonr-4306(00), June 1968

2. Meyer, W. A., "A Correlation of the Frictional Characteristics for Turbulent Flow of Dilute Viscoelastic Non-Newtonian Fluids in Pipes," AIChEJ 12, 522-525, May 1966

3. Pruitt, G. T. and H. R. Crawford, "Investigation for the Use of Additives for the Reduction of Pressure Losses," Final Report Contract No. DA-23-072-AMC-309 (T) for Army Tank Automotive Center, January 1965

4. Pruitt, G. T., and H. R. Crawford, "Effect of Molecular Weight and Segmental Constitution on the Drag Reduction of Water Soluble Polymers," Report No. DTMB-1, The Western Company, Richardson, Texas, conducted under Contract No. Nonr-4306(00) for the Naval Hydromechanical Laboratory, Washington, D. C., April 1965

5. Whitsitt, N. F., and H. R. Crawford, "Friction Drag Loss Characteristics of Enclosed Rotating Disks Operating in a Viscoelastic Fluid Media," The Western Company, Research Division, Richardson, Texas, April 1967, prepared for U. S. Naval Ordnance Test Station, Pasadena, Contract No. N60530-12741

6. Rodriquez, J. M., J. L. Zakin, and G. K. Patterson, "Correlation of Drag Reduction with Modified Deborah Number for Dilute Polymer Solutions," SPE 1678, Presented at the Symposium on Mechanics of Rheologically Complex Fluids, Houston, Texas, December 15-16, 1966

7. Ram, A., E. Finkelstein, and G. Elata, "Reduction of Friction in Oil Pipelines by Polymer Additives," I&EC, Process Design and Development $\underline{6}$, 3, July 1967

8. Metzner, A. B., J. L. White, and M. M. Denn, "Constitutive Equations for Viscoelastic Fluids for Short Deformation Periods and for Rapidly Changing Flows: Significance of the Deborah Number," AIChEJ, $\underline{12}$, 5, 1966

THE USE OF PITOT-STATIC TUBES AND HOT-FILM ANEMOMETERS IN

DILUTE POLYMER SOLUTIONS

Carl A. Friehe and W. H. Schwarz

The Johns Hopkins University

ABSTRACT

The operation of Pitot-static tubes in dilute polyacrylamide-water solutions was verified experimentally by using an independent method to measure the velocity. Measurement of the heat transfer characteristics of cylindrical hot-film anemometer probes in these solutions revealed reduced heat transfer in addition to the following anomalous results. In certain velocity ranges, the Nusselt number was independent of velocity. At high velocities, a form of vortex shedding from the probe occurred, and the Nusselt number was proportional to the square-root of velocity. The dependence of the Nusselt number on the angle of incidence was, for the most concentrated solution, opposite to that for pure water. The above results indicate that these probes cannot be used to measure velocity in certain cases, and interpretation of turbulence measurements would seem to be open to question. Calibration of a conical hot-film probe revealed only slightly reduced heat transfer. Measurement of the one-dimensional velocity spectrum in a polymer solution indicated that the cylindrical probe gave a power-law dependence on the wave number at high wave numbers; whereas the data obtained with the conical probe was qualitatively similar to Newtonian spectral data.

INTRODUCTION

The Pitot-static tube (or a Pitot-impact tube and a static tap) is the basic device used to measure local velocities in Newtonian fluids, where the Bernoulli equation is used to determine the velocity from the measured pressure difference. In non-Newtonian fluids, the use of Pitot-static tubes, together with Bernoulli's

equation, appears questionable because of possible effects due to
normal stresses and shear-dependent viscosities. Experiments were
performed to assess the use of this device in a uniform, non-turbulent
flow of dilute polymer solutions. The velocity was measured independently by using small hydrogen bubble tracers.

The basic device which is used to measure the fluctuating
velocity components of a turbulent field is the hot-wire anemometer.
Recently, the hot-film anemometer has become popular, since insulated
probes suitable for use in electrically conducting liquids have
become commercially available. The current interest in these devices
has been motivated by the desire to study turbulence in the presence
of friction-reducing agents, typical of which is polyacrylamide,
a high molecular weight polymer. Extremely dilute solutions of this
and other similar materials have been found to markedly reduce the
pressure drop in pipes when the flow is turbulent. To better
understand the physics of this phenomenon, measurements of the
fluctuating turbulence components are needed.

Experiments were conducted to determine the steady-state heat
transfer characteristics of hot-film probes in the uniform flow of
dilute solutions of polyacrylamide in water, since turbulence
measurements are interpreted from the steady-state response. The
anomalous behaviour of the heat transfer to water containing friction-
reducing agents that has been recently reported by Fabula (Ref. 4),
James (Ref. 7), and Smith et al. (Ref. 9), indicates that this
device becomes insensitive to variations in velocity under certain
conditions. Some additional results of this nature are reported
here. In addition, we have observed an anomalous behavior of the
heat transfer when cylindrical probes are orientated at an angle
to the velocity vector. The knowledge of the angular dependence of
the heat transfer is crucial for the measurement of turbulent velocity
components transverse to the mean velocity.

With both cylindrical and conical hot-film probes, the one-
dimensional velocity spectrum for a grid-generated turbulent field
was measured in a dilute polymer solution, to determine the relative
difference in response of the transducers.

EXPERIMENTAL DETAILS

The experiments were performed in the 15 x 15 cm test section
of a closed-return, fluid tunnel having a uniform, low-turbulence
flow field. For the calibration of the Pitot-static tubes, the
velocity was measured independently, using small electrochemically
generated hydrogen bubbles which were electronically timed over a
known distance to give the absolute velocity, U_W. (Details of the
experimental system and other aspects of the work presented here are
available elsewhere (Ref. 5).)

The anemometer probes were quartz coated, platinum-film cylinders (Thermo-Systems, Inc.) with nominal diameters of 0.001, 0.002, and 0.006 inch, and length-to-diameter ratios of 16.2, 19.5, and 12.2, respectively. Except when noted, the probe supports for the probes were placed transverse to the flow direction. Provision was made for yawing the cylindrical probes at various angles of incidence, a, to the flow direction. Some experiments were also made with small conical shaped probes where the heated section was located behind the apex of the cone. The probes were operated at constant temperature in the bridge circuit of a commercial Thermo-Systems unit (Model 1010A) at various temperatures, proportional to the overheat ratio, N.

The polymer used was Dowell J-100, an ionic polyacrylamide with an estimated molecular weight of 2 to 3 x 10⁶; and the concentration range was from 10 to 300 ppm (parts per million) in deionized water.

Viscometric data for a 300 ppm solution are shown in Figure 1, where the shear dependent viscosity μ is plotted versus the rate-of-deformation, κ (sec^{-1}). These data were obtained with a Weissenberg rheogoniometer for low rates of shear using the cone-and-plate geometry. For the data obtained at high rates of shear,

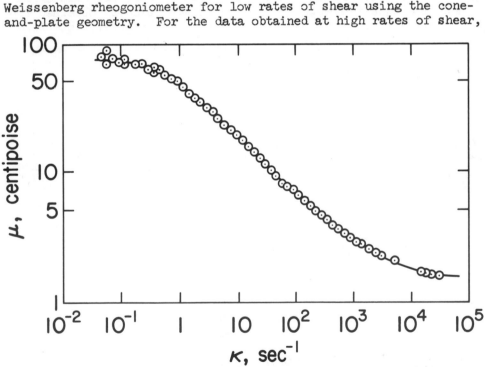

Figure 1   Shear Dependent Viscosity for 300 ppm of J-100 in
Deionized Water

(T = 25°C)

a variable pressure capillary viscometer was used. With the
rheogoniometer, no normal stresses were observed for the concentrations used in this work. The shape of the viscosity curve is
typical of a shear-thinning or pseudoplastic material and exhibits
both a lower and upper-limiting viscosity, $\mu_o = 75$ and $\mu_{oo} = 1.4$
centipoise respectively. Similar data covering a wide range of
concentrations for a polyacrylamide polymer have been obtained by
Bruce and Schwarz (Ref. 1), and it was observed that the viscosity
was shear dependent for concentrations as low as 25 ppm.

RESULTS

Pitot-Static Tubes

Typical results of the Pitot-static tube calibrations are presented in Figure 2, where the ratio U_p/U_w is plotted versus U_w.
U_p is the velocity obtained from measured pressure difference and
Bernoulli's equation, and U_w is the absolute velocity obtained from
the bubble tracers. The results indicate that the Pitot-static

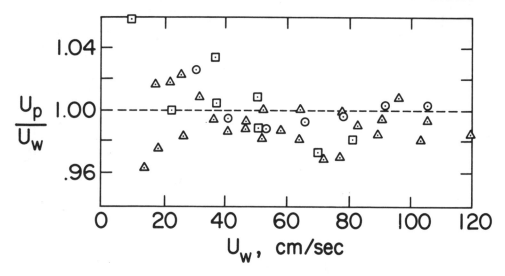

Figure 2 Ratio of Measured to Absolute Velocity:
Pitot-Static Tube Diameter: 0.953 cm

⊙ 0.015%	J-100
△ 0.03%	J-100
⊡ 0.15%	J-100

tube adequately measures the local velocity. For smaller tubes, there is a trend toward low readings ($U_p/U_w = 0.96$) at high velocities, but this small error would be negligible for most purposes.

Hot-Film Anemometer Probes

Water Calibration. For reference, the heat transfer results for water for the cylindrical sensors at $a = 0°$ are compared to Kramers' (Ref. 8) correlation,

$$Nu = 0.42\ Pr^{0.2} + 0.57\ Pr^{0.33}\ Re^{0.50}$$

where Nu is the Nusselt number, Re is the Reynolds number, and Pr is the Prandtl number. We may rewrite Kramers' formula, following Delleur et al (Ref. 3), as

$$Y_f = \frac{Nu_f - 0.42\ Pr_f^{0.2}}{Pr_f^{0.33}} = 0.57\ Re_f^{0.50} \qquad (1)$$

(where the subscript f denotes the film temperature) for comparison to the present experiments. The results for four sensors, covering the range 0.001 inch d to 0.006 inch d, are shown in Figure 3. The

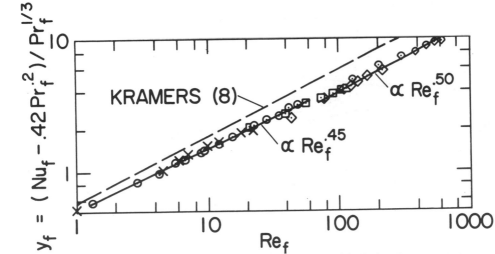

Figure 3   Heat Transfer Correlation for Cylindrical Hot-Film
           Probes: Water

⊙ 0.0017 in. d, $\ell/d = 11.1$, $\Delta T = 38°F$
⊡ 0.00114in. d, $\ell/d = 16.2$, $\Delta T = 77°F$
◇ 0.00214in. d, $\ell/d = 19.5$, $\Delta T = 77°F$
◉ 0.00615in. d, $\ell/d = 12.2$, $\Delta T = 77°F$
✕ 0.002 in. d, $\ell/d = 18.3$, $\Delta T = 22°F$ (Ref. 7)

data lie somewhat lower than predicted by equation (1), and fall
into two regimes with a transition at approximately Re ~50, which
is the value for the onset of vortex shedding.

Polymer Solutions. The heat transfer results for the polymer
solutions for $a = 0°$ are not directly compared to equation (1),
since this equation contains the Newtonian viscosity, μ_f. As
shown in the experimental section, the viscosity for the most
concentrated solution, for example, was found to be quite non-
Newtonian (Fig. 1). The results are presented as Nu_p/Nu_w, the
ratio of the Nusselt number in the solutions to that in water, as
a function of the free-stream velocity U. More detailed results
are shown as Nu_p versus $U^{0.5}$, which for water would yield an
approximate linear relationship. (We will ignore the slight
difference between $U^{0.45}$ and $U^{0.50}$ found for water when comparisons
are made to the polymer solutions.)

For the 10 and 30 ppm solutions, the Nusselt numbers, Nu_p, were
slightly lower than those in water (Fig. 4). The Nusselt number
was found to be approximately proportional to $U^{0.5}$. For the more
concentrated solutions, however, significant deviations from
Newtonian behavior were observed. For certain velocity ranges, the
Nusselt number was found to be constant. The results for the

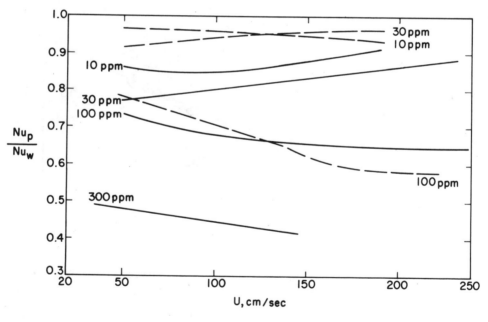

Figure 4   Plot of Nu_p/Nu_w Versus U, N = 0.10

— — — — — 0.00214 in. d sensor
———————— 0.00114 in. d sensor

300 ppm solution are presented in Figure 5, as Nu_p versus $U^{0.5}$.
The Nusselt number is practically constant up to a critical velocity,
after which a fairly sharp transition to the usual variation with
$U^{0.5}$ occurs. For this solution, the sensor supports were orientated
in two positions to determine if the anomalous results were due to
probe support effects. The placement of the supports does affect
the critical velocity and the magnitude of the Nusselt number in
the sensitive region, but the general features of the results are

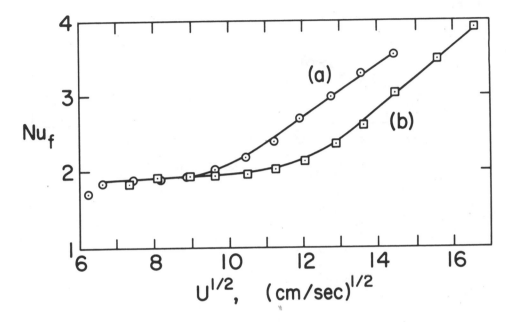

Figure 5   Heat Transfer: 300 ppm J-100; 0.00114 in.
d, ℓ /d= 16.2

⊙ Supports Transverse
▫ Supports Parallel

unchanged, including the region of constant Nusselt number. The
heat transfer coefficient is reduced to about one-half of the water
value (Fig. 4). In the 100 ppm solution for the 0.002-inch diameter
sensor, the Nusselt number was constant over a smaller range of
velocity than in the 300 ppm case, with sensitivity to $U^{0.5}$ above
and below this region. The two other sensors of different diameters
were run in this solution, and the results for the three sensors
are shown on Figure 6, where Nu_p is plotted versus $(Ud)^{0.5}$; i.e.,
the Reynolds number to the one-half without the viscosity. The
data show excellent correlation when plotted in this manner, the
constant Nusselt number region coinciding for the two larger probes.

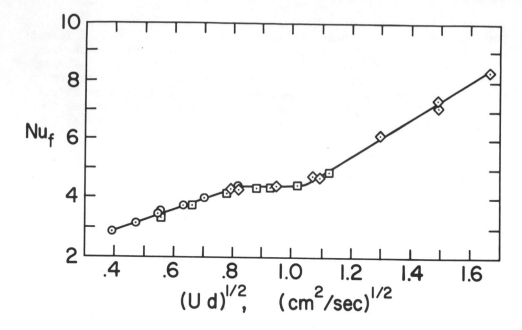

Figure 6   Correlation of Heat Transfer in 100 ppm J-100

⊙ 0.00114 in. d, ℓ /d = 16.2
△ 0.00214 in. d, ℓ /d = 19.5
□ 0.00615 in. d, ℓ /d = 12.2

(Unfortunately, for the smallest sensor, large enough values of
Ud could not be attained to verify that the constant Nu_p region
held for this probe.) In addition, the sensitive regions and the
higher critical velocity are also well correlated. As for the
other concentrations, the ratio Nu_p/Nu_w is shown in Figure 4, with
approximately a 30 percent decrease in heat transfer shown for this
solution.

The signal from the anemometer bridge was monitored with an
oscilloscope to detect vortex shedding from the sensors. In water
a well-defined sinusoidal signal was observed for Re > 50. For the
100 and 300 ppm solutions, it appeared that the transition from the
region of constant Nusselt number to the sensitive region was
associated with a form of vortex shedding. The form of the signal,
however, was not of a sinusoidal nature, but more random like a
turbulent flow, and persisted up to the highest velocities that

were attained. It appears, then, that the upper sensitive region
is associated with, or perhaps caused by, a form of vortex shedding
from the cylindrical sensors.

Similar experiments were performed with the conical shaped
sensor, where the heated section was located downstream of the apex
of the cone. The results, expressed as the square of the anemometer
voltage, E_b, which is proportional to the Nusselt number, are presented in Figure 7 for water and a 300 ppm solution. No anomalous
effects were observed, as in the case of the cylindrical probes, and
the heat transfer coefficient is only slightly less than that in
water.

Effect of Yaw. There were absolute differences in the values
of the Nusselt number for the different sets of data when the sensors
were normal to the stream, which were caused by small variations in
the velocity and the concentrations of the polymer solutions.
Therefore, the data for the yawed sensors are presented as curves of
the normalized ratio, Nu (a)/Nu(0) versus the angle of incidence,
a.

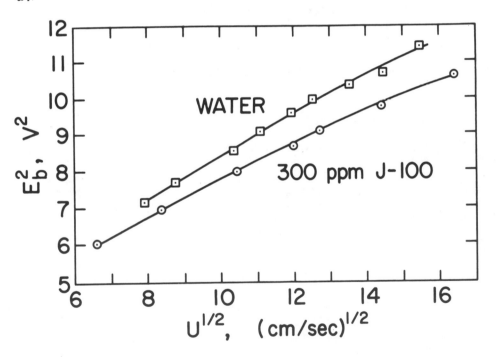

Figure 7 Heat Transfer in 300 ppm J-100: Conical Probe

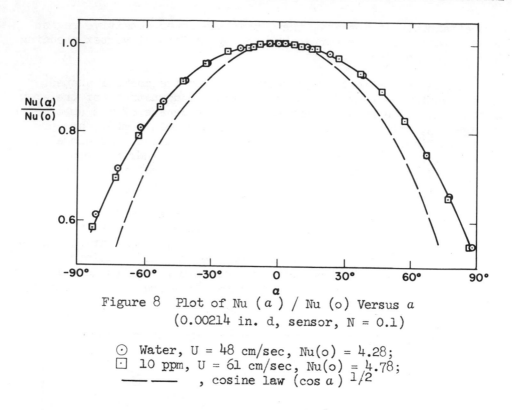

Figure 8   Plot of Nu (a) / Nu (o) Versus a
(0.00214 in. d, sensor, N = 0.1)

⊙   Water, U = 48 cm/sec, Nu(o) = 4.28;
⊡   10 ppm, U = 61 cm/sec, Nu(o) = 4.78;
────── , cosine law (cos a) $^{1/2}$

In Figure 8 the data are shown for pure water and 10 ppm J-100, using the 0.002 inch sensor. At 10 ppm there is no apparent difference from the water data. The angular dependence of an infinitely long cylinder is given by the normal component low of cooling for a Newtonian fluid, hence the cosine relation, Nu(a)/Nu(0) $\propto \cos^{1/2} a$, is also shown for comparison. The finite length of the sensor results in Nusselt numbers being slightly higher than predicted by the normal component law. This subject has been discussed in some detail by Champagne et al (Ref. 2) for a homogeneous wire in air, and by Friehe and Schwarz (Ref. 6) for cylindrical hot-films in air.

Similar data for the 0.001-inch-diameter sensor were obtained for the 30 and 100 ppm solutions (Fig. 9). One noticeable difference occurs near $a = 0°$, where slight peaks were found instead of approximate cosine law dependence. For 300 ppm, the heat transfer

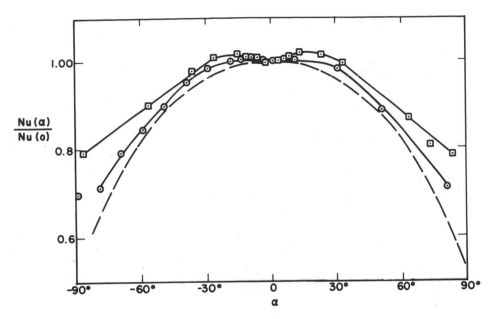

Figure 9 Plot of Nu (a) / Nu (o) Versus a
(0.00114 in. d, sensor, N = 0.1)

⊙   30 ppm, U = 50 cm/sec, Nu(o) = 2.86
⊡ 100 ppm, U = 76 cm/sec, Nu(o) = 2.88
———————— , Water data

results shown in Figure 10 are significantly anomalous, since the
Nusselt number increases with increasing angle of incidence up to
about 45° to 60°, and then decreases. The data were obtained at
two velocities, and the variation of the Nusselt number with angle
is significantly affected. The overall effect of an increase of
Nu with a was observed for this sensor and solution over a large
velocity range for both the constant and sensitive heat transfer
regions. Data were also obtained for the probe supports placed
parallel to the flow, and the effect of an increase of Nu with a
was still present, although there were minor differences in the
form of the dependence on angle.

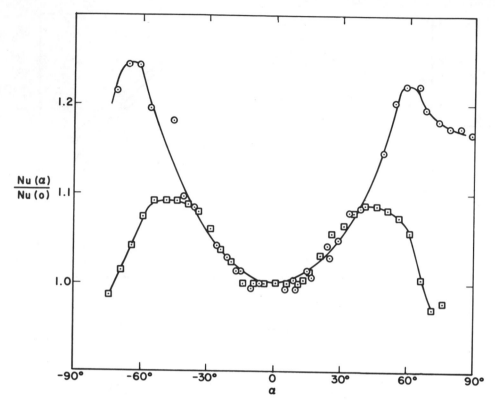

Figure 10   Plot of Nu (a) / Nu(o) Versus a
(0.00114 in.d. sensor, N = 0.10)

⊙ 300 ppm, U=25 cm/sec, Nu(o) = 1.44
⊡ 300 ppm, U=57 cm/sec, Nu(o) = 2.18

        The 0.001-inch sensor was calibrated against velocity at a
fixed angle (a = 45°) which gave a maximum value of Nu(a) for
a velocity in the constant Nusselt number region for the 300 ppm
solution.   The data are shown in Figure 11, together with the
corresponding data for water estimated from the normal component
law.   The anomalous effect of a region of constant Nusselt number
is not obtained, but the data show markedly less sensitivity to
velocity than in water.   The significant decrease in the heat
transfer is also present.

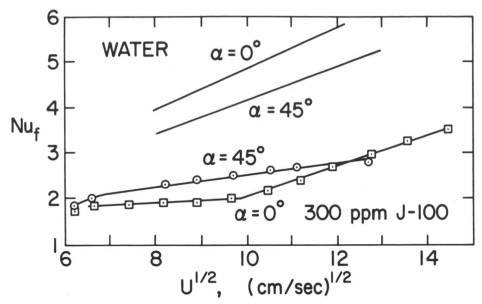

Figure 11   Heat Transfer in Water and 300 ppm J-100:
            Effect of Yaw Angle
            Sensor: 0.00114 in. d ℓ/d = 16.2

TURBULENCE MEASUREMENTS

Measurements of the stream-wise, one-dimensional velocity spectra, $\varphi(\kappa)$, were obtained in a grid-generated turbulent field using both types of probes in a polymer solution of 50 ppm, and are shown in Figure 12. The shapes of the spectra are noticeably different, with the cylindrical probe giving a power-law dependence at high wave numbers, κ; whereas the conical probe gave an exponential-like dependence as found in Newtonian fluids. In pure water, both probes gave identical results, and the spectra compared well with those obtained in air. Similar results were obtained in a 300 ppm solution. For these data, the cylindrical probes were operated at high velocities where the Nusselt number was sensitive to velocity and in the region where a form of vortex shedding is occurring. The shedding apparently causes the additional energy in the spectrum at high wave numbers.

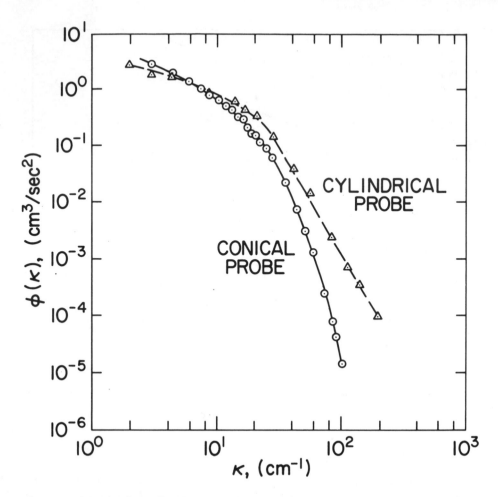

Figure 12 One-Dimensional Spectra Using Conical and Cylindrical
          (0.00114 in. d) Hot-Film Probes: 50 ppm J-100,
          U = 226 cm/sec

DISCUSSION AND CONCLUSIONS

The calibration studies of the Pitot-static tube in the dilute
polymer solutions revealed that Bernoulli's equation is adequate
for the determination of the local velocity for these devices.
There was an indication of low velocity measurements (approximately
-4 percent) at high velocities for smaller tubes, but this was
considered negligible for the present studies.

The heat transfer results presented here indicate that cylindrical hot-film anemometer probes cannot be used to measure velocity under certain conditions. Similar observations have been reported by Fabula (Ref. 4) for a wedge-shaped sensor and James (Ref. 7) for cylindrical sensors in polyethylene oxide solutions. In those studies, the Nusselt number was found to be approximately the same as in water at low velocities and exhibited a constant value at higher velocities. The velocity range in James' studies was lower than in the present work, and the sensitive region due to vortex shedding at high velocities was not observed. Smith, et al.(Ref. 9) observed anomalous results using a cylindrical probe in turbulent pipe flow of a polyethylene oxide solution. The Nusselt number was found to be approximately the same as in water at low velocities, but decreased at a Reynolds number of 40, indicating another possible effect of vortex shedding. The additional results, presented here on the anomalous angular dependence of the heat transfer, further indicate that the hydrodynamic conditions of flows in dilute polymer solutions are drastically altered over the Newtonian case. The anomalous effects seem to be associated with those flows with stagnation points, since the results with the conical probe were not markedly different from the water case.

Intuitively, turbulence measurements obtained with the cylindrical probes, in those regions where the heat transfer is sensitive to velocity, would seem unreliable. The measurements obtained for a grid-generated turbulent field for the velocity spectrum with both the cylindrical and conical probes showed significant differences. At high wave numbers (high frequency velocity fluctuations) the cylindrical probe gave a power-law dependence on wave number and additional energy than that measured with the conical probe, due to the vortex shedding around the probe itself. Measurements were not taken of the turbulent velocity components transverse to the flow direction, but in view of the opposite behavior of the heat transfer-angle relationship in the most concentrated solution compared to the Newtonian case, such measurements would seem to be difficult to interpret.

The anomalous behavior of the heat transfer in dilute polymer solutions with the cylindrical probes is particularly disadvantageous in view of the small sizes of these probes compared to the conical probes. Small probes are required for measurements near solid boundaries, although it should be noted that the effect of a shear field, present in flows with solid boundaries, on the above results is not known.

ACKNOWLEDGMENTS

This work was performed at Stanford University and supported by the National Science Foundation, under Grant GK 1245.

REFERENCES

1. Bruce, C. A., and W. H. Schwarz,"Rheological Properties of Ionic
    and Nonionic Polyacrlyamide Solutions," submitted to J. Poly. Sci.,
    1968

2. Champagne, F. H., C. A. Sleicher, and O. H. Wehrmann, "Turbulence
    Measurements with Inclined Hot-Wires, Part 1," J. Fluid Mech.,
    6, 357, 1968

3. Delleur, J. W., G. H. Toebes, and C. L. Liu, "Hot Wire Physics
    and Turbulence Measurements in Liquids," Report No. 13, Dept.
    of Civil Engineering, Purdue University, 1966

4. Fabula, A. G., "An Experimental Study of Grid Turbulence in
    Dilute High-Polymer Solutions," Ph.D. Thesis, Pennsylvania State
    University, 1966

5. Friehe, C. A., "Velocity Measurements in Dilute Polymer Solutions,"
    Ph.D. Thesis, Stanford University, 1968

6. Friehe, C. A., and W. H. Schwarz, "Deviations from the Cosine
    Law for Yawed Cylindrical Anemometer Sensors," to be published
    in J. Appl. Mech.

7. James, D. F., "Laminar Flow of Dilute Polymer Solutions Around
    Circular Cylinders," Ph.D. Thesis, California Institute of
    Technology, 1967

8. Kramers, H., "Heat Transfer from Spheres to Flowing Media,"
    Physica, 12, 61, 1946

9. Smith, K. A., E. W. Merrill, H. S. Mickley, and P. S. Virk,
    "Anomalous Pitot Tube and Hot Film Measurements in Dilute
    Polymer Solutions," Chemical Engineering Science, 22, 619, 1967

SOME OBSERVATIONS ON THE FLOW CHARACTERISTICS OF CERTAIN

DILUTE MACROMOLECULAR SOLUTIONS

A. White

Hendon College of Technology, London

ABSTRACT

The flow characteristics of some dilute macromolecular solutions have been studied in a number of systems, including smooth pipes, rough pipes, submerged jets, flow around spheres, and wall-attachment experiments.

The primary effect of the additives in turbulent boundary layer flow is to cause a thickening of the viscous sublayer adjacent to a wall, the structure of the remaining portion of the boundary layer being little changed. Certain polymeric additives exhibit a secondary "bulk effect" which can cause a suppression of free turbulence away from a wall. This latter phenomenon does not occur with all effective additives and disappears on aging the solution. At the same time, the well defined threshold stress above which drag reduction occurs is somewhat increased.

Anomalous results from experiments with submerged jets, sphere drag, and wall attachment are discussed; and it seems that the secondary bulk effect only occurs with solutions which exhibit detectable elastic properties.

Some complex soap systems are also extremely effective drag reducers, and some unusual flow characteristics exhibited by one such system are also discussed in this paper.

INTRODUCTION

The reduction of frictional drag under turbulent flow conditions by introducing very small quantities of certain long chain additives to a liquid has become an extremely popular topic for study and research. Quite apart from the high academic interest, the fact that skin friction can be more than halved with the addition of only a few parts per million of the additive provides a great incentive for practical application.

Despite intensive efforts by many researchers, an overall explanation for the drag reduction mechanism is still extremely difficult. Even if the study is restricted to very dilute solutions in which the viscosity is but little affected by the additive, the problem is complicated by the fact that various additives can behave differently in different systems, although the overall effects on drag reduction in smooth pipe flow may be similar. Certainly the method of mixing, shear rate, and age of the solution can all play a part in the effectiveness of an additive.

A general review of the Toms effect is not presented in detail here, since a number of excellent surveys, bibliographies, and other papers already exist (Refs. 1-4). Instead a number of experimental results are presented which illustrate some important secondary anomalies which involve particular effects associated with shear rate, age, and elasticity.

SOME EXPERIMENTS WITH PIPE FLOW AND FREE TURBULENCE

During the past few years, considerable pressure loss data have appeared in the literature for the flow of drag reducing fluids in smooth pipes, and, to a somewhat lesser extent, velocity profile measurements are also well represented. A number of general observations can be made from these results. With most additives, drag reduction only occurs when a certain wall shear stress is exceeded, the value of which depends on the polymer, its concentration, and molecular weight. Below this threshold stress, the normal Newtonian laminar and turbulent flow occur; although in a small bore pipe the threshold stress may be exceeded in the laminar regime, and fully turbulent flow is then never established.

Velocity profile measurements show an important effect with concentrations below that at which detectable shear thinning occurs. These exhibit the same logarithmic core region with the same classical slope (same mixing constant, k) as in Newtonian turbulent flow but with an increased thickness of the viscous sublayer adjacent to a wall. This is seen from results by Wells (Ref. 5) and Elata, et al (Ref. 6) with guar gum solution; Ernst (Ref. 7) with C. M. C., Costrell (Ref. 8) and Virk, et al (Ref. 4) with Polyox, among others.

These results indicate that the drag reduction is a wall

effect, the structure of the turbulent core being little changed.
However, some velocity profile measurements by Goren (Ref. 9),
using freshly mixed Polyox solution injected into the flow well
upstream from the measuring section, do indicate some small change
in the core region since the slope of the logarithmic zone is very
slightly increased and k is reduced somewhat. The effect was not
apparent with a solution that had been thoroughly premixed and
slightly degraded during the mixing process.

The lack of significant turbulence damping in the inertial
core region, evidenced by the preceding results, might suggest
that "free" turbulence in the absence of a wall would be unaffected
by dilute solutions of these drag reducing additives, but this is
not always the case. Wu (Ref. 10) has measured the rate of spread
and decay of turbulence created by a paddle which was given a
single oscillation in a large tank of solution, and found a considerable suppression of free turbulence with Polyox above 25 ppm
which was the lowest concentration used.

Submerged jets provide another means to study the turbulence
damping properties of various additives without the influence of a
wall. Goren (Ref. 9) and Jackley (Ref. 11) both found little
difference between a polymer jet and one of water using respectively
Polyox and a polyacrylamide. Gadd (Ref. 1), on the other hand,
observed that the small-scale turbulence was greatly diminished with
Polyox at 30 ppm concentration. Some jet studies have also been
carried out by the author with a small jet and a much larger one,
using solutions of guar gum, Polyox (WSR 301), and a nonionic
polyacrylamide (Separan NP 10). The results show that with the
latter two polymers a certain solution concentration is required
before any change in the jet diffusion pattern becomes visibly
apparent.

The small jet was produced by a rounded entry nozzle, 0.24
centimeter in diameter, which was supplied with either water or
polymer solution from a constant head tank, and the jet discharged
into a Perspex tank containing a solution identical to the jet.
A dye was injected into the supply pipe just upstream to the nozzle
in order to render the jet diffusion pattern visible.

The experiments carried out with guar gum solution up to a
concentration of 500 wppm showed no significant difference from a
pure water jet, although this concentration brings about an enormous
reduction in drag with turbulent pipe flow. Polyox jets on the
other hand exhibited a turbulence damping effect with concentrations
greater than about 10 wppm, although the effect was not really

apparent for lower concentrations. With higher concentrations, the
turbulence damping was much more pronounced, and flow patterns
similar to Gadd's were observed. The submerged jets of Separan
solution were similar in nature to the Polyox jets except that a
concentration of about 70 wppm was required to produce an observable damping effect. No significant differences in the jet
patterns were observed over the whole of the Reynolds number range
investigated — between 3,500 and 20,000.

     For the larger scale experiments, the jet was produced by a
straight length of 3/4-inch diameter pipe, which was again supplied
with fluid from a header tank and discharged into a transparent
container. Dye was injected into the center of the jet pipe 8 inches
from the exit end. For all the tests the jet patterns were very
similar to those observed with the smaller apparatus. A comparison
between a water jet with 50 wppm Polyox solution can be made from
Figures 1 and 2, and it can be seen that the small-scale high
frequency turbulence has been supressed by the polymer additive.

Figure 1   Water, Jet Diameter   Figure 2   Polyox WSR 301,
              3/4 inch,   50 wppm, Jet
              Re = 60,000   Diameter 3/4 inch

After aging the Polyox solution for about a week, no detectable suppression was observed in the submerged jet although the same solution still gave an enormous drag reduction in smooth pipe flow.

From the available evidence, it seems that suppression of free turbulence only occurs with solutions which exhibit detectable elastic effects. For example Gadd (Ref. 12) has found measurable second normal stress differences with fresh Polyox solution in an annular shear flow, but not with dilute guar gum solution.

Brennen and Gadd (Ref. 13) showed that the elastic effects with dilute Polyox disappear after storing the solution for several days, but that the solution was still very effective in reducing turbulent skin friction.

Some further evidence has been derived from rough bore pipe flow experiments (Refs. 14,15) in an attempt to obtain flow resistance data with the sublayer effect eliminated. This was achieved by constructing a pipe with a threaded bore of 5/8-inch Whitworth thread form so that the roughness height projected well beyond the sublayer thickness into the inertial core region. Some of the results obtained are presented in Figures 3 to 6, in which the

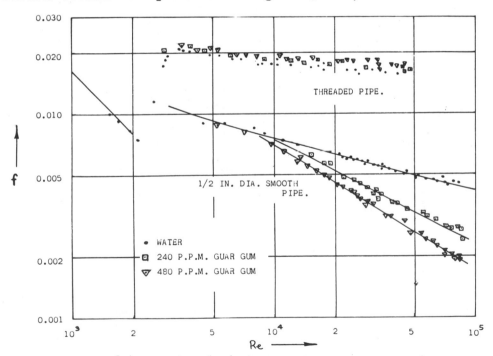

Figure 3   Effect of Extreme Roughness with Guar Gum Solution

mean flow velocity and Reynolds number have been conveniently based
on the core diameter of the threaded pipe. A selection of smooth
pipe data is also shown for comparison. It is seen that guar gum
molecules have little significant effect on the pressure drop along
the rough pipe, up to a concentration of 480 ppm, which was the
highest used, although an enormous drag reduction is found with
smooth pipes.

Preliminary test results with fresh Polyox solution showed
considerable scatter — much more than could be accounted for by
errors of experimental measurement. The pressure loss characteristics appeared to depend somewhat on the prehistory of the
polymer solution, and it was only by adopting a standard mixing
procedure that any degree of repeatability of the reading could be
obtained. The measured quantity of polymer was first dissolved
in a bucket of water and very gently stirred for a period of 1/2
hour. The solution was then mixed with the water in a header
tank and left for a further 1/2-hour period. A further gentle
stirring then preceded the tests. Mixing procedure had a much
lesser effect on the performance in smooth pipe.

The results of the experiments are shown in Figure 4, and

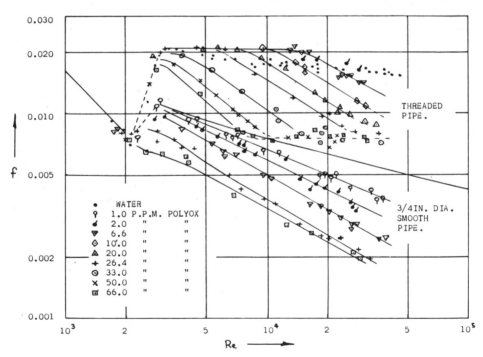

Figure 4 Effect of Extreme Roughness with Freshly Mixed
Polyox WSR 301 Solution

despite the scatter, some clear and rather unexpected trends are
discernible. It is seen that the Polyox additive can result in
drag reduction for all except the very lowest concentrations.
This would indicate that the core turbulence is partially suppressed
by the polymer molecules, and is in agreement with the experimental
results quoted earlier in this paper.

It is tempting to postulate the following physical explanation:-

Barenblatt (Ref. 16) has suggested that surrounding water
molecules may be entrapped by the polymer molecules to produce
a larger effective inertial mass, and certainly the effect would
be enhanced if several molecules become mechanically interlinked
to form clusters or networks. The tendency to cluster would
presumably be increased to some extent with an increase of the
polymer concentration, and the larger the clusters, the longer
would be their relaxation time and physical size in relation to
small eddies. This would expose a greater portion of the turbulence
spectrum to their damping influence and could, therefore, explain
the reduction of turbulent mixing as the polymer concentration is
increased.

The drag reduction tends to a maximum value at a moderately
high value of the Reynolds number. Possibly the clusters are
partially broken down by the high turbulence intensity, thus
decreasing their relaxation time and dissipating effect and reducing
their stabilizing influence.

Figures 5 and 6 show a direct comparison between the performance
of a freshly mixed Polyox solution and one that had been stored for
several days prior to the tests. It can be seen that the aged
solution gives no drag reduction in rough pipe flow and in smooth
pipes the threshold stress is somewhat increased. (Slight differences
between Figures 4 and 5 are due to a different batch of polymer
being used.)

It is interesting to consider some results by Fabula (Ref. 17)
in connection with the above. Measurement of turbulence in Polyox
solution behind a grid revealed some anomalous ragged signals
which were not due to velocity and could well have been clusters
of molecules. These clusters may have been brought together by
the straining of the fluid across the grid, since they were not
detectable in the absence of the grid; furthermore, the raggedness
of signal disappeared with age of the solution.

It is possible that aggregates are formed by the intensive
vorticity in the case of the threaded pipe, but it is difficult

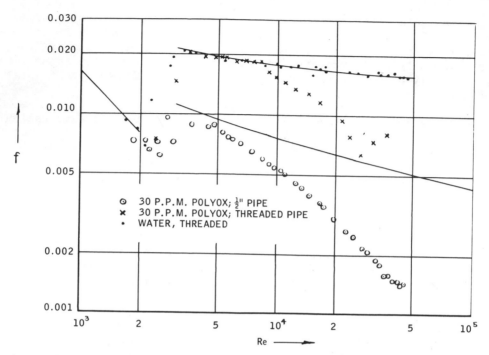

Figure 5   Pipe Flow Characteristics - Polyox WSR 301 (Freshly Mixed)

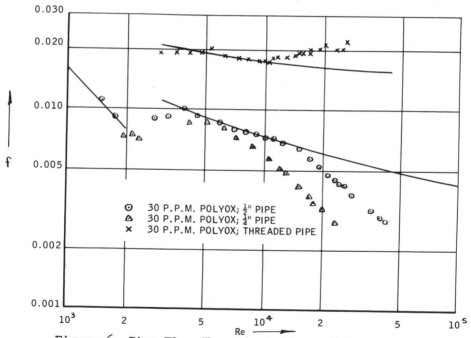

Figure 6   Pipe Flow Characteristics - Polyox WSR 301
(Aged for 17 Days)

to reconcile this with the great dependence of drag reduction in mixing procedure referred to previously.

Gadd (Ref. 18) has reported an experiment which shows that fresh Polyox, polyacrylamide solution, and a complex micellar system of centrimide and naphthol (see later) all have the ability to inhibit the stretching of moderately large vortics. Aged Polyox and guar gum solutions do not exhibit this property. This is consistent with the previous observations on "coarse" turbulence, but the effect of all the additives on vortex stretching with fine-scale turbulence in the highly sheared layer near a wall remain unexplored. These ideas on the suppression of vortex stretching were proposed by Pfenninger (Ref. 19) and do provide another plausible explanation for many of the anomalous effects.

Some unusual pipe flow characteristics are exhibited with solutions of certain complex soap systems. Figure 7 shows some effects found with an equimolar solution of cetyltrimethylammonium bromide and 1-naphthol. It is seen that the drag reduction ter-minates at some upper Reynolds number, depending on the pipe diameter, and which corresponds roughly to a fixed value of the wall shear stress (Ref. 20). The solution is very stable with respect to mechanical shearing in a closed-loop system, and the drag reduction reappears if the flow rate is reduced below the

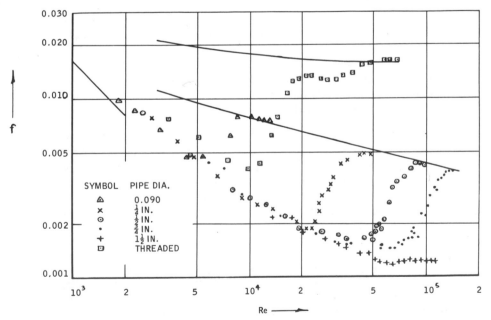

Figure 7   Pipe Friction Reduction with CTAB/1-Naphthol; Equimolar
           Solution Total Concentration 508 ppm

upper limiting Reynolds number. Similar results have been reported
by Savins (Ref. 21) with another soap system, and the effect is
probably caused by a reversible scission of the micelles when the
critical stress is exceeded. It should be noted that a somewhat
similar drag reduction limit has been observed with Polyox solutions
at very high shear rates, but in this case the scission is permanent
and the solution becomes degraded and ineffective.

Another interesting feature shown in Figure 7 is the apparent
absence of a threshold stress, evidenced by the lack of any diameter
effect in the reduced drag zone. It is likely that, if the micelles
are permanently stretched out in solution, a wide range of the
turbulence structure is exposed to their stabilizing influence.
The reduced drag curve with the soap system is roughly similar to
the friction reduction obtained with polymer additives at their
optimum concentration. The micellar system has also exhibited turbulence suppression in a submerged jet and in rough pipes.
Reference 15 may be consulted for further data showing the effects
of temperature, concentration, and oxidation with age.

EXTERNAL FLOWS

The performance of additives in reducing drag on an immersed
body is complicated by a number of factors. Certainly, with well
streamlined bodies, drag reduction is effected through reduced
skin friction just as with internal flows. With blunter bodies,
however, the drag consists primarily of form drag and is dominated
by the wake size and point of flow separation, skin friction
frequently being negligible in comparison.

Results from an early experiment clearly indicated that in
an extreme case the drag on an immersed body could be increased
by Polyox addition (Ref. 22). A large sphere dropped through a
tank of water with a Reynolds number $> \simeq 2 \times 10^5$ shows the small
wake associated with a turbulent boundary layer. With Polyox
solution, the wake was much larger, corresponding more nearly with
the early flow separation associated with a laminar boundary
layer, and consequently the drag was increased.

Drag measurements on spheres are simple and have been reported
by a number of investigators (Refs. 23, 24, 25). Some results
previously reported by the author (Ref. 26) are shown in Figure 8
and are generally consistent with the findings of others. Below
the critical Reynolds number, freshly mixed Polyox can delay
laminar separation and give rise to reduced form drag. This is

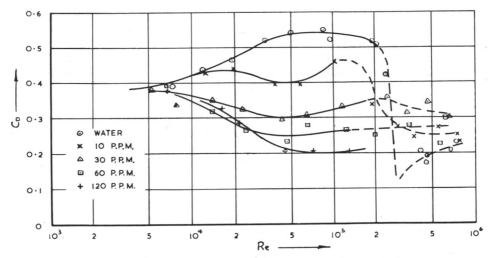

Figure 8   Drag of Spheres in Fresh Polyox (WSR 301) Solution

also seen in photographs by Lang and Patrick (Ref. 24).   The complex soap system previously mentioned can also bring about similar effects (Ref. 26).

Although guar gum solution is very effective in reducing skin friction, it was found to have no effect on the drag of spheres for concentrations up to 500 ppm.   Furthermore, it was observed that sphere drag reduction with Polyox disappeared on aging (Table 1), although this same aged solution retained skin friction reducing properties.

TABLE 1

Sphere diameter 1/2 inch (C_d in water = 0.475)
30 ppm Polyox WSR301

AGE	CD
Fresh	0.324
1 Day	0.346
2 Days	0.326
3 Days	0.390
6 Days	0.445

From these results it certainly seems that the delayed laminar separation is caused by elastic effects, since the phenomenon only occurs with solutions which exhibit detectable normal stress differences in sheared flow.   It is likely that the stress system set up by the shear flow in the boundary layer tends to strangle

the fluid onto the sphere in a similar way to the Weissenberg
effect with flow in an annulus with an outer rotating cylinder.

It should be noted that sphere drag reduction has been measured
by Ruszczycky (Ref. 27) using guar gum solution at much greater
concentrations. At such concentrations the solution is extremely
pseudoplastic and Bizzell and Slattery (Ref. 28) have shown that
for a power law fluid the separation point would move towards the
rear of a sphere as the flow index is decreased. Viscoelastic
properties are also exhibited by guar gum solutions at higher
concentrations.

Finally, we will consider the results of a simple wall attachment (Coanda effect) experiment. Figure 9 shows the layout of the

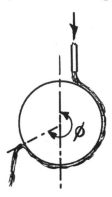

FIG. 9

apparatus used. Liquid was supplied to a 1/8-inch diameter pipe
from a constant head container, and the jet from this pipe was
directed onto a 3.5-inch-diameter cylinder. The flow rate was
slowly increased and the maximum value of the angle ϕ to the "peel-
off point" was noted. (Although ϕ oscillated, only the maximum
value was recorded). The same maximum value $\phi = 240°$, was obtained
with both water and filtered guar gum solutions up to 500 ppm
concentration. On the other hand, with fresh Polyox solution a
value $\phi = 270°$ was easily achieved for concentrations between 30
and 150 ppm. With higher concentrations, the energy dissipation
caused by the increased viscosity resulted in ϕ becoming less than
that observed with water.

CONCLUSIONS

The preceding results indicate at least two effects which may
or may not occur simultaneously, depending on the polymer and the
system considered. Practically all the experimental evidence with
pipe and boundary layer flow supports the view that the drag
reduction is associated with an increased thickness of the viscous

sublayer, the remaining portion of the boundary layer remaining essentially Newtonian in structure. This has received considerable discussion in the **literature**; and a number of useful semiempirical data correlations have been proposed based on the single two-zone model, although most of the early results correlated equally well in the form of a wall stress plot (Ref. 29).

The performance of the effective skin friction reducers in suppressing coarse free turbulence is somewhat different and it seems that only those additives which produce measurable elastic effects are successful in this connection. Similarly, elastic effects also seem primarily responsible for changes in a boundary layer separation point and wall attachment. Further detailed experiments are necessary to throw more light on these anomalies.

ACKNOWLEDGMENTS

This work has been aided by conversation and correspondence with a number of persons. Particular acknowledgment is made to Dr. G. E. Gadd (NPL Ship Division) and Dr. H. Barrow (University of Liverpool) for some useful discussions.

NOMENCLATURE

d	Pipe diameter
f	Friction factor $(\tau_w/(1/2)\rho u^2)$
u	Mean axial velocity
Re	Pipe flow Reynolds number (ud/υ)
υ	Kinematic viscosity
ρ	Fluid density
τ_w	Wall shear stress
C_d	Drag coefficient (Drag/area $1/2\rho u^2$)

Other symbols are defined in the text where they appear.

REFERENCES

1. Gadd, G. E., "Reduction of Turbulent Friction in Liquids by Dissolved Additives," Nature 212, No: 5065, 874, 1966

2. Lumley, J. L., "The Toms Phenomenon; Anomolous Effect in Turbulent Flow of Dilute Solutions of High Molecular Weight Linear Polymers," Applied Mech. Rev. 20. No. 12, 1139, 1967

3. Fabula, A. G., "Some Interpretations of the Toms Effect," <u>Modern Development in the Mechanics of Continua</u>, Academic Press 1966, p. 146

4. Virk, P. S., "The Toms Phenomenon; Turbulent Pipe Flow of Dilute Polymer Solutions," <u>J. Fluid Mech</u>. <u>30</u>. 305, 1967

5. Wells, C. S., "On the Turbulent Shear Flow of an Elastico-Viscous Fluid," <u>AIAA</u> preprint 64-36, 1964

6. Elata, C., "Turbulent Shear Flow of Polymer Solutions," <u>Israel Journ. of Tech</u>. <u>4</u>, No. 1, 87, 1966

7. Ernst, W. D., "Turbulent Flow of an Elasticoviscous Non-Newtonian Fluid," <u>AIAA Journ</u>. <u>5</u>, No. 5, 906, 1967

8. Costrell, J. A., "Preliminary Measurements of the Effect of Polymer Additives on the Velocity Distribution in Turbulent Pipe Flow," Thesis; West Virginia University, 1966

9. Goren, Y., "The Effect of Polymer Additives on Turbulent Shear Flow," Thesis, University of Liverpool, 1966

10. Jin, Wu, "Experiments on Free Turbulence in Viscoelastic Fluids," Hydronautics, Inc., Technical Report, 353-1

11. Jackley, D. N., "Drag Reducing Fluids in a Free Turbulent Jet," Int. Shipbuilding Prog. <u>14</u> 158, 1967

12. Gadd, G. E., "Differences in Normal Stress in Aqueous Solutions of Turbulent Drag Reducing Additives," <u>Nature 212</u>, No. 5069, 1348, 1966

13. Brennan, C. and Gadd, G. E., "Aging and Degradation in Dilute Polymer Solutions," <u>Nature 215</u>, 1368, 1967

14. White, A., "Turbulence and Drag Reduction with Polymer Additives," Hendon Coll. of Tech. Res. Bull. Nos. 4, 75, 1967

15. White, A., "Studies of Flow Characteristics of Dilute High Polymer Solutions," Hendon Coll. of Tech. Res. Bull. Nos. 5, 113, 1968

16. Barenblatt, G. I., J. Prikl. Mech. Tech. Fig. 5. 147, 1965

17. Fabula, A. G., "An Experimental Study of Grid Turbulence in Dilute High Polymer Solutions," Thesis, Pennsylvania State University, 1966

18. Gadd, G. E., "Effects of Drag Reducing Additives on Vortex Stretching," Nature 217, No. 5133, 1040, 1968

19. Pfenninger, W., Northrop Corp. Norair Div. Report. BLC -179, 1967

20. White, A., "Flow Characteristics of Complex Soap Systems," Nature 214, No. 5088, 585, 1967

21. Savins, J. G., "A Stress Controlled Drag Reduction Phenomenon," Soc. Petroleum Eng. Preprint SPE 1724, 1966

22. White, A., "Effect of Polymer Additives on Boundary Layer Separation and Drag of Submerged Bodies," Nature 211, No. 5056, 1390, 1966

23. White, D. A., "Drag Coefficients for Spheres in High Reynolds Number Flow of Dilute Solutions of High Polymers," Nature 212, No. 5059, 277, 1966

24. Lang, T. G. and Patrick, H. V. L., "Drag of Blunt Bodies in Polymer Solutions," ASME preprint 66-WA/FE-33, 1966

25. Sanders, J. V., "Drag Coefficients of Spheres in Poly (Ethylene Oxide) Solutions," Int. Shipbuilding Prog. 14, 140, 1967

26. White, A., "Drag of Spheres in Dilute High Polymer Solutions," Nature 216, No. 5119, 994, 1967

27. Ruszczycky, M. A., "Sphere Drop Tests in High Polymer Solutions," Nature 206, No. 4984, 614, 1965

28. Bizzell, G. D., and Slattery, J. C., "Non-Newtonian Boundary Layer Flow," J. Chem. Eng. Sci. 17, 777, 1962

29. White, A., "Turbulent Drag Reduction with Polymer Additives," J. Mech. Eng. Sci. 8, No. 4. 452, 1966

THE EFFECT OF DRAG REDUCTION AND OTHER IMPROVEMENTS

ON THE DESIGN AND PERFORMANCE OF SUBMERGED VEHICLES

Thomas G. Lang

Naval Undersea Warfare Center

ABSTRACT

A nondimensional method is utilized to provide the size of a submerged vehicle and its primary internal components as a function of the performance specifications, drag coefficient, propulsion system, and payload. The effect of technological improvements or of changes in the specified quantities is presented in the form of design changes in vehicle size, speed and range, or combinations thereof. The relative improvement in vehicle performance or size, resulting from individual technological improvements, aids in determining which type of technological improvement is the most important for a given vehicle.

INTRODUCTION

The objective of this paper is to present a simple method for predicting the size of submerged vehicles and determining the effect of design improvements on design size or vehicle performance. Submerged vehicles are defined as the class of self-propelled devices which travel through a fluid and whose weight is principally supported by buoyancy force.

This analysis is nondimensional in order to apply equally well to submarines, torpedoes, and airships, such as those shown in Figure 1. The results of this analysis aid in determining whether research or development should be conducted on any or all of the possible types of technical improvements, and in determining the trade offs resulting from changes in the performance specifications.

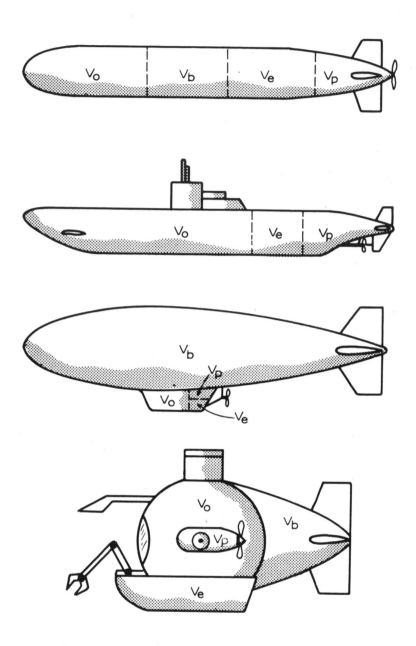

Figure 1   Possible Forms of Submerged Vehicles

PHYSICAL EQUATIONS

This analysis is based upon the generalized engineering design procedure presented in Reference 1 in which one chapter is devoted to the design of submerged vehicles. The basic equations relating to the design size of submerged vehicles and of their component parts are:

$$V = V_o + V_p + V_e + V_b \tag{1}$$

$$W = W_o + W_p + W_e + W_b \tag{2}$$

$$D = C_d V^{2/3} (1/2) \rho U^2 \tag{3}$$

where V = vehicle volume; V_p is the volume of the power-dependent components and the associated hull structure; V_e is the volume of the energy-dependent components and the associated hull structure; V_b is the volume of the buoyancy sections and the associated hull structure; and V_o is the volume of all remaining components which includes the payload, electronics, living quarters and personnel, if any, controls, stabilizing fins, ballast tanks, and all associated hull structure; W is the vehicle weight; W with each subscript is the weight of each vehicle component where the subscript has the same meaning as defined above; D is the vehicle drag; C_d is the drag coefficient which varies from about 0.025 for well-streamlined vehicles to as much as 0.100 or more for poorly streamlined vehicles with many appendages (Refs. 2 and 3); ρ is the mass density of the fluid; and U is the vehicle speed.

The volumes V_p and V_e are defined as:

$$V_p = \alpha_p \, DU \tag{4}$$

$$V_e = \alpha_e \, DR \tag{5}$$

where a_p is the volume per unit of net power output (i.e., V_p divided by the product of shaft power and propulsive efficiency), a_e is the volume per unit of net energy output (i.e., V_e divided by the product of the energy content of the fuel, the power plant efficiency, and the propulsive efficiency), and R is the range. All dimensional units should be consistent. The associated portion of the hull structure has been included in the volume and weight allotment for each component in order to provide for designs where some components are not placed within a single pressure hull.

Substituting Equations (3), (4), and (5) into Equation (1) gives:

$$V = V_o + C_d \, V^{2/3}\left(1/2 \rho U^2 (\alpha_p U + \alpha_e R)\right) + V_b. \tag{6}$$

Introducing the density of each component as W/gV (with the appropriate subscripts) into Equation (2) and dividing by $g\rho_b V_o$ gives:

$$\frac{\rho_v V}{\rho_b V_o} = \frac{\rho_o}{\rho_b} + \frac{\rho_p V_p}{\rho_b V_o} + \frac{\rho_e V_e}{\rho_b V_o} + \frac{V_b}{V_o}. \tag{7}$$

Substituting Equations (3), (4), and (5) into Equation (7), solving Equation (7) for V_b/V_o, substituting the result into Equation (6), and rearranging, gives

$$\left(\frac{V}{V_o}\right)^{1/3} - \left(\frac{V_o}{V}\right)^{2/3}\left(\frac{\rho_o - \rho_b}{\rho_v - \rho_b}\right) = \frac{C_d}{2}\left(\frac{\alpha_p \rho U^3}{V_o^{1/3}}\right)\left(\frac{\rho_p - \rho_b}{\rho_v - \rho_b}\right)$$

$$+ \frac{C_d}{2}\left(\frac{\alpha_e \rho U^2 R}{V_o^{1/3}}\right)\left(\frac{\rho_e - \rho_b}{\rho_v - \rho_b}\right). \tag{8}$$

In the cases where vehicle density is unimportant, or where no volume is used for buoyancy, then $V_b = o$ and Equation (6) becomes

$$\left(\frac{V}{V_o}\right)^{1/3} - \left(\frac{V_o}{V}\right)^{2/3} = \frac{C_d}{2}\left(\frac{\alpha_p \rho U^3}{V_o^{1/3}}\right) + \frac{C_d}{2}\left(\frac{\alpha_e \rho U^2 R}{V_o^{1/3}}\right). \tag{9}$$

Defining a nondimensional design problem as a design mission, let m_1 to m_7 be defined as the mission parameters which describe the requirements of a design mission where

$$m_1 = \frac{C_d}{2}\frac{\alpha_p \rho U^3}{V_o^{1/3}} = \frac{V_p}{V}\left(\frac{V}{V_o}\right)^{1/3} \tag{10}$$

$$m_2 = \frac{C_d}{2}\frac{\alpha_e \rho U^2 R}{V_o^{1/3}} = \frac{V_e}{V}\left(\frac{V}{V_o}\right)^{1/3} \tag{11}$$

$$m_3 = \frac{C_d}{2}\frac{\alpha_p \rho U^3}{V_o^{1/3}}\left(\frac{\rho_p - \rho_b}{\rho_v - \rho_b}\right) = m_1\left(\frac{\rho_p - \rho_b}{\rho_v - \rho_b}\right) \tag{12}$$

$$m_4 = \frac{C_d}{2} \frac{\alpha_e \rho U^2 R}{V_o^{1/3}} \left(\frac{\rho_e - \rho_b}{\rho_v - \rho_b}\right) = m_2 \left(\frac{\rho_e - \rho_b}{\rho_v - \rho_b}\right) \qquad (13)$$

$$m_5 = \frac{\rho_o - \rho_b}{\rho_v - \rho_b} \qquad (14)$$

$$m_6 = m_1 + m_2 = \frac{C_d}{2} \frac{\rho U^2}{V_o^{1/3}} \, (\alpha_p U + \alpha_e R)$$

$$= \left(\frac{V}{\overline{V}_o}\right)^{1/3} \left(\frac{V_p + V_e}{V}\right) \qquad (15)$$

$$m_7 = m_3 + m_4 = m_1 \left(\frac{\rho_p - \rho_b}{\rho_v - \rho_b}\right) + m_2 \left(\frac{\rho_e - \rho_b}{\rho_v - \rho_b}\right) . \qquad (16)$$

Substituting m_5 to m_7, Equations (9) and (8) become

$$\left(\frac{V}{\overline{V}_o}\right)^{1/3} - \left(\frac{V_o}{V}\right)^{2/3} = m_6 \quad (\text{for } V_b = o) \qquad (17)$$

$$\left(\frac{V}{\overline{V}_o}\right)^{1/3} - m_5 \left(\frac{V_o}{V}\right)^{2/3} = m_7 . \qquad (18)$$

Equation (17) provides the net vehicle volume (i.e., V/V_o) when $V_b = o$ and Equation (18) pertains when vehicle density is specified. Notice that if m_8 is defined as the ratio V_p/V_e where

$$\frac{\alpha_p U}{\alpha_e R} = \frac{m_1}{m_2} = \frac{V_p}{V_e} = m_8 \qquad (19)$$

then m_8 may be considered as a classification parameter where if $m_8 > 1$, the vehicle has relatively high speed and low range, while if $m_8 < 1$, the vehicle has relatively low speed and long range. Similarly, m_6 may be considered as another classification parameter where $m_6 > 1$ indicates a high performance vehicle (i.e., high speed and/or long range) and $m_6 < 1$ indicates a low performance vehicle.

Equations (17) and (18) are graphed in Figure 2 where V/V_0 is shown as a function of m_6 when $V_b = 0$, and as a function of m_5 and m_7 when vehicle density is specified.

The relative sizes of power, energy, and buoyancy components, V_p/V, V_e/V, and V_b/V, are obtained from Equations (3), (4), and (10), Equations (3), (5), and (11), and Equation (1), respectively as

$$\frac{V_p}{V} = \left(\frac{V_0}{V}\right)^{1/3} m_1 \tag{20}$$

$$\frac{V_e}{V} = \left(\frac{V_0}{V}\right)^{1/3} m_2 = \frac{V_p}{V} \cdot \frac{1}{m_8} \tag{21}$$

$$\frac{V_b}{V} = 1 - \frac{V_0}{V} - \frac{V_p}{V} - \frac{V_e}{V} . \tag{22}$$

The weight-to-drag ratio W/D is sometimes desired as a means of comparison with the lift-to-drag ratios of surface craft or aircraft. Utilizing Equation (3),

$$\frac{W}{D} = \frac{\rho g V}{C_d V^{2/3} (1/2)\rho U^2} = \frac{2}{C_d}\left(\frac{gV^{1/3}}{U^2}\right) = \frac{2}{C_d}\left(\frac{gV_0^{1/3}}{U^2}\right)\left(\frac{V}{V_0}\right)^{1/3} . \tag{23}$$

EFFECT OF TECHNOLOGICAL IMPROVEMENTS AND SPECIFICATION MODIFICATIONS ON VEHICLE DESIGN AND PERFORMANCE.

Using a sub x to denote a change in design or performance, Equation (6) is rewritten as follows to pertain for a new vehicle configuration:

$$V_x = V_{ox} + (C_{dx})_0 \, V_x^{2/3} \, (1/2)\rho_x U_x^2 (\alpha_{px} U_x + \alpha_{ex} R_x) + V_{bx} \tag{24}$$

where $(C_{dx})_0$ is an equivalent drag coefficient which includes the effect of drag reduction equipment when the drag is reduced. An expression will be presented later for calculating $(C_{dx})_0$ as a function of the actual drag coefficient C_{dx} and the volume of drag reduction equipment V_d which is required.

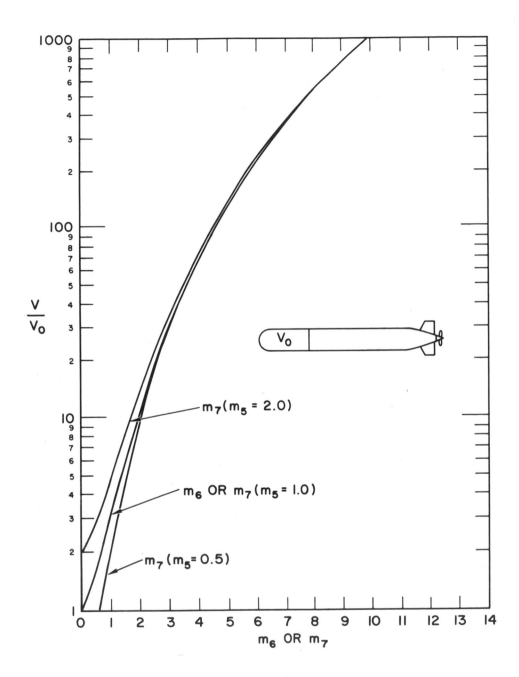

Figure 2   Size of Submerged Vehicles

Subtracting Equation (24) from Equation (6), rewriting and utilizing Equations (3) and (5), gives

$$1 - \frac{V_x}{V} = \frac{V_o}{V}\left(1 - \frac{V_{ox}}{V_o}\right) + \frac{V_b}{V}\left(1 - \frac{V_{bx}}{V_b}\right) + \frac{V_p}{V}\left[1 - \frac{(C_{dx})_o}{C_d}\left(\frac{V_x}{V}\right)^{2/3}\frac{\rho_x}{\rho}\left(\frac{U_x}{U}\right)^3\frac{\alpha_{px}}{\alpha_p}\right]$$

$$+ \frac{V_e}{V}\left[1 - \frac{(C_{dx})_o}{C_d}\left(\frac{V_x}{V}\right)^{2/3}\frac{\rho_x}{\rho}\left(\frac{U_x}{U}\right)^2\frac{R_x}{R}\frac{\alpha_{ex}}{\alpha_e}\right]. \qquad (25)$$

CHANGE IN DRAG COEFFICIENT

In case a reduction in drag is used to reduce vehicle volume, keeping all other parameters fixed, Equation (25) reduces to

$$1 - \frac{V_x}{V} = \frac{V_p}{V}\left[1 - \frac{(C_{dx})_o}{C_d}\left(\frac{V_x}{V}\right)^{2/3}\right] + \frac{V_e}{V}\left[1 - \frac{(C_{dx})_o}{C_d}\left(\frac{V_x}{V}\right)^{2/3}\right]. \qquad (26)$$

Rewriting, the drag reduction factor required to reduce vehicle volume by a factor V/V_x is

$$\begin{Bmatrix} C_d \text{ and} \\ V \text{ vary} \end{Bmatrix} \qquad \frac{C_d}{(C_{dx})_o} = \frac{(V_x/V)^{2/3}}{1 - \dfrac{1 - (V_x/V)}{(V_e/V) + (V_p/V)}} \qquad . \qquad (27)$$

Alternatively, the effect of a change in drag coefficient on vehicle volume can be obtained directly from Figure 2 by multiplying m_6 (or m_7) by the ratio $(C_{dx})_o/C_d$ and finding the new value of V/V_o. Notice that drag reduction has a strong influence on vehicle size reduction if $m_6 > 1$, while it has little influence if m_6 is close to zero. For example, if $m_6 = 10$ and the drag coefficient is reduced by a factor of 2.0, Figure 2 shows that the vehicle size is reduced by a factor of 8.0. The reason is that a reduction in drag coefficient reduces the required values of V_e and V_p, which in turn reduces the wetted surface area, which then further reduces V_e and V_p resulting in a greater reduction of wetted surface area, etc. On the other hand, when m_6 is close to zero, very little volume is used for V_e and V_p, so the effect of drag reduction on vehicle size is negligible.

Now consider the case where drag reduction is used to increase the speed of a vehicle. In this case, Equation (25) reduces to

$$\begin{Bmatrix} C_d \text{ and} \\ U \text{ vary} \end{Bmatrix} \quad \left(\frac{C_d}{C_{dx}}\right)_o = \left(\frac{U_x}{U}\right)^3 \left[\frac{1 + \dfrac{V_p}{V_e}\dfrac{U_x}{U}}{1 + \dfrac{V_p}{V_e}}\right] \tag{28}$$

which provides the drag reduction factor required to increase speed by a factor of U_x/U.

In case drag reduction is used to increase the vehicle range, Equation (25) shows that the range increase factor is

$$\begin{Bmatrix} C_d \text{ and} \\ R \text{ vary} \end{Bmatrix} \quad \frac{R_x}{R} = \frac{C_d}{(C_{dx})_o}\left[1 + \frac{V_p}{V_e}\right] - \frac{V_p}{V_e} . \tag{29}$$

CHANGE IN POWER PLANT EFFECTIVENESS

In case the volume per unit of net power output is reduced by a factor a_p/a_{px}, the vehicle volume reduction factor V/V_x can be obtained from Equation (25), assuming that nothing else changes, which reduces to

$$\begin{Bmatrix} a_p \text{ and} \\ V \text{ vary} \end{Bmatrix} \quad \frac{a_p}{a_{px}} = \frac{\dfrac{V_p}{V}\left(\dfrac{V_x}{V}\right)^{2/3}}{\dfrac{V_x}{V} - 1 + \dfrac{V_p}{V} + \dfrac{V_e}{V}\left[1 - \left(\dfrac{V_x}{V}\right)^{2/3}\right]} . \tag{30}$$

Utilizing a reduction in a_p to increase the speed, Equation (25) provides the following relationship:

$$\begin{Bmatrix} a_p \text{ and} \\ U \text{ vary} \end{Bmatrix} \quad \frac{a_p}{a_{px}} = \frac{\dfrac{V_p}{V_e}\left(\dfrac{U_x}{U}\right)^3}{\dfrac{V_p}{V_e} + 1 - \left(\dfrac{U_x}{U}\right)^3} . \tag{31}$$

Similarly, the relationship between a change in α_p and a change in range is

$$\left\{\begin{matrix}\alpha_p \text{ and}\\ R \text{ vary}\end{matrix}\right\} \quad \frac{R_x}{R} = 1 + \frac{V_p}{V_e}\left(1 - \frac{\alpha_{px}}{\alpha_p}\right).$$ (32)

CHANGE IN ENERGY CONTENT OF THE FUEL

Utilizing Equation (25), the following expressions provide the effect of a change in α_e on size, speed, and range:

$$\left\{\begin{matrix}\alpha_e \text{ and}\\ V \text{ vary}\end{matrix}\right\} \quad \frac{\alpha_e}{\alpha_{ex}} = \frac{\dfrac{V_e}{V}\left(\dfrac{V_x}{V}\right)^{2/3}}{\dfrac{V_x}{V} - 1 + \dfrac{V_e}{V} + \dfrac{V_p}{V}\left[1 - \left(\dfrac{V_x}{V}\right)^{2/3}\right]}$$ (33)

$$\left\{\begin{matrix}\alpha_e \text{ and}\\ U \text{ vary}\end{matrix}\right\} \quad \frac{\alpha_e}{\alpha_{ex}} = \frac{\left(\dfrac{U_x}{U}\right)^2}{1 + \dfrac{V_p}{V_e}\left[1 - \left(\dfrac{U_x}{U}\right)^3\right]}$$ (34)

$$\left\{\begin{matrix}\alpha_e \text{ and}\\ R \text{ vary}\end{matrix}\right\} \quad \frac{R_x}{R} = \frac{\alpha_e}{\alpha_{ex}}$$ (35)

CHANGE IN SPEED

The effect of a change in speed on design size or design range is obtained using Equation (25) which provides

$$\left\{\begin{matrix}U \text{ and}\\ V \text{ vary}\end{matrix}\right\} \quad \left(\frac{U_x}{U}\right)^2\left(\frac{U_x}{U}\frac{V_p}{V} + \frac{V_e}{V}\right) = \frac{\dfrac{V_x}{V} + \dfrac{V_p}{V} + \dfrac{V_e}{V} - 1}{\left(\dfrac{V_x}{V}\right)^{2/3}}$$ (36)

$$\left\{\begin{array}{l}U \text{ and}\\ R \text{ vary}\end{array}\right\} \quad \frac{R_x}{R} = \frac{1 + \dfrac{V_p}{V_e}\left[1 - \left(\dfrac{U_x}{U}\right)^3\right]}{\left(\dfrac{U_x}{U}\right)^2} \tag{37}$$

Since Equation (36) is not in explicit form, the effect of a change in speed on a change in vehicle size is most easily obtained from Figure 2 where the new value of m_6 (or m_5 and m_7) directly provides the new value of V/V_o.

CHANGE IN RANGE

The effect of a change in range on vehicle volume is obtained from Equation (25) as

$$\left\{\begin{array}{l}R \text{ and}\\ V \text{ vary}\end{array}\right\} \quad \frac{R_x}{R} = \frac{\dfrac{V_x}{V} - 1 + \dfrac{V_e}{V} + \dfrac{V_p}{V}\left[1 - \left(\dfrac{V_x}{V}\right)^{2/3}\right]}{\dfrac{V_e}{V}\left(\dfrac{V_x}{V}\right)^{2/3}}, \tag{38}$$

CHANGE IN FLUID DENSITY

The following expressions are derived from Equation (25):

$$\left\{\begin{array}{l}\rho \text{ and}\\ V \text{ vary}\end{array}\right\} \quad \frac{\rho}{\rho_x} = \left(\frac{V_x}{V}\right)^{2/3} \frac{1}{1 + \left(\dfrac{\dfrac{V_x}{V} - 1}{\dfrac{V_p}{V} + \dfrac{V_e}{V}}\right)} \tag{39}$$

$$\left\{\begin{array}{l}\rho \text{ and}\\ U \text{ vary}\end{array}\right\} \quad \frac{\rho}{\rho_x} = \left(\frac{U_x}{U}\right)^2 \frac{1 + \dfrac{V_p}{V_e}\left(\dfrac{U_x}{U}\right)}{1 + \dfrac{V_p}{V_e}} \tag{40}$$

$$\begin{Bmatrix} \rho \text{ and} \\ R \text{ vary} \end{Bmatrix} \quad \frac{R_x}{R} = \frac{\rho}{\rho_x}\left(1 + \frac{V_p}{V_e}\right) - \frac{V_p}{V_e}. \tag{41}$$

CHANGE IN V_o

If the payload volume or the volume of the various components comprising V_o can be reduced, the vehicle performance can be improved or the net vehicle volume can be reduced. The following equations derived from Equation (25) show the results of changing V_o:

$$\begin{Bmatrix} V_o \text{ and} \\ V \text{ vary} \end{Bmatrix} \quad \frac{V_o}{V_{ox}} = \frac{V_o/V}{\frac{V_x}{V} - 1 + \frac{V_o}{V} + \left(\frac{V_p}{V} + \frac{V_e}{V}\right)\left[1 - \left(\frac{V_x}{V}\right)^{2/3}\right]} \tag{42}$$

$$\begin{Bmatrix} V_o \text{ and} \\ U \text{ vary} \end{Bmatrix} \quad \frac{V_o}{V_{ox}} = \frac{V_o/V}{\frac{V_o}{V} + \frac{V_p}{V}\left[1 - \left(\frac{U_x}{U}\right)^3\right] + \frac{V_e}{V}\left[1 - \left(\frac{U_x}{U}\right)^2\right]} \tag{43}$$

$$\begin{Bmatrix} V_o \text{ and} \\ R \text{ vary} \end{Bmatrix} \quad \frac{R_x}{R} = 1 + \frac{V_o}{V_e}\left(1 - \frac{V_{ox}}{V_o}\right). \tag{44}$$

CHANGE IN V_b

Equation (25) is used to provide the following relationships:

$$\begin{Bmatrix} V_b \text{ and} \\ V \text{ vary} \end{Bmatrix} \quad \frac{V_b}{V_{bx}} = \frac{V_b/V}{\frac{V_b}{V} + \frac{V_x}{V} - 1 + \left(\frac{V_p}{V} + \frac{V_e}{V}\right)\left[1 - \left(\frac{V_x}{V}\right)^{3/3}\right]} \tag{45}$$

$$\begin{Bmatrix} V_b \text{ and} \\ U \text{ vary} \end{Bmatrix} \quad \frac{V_b}{V_{bx}} = \frac{V_b/V}{\frac{V_b}{V} + \frac{V_p}{V}\left[1 - \left(\frac{U_x}{U}\right)^3\right] + \frac{V_e}{V}\left[1 - \left(\frac{U_x}{U}\right)^2\right]} \tag{46}$$

$$\left\{ \begin{matrix} V_b \text{ and} \\ R \text{ vary} \end{matrix} \right\} \quad \frac{R_x}{R} \ = \ 1 + \frac{V_b}{V_e}\left(1 - \frac{V_{bx}}{V_b}\right). \tag{47}$$

PENALTY PAID FOR DRAG REDUCTION EQUIPMENT

If the drag coefficient is reduced by a factor C_d/C_{dx} and V_d is the volume of drag reduction equipment needed, the equivalent drag reduction factor $C_d/(C_{dx})_o$ (which assumes that $V_d = 0$) used in the above equations is less than C_d/C_{dx} and thereby reflects the penalty paid for the drag reduction equipment. Rewriting Equation (24) for the two methods of treating drag reduction, in which the first includes the added volume V_d, gives

$$V_x \ = \ V_{ox} + V_{bx} + V_d + C_{dx}\, V_x^{2/3}(1/2)\rho_x U_x^2\left(\alpha_{px}U_x + \alpha_{ex}R_x\right) \tag{48}$$

$$V_x \ = \ V_{ox} + V_{bx} + (C_{dx})_o V_x^{2/3}(1/2)\rho_x U_x^2(\alpha_{px}U_x + \alpha_{ex}R_x). \tag{49}$$

Combining Equations (48) and (49) provides

$$\frac{C_d}{C_{dx}} \ = \ \left(\frac{C_d}{C_{dx}}\right)_o\left[\frac{1}{1 - \left(\dfrac{V_d}{V_x - V_{ox} - V_{bx}}\right)}\right] \tag{50}$$

which shows the actual (increased) drag reduction factor C_d/C_{dx} which is required to provide the same vehicle improvement as the factor $C_d/(C_{dx})_o$ in which no drag reduction equipment is assumed.

In case the values of V, V_o, and V_b remain fixed when drag reduction is applied, Equation (50) becomes

$$\frac{C_d}{C_{dx}} \ = \ \left(\frac{C_d}{C_{dx}}\right)_o\left[\frac{1}{1 - \dfrac{V_d}{V - V_o - V_b}}\right]. \tag{51}$$

EFFECT OF MULTIPLE IMPROVEMENTS

In case several improvements are made to a vehicle simultaneously, their net effect on the design or performance can be obtained by applying each improvement in series by making use of the appropriate equation. For example, if drag reduction and a change in a_e are used to increase vehicle range, Equations (29) and (35) would be used in series; however, the new values of the component volumes resulting from the last step in the series must be used for each new step. Alternate methods for determining the effect of multiple improvements are to determine the new component volumes and vehicle size directly by using Figure 2 and Equations (20) to (22), or to utilize Equation (25).

VEHICLE DESIGN EXAMPLE

The torpedo design presented in Reference 1 is used as an example of this design procedure. The specifications and basic design data are: $U = 80$ ft/sec, $R = 30,000$ ft, $V_0 = 1.0$ ft3, $\rho = 2.0$ slugs/ft3, $\rho_v = 2.4$ slugs/ft3, $\rho_b = 0.4$ slugs/ft3, $a_p = 1.5$ x 10^{-5}ft3/(ft-lb/sec), $\rho_p = 6.2$ slugs/ft3, $a_e = 1.0$ x 10^{-7} ft3/ft-lb, and $\rho_e = 4.2$ slugs/ft3. The value of C_d for a smooth, streamlined body with a turbulent boundary layer and stabilizing fins operating at a Reynolds number of about 4 x 10^7 is 0.023, according to Reference 2.

Using Equations (10) to (16), $m_1 = 0.177$, $m_2 = 0.442$, $m_3 = 0.513$, $m_4 = 0.840$, $m_5 = 2.0$, $m_6 = 0.619$, and $m_7 = 1.353$. Using Figure 2, $V/V_0 = 6.8$. A more accurate value of $V/V_0 = 6.9$ is obtained from Equation (18). Consequently, $V = 6.90$ ft3 and $W = \rho_v g V = 534$ lb. Using Equations (20) to (22), $V_p = 0.641$ ft3, $V_e = 1.60$ ft3, and $V_b = 3.24$ ft3. From the known densities, $W_p = 128$ lb, $W_e = 217$ lb, $W_b = 42$ lb, and $W_0 = 142$ lb. The vehicle drag is obtained from Equation (3) as 533 lb. The net power output is DU/550 or 77.7 horsepower. The shaft horsepower is 77.7 divided by the propulsive efficiency. The W/D ratio is approximately one.

EXAMPLE OF DESIGN IMPROVEMENTS

Selecting the above torpedo, let the following improvements be made: $C_d/(C_{dx})_0 = 1.5$, $a_p/a_{px} = 2.0$, and $a_e/a_{ex} = 1.5$. Equations (12) and (13) show that the new values for m_3 and m_4 are $m_{3x} = 0.171$ and $m_{4x} = 0.374$ which provide the value $m_{7x} = m_{3x} + m_{4x} = 0.545$. Figure 2 shows that the new volume ratio is $V_x/V_0 = 3.1$. Therefore, $V_x = 3.1$ ft3 which represents a reduction in vehicle size and weight by a factor of 2.2.

Alternatively, if the vehicle volume had remained constant and the improvements were used to increase speed, Equations (28), (31), and (34) can be used in series by solving each equation iteratively and calculating the new ratio of V_p/V_e at the end of each step. Perhaps a quicker method of solution is to use Equation (25) which reduces for this case to

$$\left(\frac{U_x}{U}\right)^2 \frac{\alpha_{ex}}{\alpha_e} + \left(\frac{U_x}{U}\right)^3 \frac{V_p}{V_e} \frac{\alpha_{px}}{\alpha_p} = \frac{C_d}{(C_{dx})_o}\left[1 + \frac{V_p}{V_e}\right] \tag{52}$$

which can be solved iteratively to give $U_x/U = 1.48$.

Improvements due to individual advancements can best be calculated using the appropriate equation which has already been developed. For example, the range increase factor R_x/R due to factor of two improvements of $C_d/(C_{dx})_o$, α_p/α_{px}, and α_e/α_{ex}, respectively, for the example torpedo where $V_p/V_e = 0.40$ is shown by Equations (29), (32), and (35) to be 2.4, 1.2, and 2.0. In this particular case, work on improving (reducing) C_d or α_e is more important than work on improving the power plant.

TYPICAL COMPARISONS OF THE EFFECTIVENESS OF TECHNOLOGICAL IMPROVEMENTS

One method of comparing the effectiveness of various technological improvements is presented in Figure 3, where the improvement factors required to provide a vehicle speed increase of 25 percent are graphed. The curves on the graph were obtained from Equations (28), (31), (35), and (37), assuming that V_o, V, and V_b remain constant. The graph shows that all vehicles which are to utilize some type of improvement for speed increase can be classified by the parameter V_p/V_e (the ratio of the volume of the power-dependent components to the volume of the energy-dependent components). Notice that drag reduction is the most effective means for increasing speed. Also note that the speed can be increased 25 percent by a reduction in range, R/R_x, or an improvement in the energy content of the fuel, α_e/α_{ex}, only if V_p/V_e is less than about 0.85. Alternatively, the vehicle speed can be increased 25 percent by an improvement in the power plant, α_p/α_{px}, only if V_p/V_e is greater than about 0.85.

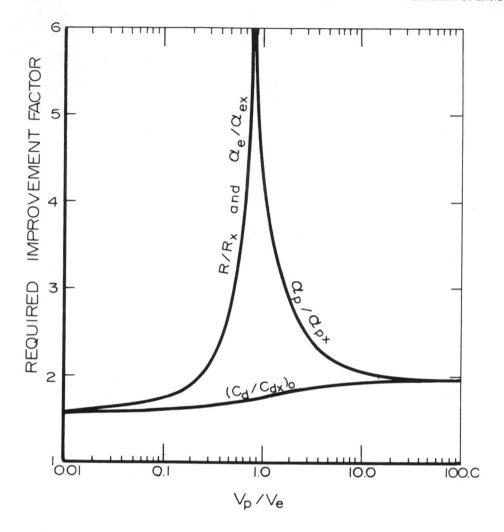

Figure 3   Improvement Factors Required for a Speed Increase of 25%

Another method of comparing the effectiveness of various technological improvements is presented in Figure 4 which shows the
range increase graphed as a function of each improvement factor.
Notice that submerged vehicles are again classified by the ratio
V_p/V_e.

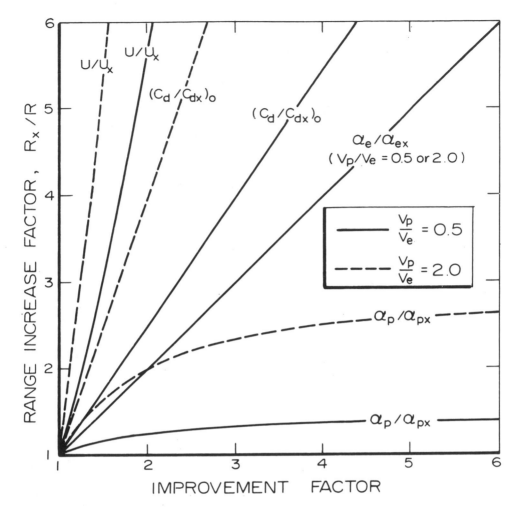

Figure 4   Effect of Technological Improvements

on Increasing the Range

Many other types of comparative presentations may be made. Such comparisons show which kinds of improvements should be pursued for a given submerged vehicle.

ACKNOWLEDGMENT

This paper is based upon one chapter of the author's unclassified PhD thesis "A Generalized Engineering Design Procedure," Pennsylvania State University, June 1968. His advisor and principal reviewer was Professor G. F. Wislicenus.

REFERENCES

1. Lang, T. G., "A Generalized Engineering Design Procedure," PhD
    thesis, Pennsylvania State University, Aerospace Department,
    June, 1968

2. Greiner, Leonard, editor, Underwater Missile Propulsion, (Compass
    Publications, Inc., Arlington, Virginia, 1967), pages 117-146,
    "Simplified Methods for Estimating Torpedo Drag" by J. D. Brooks
    and T. G. Lang

3. Hoerner, S. F., Fluid-Dynamic Drag (published by the author,
    Midland Park, N. J., 1965)

DRAG REDUCTION IN EXTERNAL FLOWS

OF ADDITIVE SOLUTIONS

Jin Wu

HYDRONAUTICS, Incorporated

ABSTRACT

A series of measurements of the turbulent drag on a flat
plate using homogeneous solutions of high-molecular-weight
additives, and a series of visual studies concerning diffusion
and entrainment of jets with additive solutions flowing into a
turbulent stream of pure water have been conducted. The experiments
include tests with additive solutions of various concentrations
and different channel velocities. The drag reduction obtained in
these experiments is generally lower than that for pipe flows
without taking into account differences in experimental Reynolds
numbers; however, the maximum reduction occurs at about the same
concentration (50-100 ppmw) in both cases. A comparison between
the ejection study (studies with additive solutions ejected into
a pure water boundary layer) data and the present results indicates very poor mixing between the ejected fluid and its surroundings. Photographs of submerged jets confirm that additives suppress
turbulent diffusion. The flat plate results also suggest that
for efficient drag reduction, the solution ejected into the boundary
layer should be dilute and that the rate of ejection should be
comparable to the discharge within the inner boundary layer (the
wall controlled region). These findings suggest that smaller
amounts of additive are needed for ejection than are usually
estimated, and therefore brighten the hope for the practical
application of additives to achieve drag reduction in external
flow cases, such as on a ship hull.

INTRODUCTION

Many experiments, reported within the last five years, show
the capability of additives of high molecular weight to reduce

turbulent friction. Most measurements refer to the pressure drop
in turbulent pipe flows with additives homogeneously mixed in
water —— e.g., Hoyt and Fabula (Ref. 1); some measurements,
however, have been made of the turbulent skin friction on a flat
plate with concentrated additive solution ejected into a pure-water
boundary layer —— e.g., Love (Ref. 2). Very few measurements of
drag reduction on a flat plate due to homogeneous additive solutions have been reported. This measurement becomes important in
view of the suggestion that drag reduction due to polymer solution is less effective for flow along a plate (external flow)
than inside a pipe (internal flow), Elata (Ref. 3), and in view of
the uncertainty about techniques for the most efficient ejection
into external flows. Therefore, a set of direct measurements of
turbulent drag on a flat plate using homogeneous solutions of
various additive concentrations has been conducted. The results
reveal the difference in drag reduction between internal and external flows. These results, together with visual studies of turbulent mixing between additive solutions and pure water, also
reported herein, are helpful in finding the most efficient ejection
for external flows.

     It has been commonly taken for granted that for effective
drag reduction in external flow cases, the entire boundary layer
should be filled with polymer solution, not recognizing or be-
lieving that major effects due to the presence of an elastic
fluid occur very close to the wall and certainly within the
inner boundary layer (wall turbulence region), Tulin (Ref. 4).
For very dilute solutions this is specially true, as shear-stiffening
occurs in the turbulent region closest to the wall and, it is believed, accounts for the reduction of turbulent skin friction due
to its action there. It has been commonly believed that a concentrated additive solution should be ejected at the wall and that
turbulent mixing inside the boundary layer will satisfactorily
dilute the ejected solution; this does not contend with the fact
that turbulent mixing between the ejected solution and the pure
water surrounding may be highly suppressed and that the ejected
solution may remain rather concentrated and therefore lose its
effectiveness. The present study confirms these possibilities
through an analysis of drag reduction data from experimental
studies with both homogeneous solutions and with boundary layer
ejections.

<h2 style="text-align:center">EXPERIMENTAL TECHNIQUES</h2>

     The experiments have been performed in a circulating water
channel with a closed test section 44 inches long, 15 inches wide,
and 7.5 inches deep. The test fluid consists of homogeneous solutions of variously concentrated polyethylene oxide (Polyox WSR-301)

additive in water. Shear degradation of the testing fluid is inevitable and will be discussed in a later section.

   A part of the cover plate at the test section, 1 foot wide
and 2 feet long, is cut from the rest with a clearance of 1/64
inch along four sides. This part of the cover plate is held by a
strain gage support whose output is indicated on a digital readout
device (Figs. 1a, b). Two rows of pins, 1/8 inch in diameter and
1/10 inch in height, are installed in a staggered fashion ahead of
the drag-measuring plate, with a 1/2-inch spacing between rows and
1 inch between pins along each row. The last row is 1 inch upstream
from the leading edge of the drag-measuring plate. Therefore, the
pins serve as turbulence stimulators, but exclude themselves from
the drag measurements. This setup has been checked by taking
measurements in pure water and comparing the results with the
conventional turbulent frictional coefficient formula for a plane
boundary (Fig. 1c).

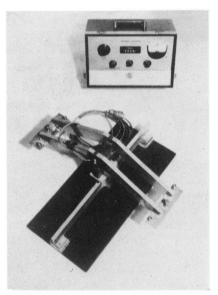

(a) Drag-Measuring Plate, Strain-Gage   (b) Calibration Curve of
    Support and Read-Out Device   Strain Gage

Figure 1 - Calibration of Equipment and Instrument (Continued)

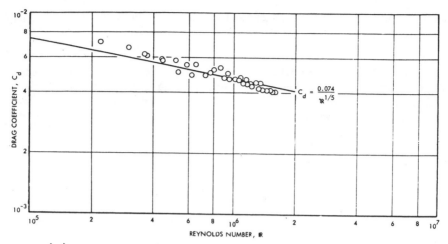

(c) Mean Surface Resistance of Drag-Measuring Plate

Figure 1 - Calibration of Equipment and Instrument (Concl.)

The velocity in the channel is determined by photographing a 1/10-inch diameter plastic particle, with near unit specific gravity, released at the upstream end of the test section. The time exposure picture of the path of the particle, illuminated by a strobe light, is shown as a series of bright dots on film. By comparing the distance between dots and the time interval between flashes, counted by an electronic counter, the channel speed is accurately determined.

A separate experiment was conducted to study problems involved in the use of polymer additives for ejection into external flows. In this case, the mixing characteristics of the ejected fluid with pure water dictate the ejection technique for the most efficient drag reduction. The mixing problem was studied by observing the spreading of a submerged jet, 3/16-inch initial diameter, of additive solutions into a pure water stream which has passed through a turbulence grid. The latter was installed at the upstream end of the test section and is made of 1/32-inch diameter wires with 1/4-inch spacing (Fig. 2).

Nozzle and Grid

Additive Concentration 200 ppmw

Additive Concentration 0 ppmw

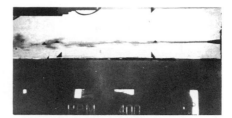

Additive Concentration 400 ppmw

Additive Concentration 50 ppmw

Additive Concentration 700 ppmw

Additive Concentration 100 ppmw

Additive Concentration 1000 ppmw

Figure 2 - Submerged Jets with Additive Solutions Flowing into
a Turbulent Stream of Pure Water

RESULTS AND DISCUSSIONS

Drag Reduction and Shear Degradation

The drag coefficients of the cover plate (a plane boundary), C_d, obtained with various additive concentrations are separately plotted in Figure 3 versus the Reynolds number, $R = U\ell/\nu$ (U is the

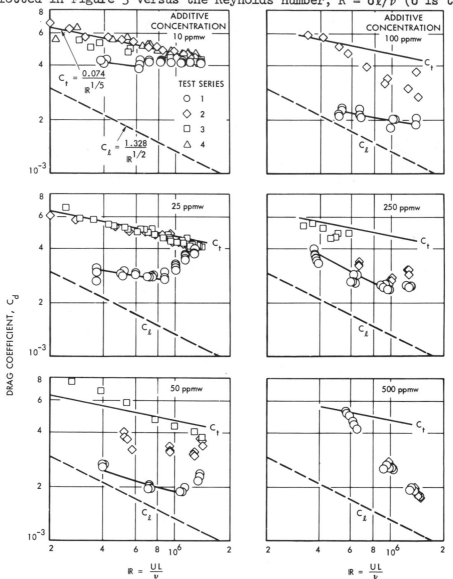

Figure 3 - Mean Drag Coefficient of a Plane Boundary Using Variously Concentrated Polyox-Additive Solutions

channel velocity, ℓ is the plate length and ν is the kinematic viscosity of water). In the same figure, the turbulent drag coefficient, C_t, for pure water

$$C_t = \frac{0.074}{R^{1/5}} \tag{1}$$

is drawn as a continuous curve, and the laminar drag coefficient, C_ℓ,

$$C_\ell = \frac{1.328}{R^{1/2}} \tag{2}$$

is drawn as a dashed curve. Several series of tests have been conducted for each concentration. During each series, the channel speed was varied monotonically with an alternate increase and decrease of speed from series to series. It can be seen from Figure 3 that the data, especially those of the initial series, deviate from the turbulent drag coefficients and become more laminar-like.

Shear degradation (the fluid loses its effectiveness as a drag reducing agent) suffered by the testing fluid is shown in Figure 3; this phenomenon prevents us from studying the Reynolds number influence on drag reduction without ambiguity. Quantitative values of the drag reduction, ΔC_d,

$$\Delta C_d = \frac{C_t - C_d}{C_t} \tag{3}$$

can be obtained from Figure 3 for cases where the shear degradation is not in evidence. These typical values of drag reduction, plotted in Figure 4, show that the polyox additive changes its drag-reducing capability with concentration rather rapidly and that the additive has its optimum efficiency at 50-100 ppmw. In general, the drag reduction obtained in the present experiment over a flat plate (external flow) is less than that determined from pipe flow (internal flow), without taking into account the difference in experimental Reynolds numbers. For internal flow the solution of high concentrations (greater than 100 ppmw) loses its efficiency rather slowly as the concentration increases.

Drag measurements on a thin plate in dilute polyox additive solutions were reported by Levy and Davis (Ref. 5). Comparing ing with their data, the present results show less drag reduction at low additive concentrations (less than 50 ppmw). Both results peak at nearly the same concentration. However, their measurements

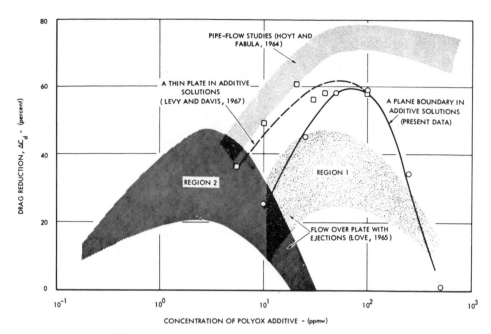

Figure 4 - Drag Reduction with Additive Solutions for
Various Experimental Set-Ups

did not extend to such high concentrations (greater than 100 ppmw)
as in the present experiments. The tests with high additive concentrations are important for external flows in order to make
comparisons with experimental results where a relatively concentrated
additive solution has been ejected into a pure water boundary layer.

    The present data also show that the effect of shear-degrada-
tion of the additive solution is closely related to the effect of
dilution. This relationship is demonstrated by comparing the results presented in Figures 3 and 4. For lower concentration at
the left (rising) side of the drag-reduction curve (Fig. 4), the
shear degradation dilutes the testing fluid and causes a decrease
in its efficiency (Fig. 3). On the other hand, for fluid with
higher additive concentrations at the right (declining) side of
the drag-reduction curve, the degradation at first improves the
additive efficiency and then causes it to deteriorate. In other

words, the change of additive capability as a drag reducing agent
due to shear degradation follows the trend of the drag reduction
curve, starting at the original additive concentration and moving
along the drag reduction curve to lower concentrations.

Suppresion of Turbulent Mixing with Additive Solutions

The suppression of turbulent diffusion in additive solutions
was studied by Wu (Ref. 6), who measured the diffusion and decay of
free turbulence by observing the spreading of a cylindrical cloud
into a nonturbulent media. Pure water and aqueous solutions of
variously concentrated polyox (WSR-301) additive were adopted as
the test media. Significantly reduced spreading of turbulent
clouds in the additive solutions was found.

In order to illustrate more carefully the suppressed turbulent mixing accompanying ejection into a boundary layer, a simula-
tion of boundary ejection is made. The turbulence is generated by
a grid, downstream of which a jet of "additive solutions" (red-
colored) is ejected into this turbulent pure water stream. A
series of photographs of these submerged jets, each of which is
typical of its own concentration, is presented in Figure 2.

For jets with pure water or with very diluted additive solutions, the flow is distinctly turbulent within the region of large
regular eddies at the boundary of the jet. The turbulent region
is marked by a cone of well mixed, red colored fluid. As the concentration increases, the large eddies extend toward the center of
the jet, and the flow pattern becomes fairly regular. The cone of
fluid is seen to be disintegrated by large eddies. This shows the
suppression of conventional turbulent diffusion by the additive
solution. Large eddies do occur at the jet boundary and are presumably generated by an instability there. However, such large
eddies can hardly be generated near a solid surface; very poor
dispersion of fluid ejected at a wall into the turbulent boundary
layer is suggested by these jet experiments.

Drag Reduction with Boundary-Layer Ejection

An experimental investigation was conducted earlier by Love
(Ref. 2), who determined the effect of ejecting (polyox WSR-301)
additive solutions into the turbulent pure water boundary layer
on a plate. The plate, having its leading and trailing edges
streamlined, is 18 inches long and 1/2 inch thick. The ejection
was made from slots at both the upper and lower faces of the plate,
1/2 inch from the leading edge. The drag was determined by the

wake survey method. Results of this ejection study are presented
into two different ways in Figure 4. Region 1 represents drag-
reduction results plotted versus the concentration of ejected
solution. Region 2 represents the same results plotted versus
the diluted concentration, obtained by diluting homogeneously
the ejected solution within the entire turbulent boundary layer,
utilizing the 1/7-power velocity distribution. The scattering
of Love's data for both regions, obtained with various rates of
ejection, suggests the importance of controlling the ejection
technique, which in turn controls the additive concentration near
the wall.

It is seen in Figure 4 that Love's data based on the undi-
luted concentration of the ejected solution (region 1) are peaked
near the same concentration as both the present data, those of
Levy and Davis, as well as those for pipe flow, and that Love's
data based on diluted concentrations (region 2) deviate far to
the left of all data shown. These facts tend to indicate that in
the case of Love's ejection system very poor mixing between the
ejected fluid and its pure water surroundings has taken place inside the boundary layer.

In order to investigate further the technique of ejection
and to optimize the rate of ejection as well as the concentration
of the ejected fluid, Love's data are regrouped and presented in
Figure 5. In the same figure, the present results are shown as a
continuous curve. The regrouping of Love's data involves averaging
the data compiled under identical ejection conditions. Data obtained from ejecting additive solutions of a concentration greater
than 500 ppmw are omitted here, because the viscoelastic effect on
pitot-tube reading might have introduced some error in Love's measurements. Below this concentration, the turbulent mixing in the
thick wake of the plate dilutes the ejected fluid to low concentration, for which no appreciable effect on the 1/16-inch outer
diameter tube, used by Love, is expected (Ref. 7).

Many other interesting trends are shown by the regrouped data
of Love. Interpretations, based on the present drag-reduction results as well as on studies of turbulent diffusion and entrainment
with additive solutions, reveal the presence of certain flow conditions near the wall following ejection. These trends and their
interpretations are summarized below:

(a) The peak of a drag reduction curve for a smaller rate
of ejection shifts toward a higher additive concentration. That
is, greater effective dilution of the ejected solution with

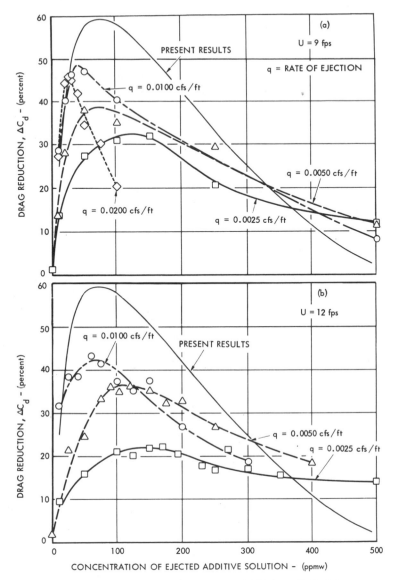

Figure 5 - Effect of Ejecting Additive Solutions on
Resistance of a Flat Plate (Love's Results
with Two Channel Velocities)

surrounding pure water occurs at lower rates of ejection in comparison to higher rates. This shift indicates that the degree of mixing, i.e., the dilution ratio (a ratio between the effective additive concentration which produces the drag reduction and the concentration of the ejected solution) should be comparable to the ratio between the concentration where the drag-reduction

curve with homogeneous additive solutions is peaked and the
concentration where the drag-reduction curve with ejection is
peaked.

(b)   For lower channel velocity (U = 9 fps) the curve corresponding to the ejection rate q = 0.005 cfs/ft and for higher velocity (U = 12 fps) the curve corresponding to the rate q = 0.01
cfs/ft are peaked at about the same concentration as the present
results obtained with homogeneous additive solutions. That is,
for these two cases, very little dilution of ejected fluid has
taken place.

(c)   For a given rate of ejection, the results obtained at
U = 9 fps are peaked at a lower concentration than those obtained
at U = 12 fps. That is, a greater rate of ejection is required
for a higher channel velocity; or for a given rate of ejection, a
higher additive concentration is demanded.

(d)   At the lower velocity, U = 9 fps, the drag reduction
curves for rates of ejection 0.02 cfs/ft are peaked at lower concentrations than the present results. It is therefore speculated
that the increasingly suppressed mixing between pure water and
ejected additive solutions of high concentrations (greater than
50-100 ppmw) causes the ejected jet effectively to conserve its
integrity and therefore to penetrate further into the stream.
Consequently, the ejected fluid is lost to the free stream or to
the outer boundary layer, causing an earlier (at lower concentrations) drop in the drag-reduction curve.

(e)   On the low concentration sides of drag reduction curves,
less drag reduction is obtained with smaller rates of ejection;
while on the high concentration sides, more drag reduction is obtained with smaller rates of ejection. This is in accordance with
the peaked drag reduction curve for homogeneous solutions, since
the dilution on the low concentration side causes the efficiency
of drag reduction to descend along the reduction curve while dilution on the high concentration side results in an increased efficiency.

In summary, much insight about the additive ejection into
external flows can be deduced from the foregoing. Considering
the extreme difficulty involved in observing the flow conditions
near the wall, especially the additive concentration profile,
the present deduction should be quite helpful in determining the
technique for most efficient ejection. (The ideal experimental
tactic would be to determine the drag reduction in cases with
various additive concentration profiles.)

Optimum Rate of Boundary Layer Injection

Based on the dynamics of molecular response to motion of the solvent, Tulin (Ref. 4) pointed out that the ability of the dis-perse phase of a solution to store energy in strain increases as the time scale of the impressed motion decreases. He further intro-duced the idea of critical strain rates and treated the problem associated with large strains from the relaxed condition. For the supercritical state (the ratio between the molecular relax-ation time and the rate of strain greater than unity), the stiffness associated with the strain and, therefore, strain energy can be several orders of magnitude greater than if molecules are relaxed. Therefore, Tulin suggested that a shear stiffening effect should occur in a turbulent flow (a motion with small time scale) when the local shear associated with the dissipation scale is high (supercritical) and when at the same time the local turbulence Reynolds number for the energy containing scale is small. The fluid stiffness then provides an enhanced mode for the extraction of turbulent energy through the generation of elastic shear waves. Finally, Tulin showed that, because of this radiation damping, thickening of the laminar sublayer occurs and drag on a solid sur-face is reduced.

Based on experimental evidence, Townsend (Ref. 8) suggested that a boundary layer along a smooth surface can be represented by a two-layer model, an inner layer and an outer layer. The former includes the laminar sublayer and the logarithmic law region; this is the "wall turbulence" region wherein most of the turbulent energy production takes place. On the other hand, the flow in the outer layer resembles a free turbulent shear flow. The principal source of turbulent energy within this layer is diffusion from the inner layer.

It appears that, according to Tulin's mechanism of radiation of shear wave energy, drag reduction in dilute additive solutions depends very much on the shear stiffening effect of the high-molecular-weight additive in a turbulent flow. This effect will effectively take place in a region very close to the wall, where the shear rate is high and the eddy scale is small. It is thus instructive to compare various rates of ejection adopted by Love (Ref. 2) with discharges within the boundary layer, the inner layer and the viscous sublayer, respectively. These discharges can be obtained by integrating the following velocity distributions (u vs y) for a smooth plate reported by Landweber and Siao (Ref. 9).

$$\frac{u}{u*} = y_* + 0.000962 \; y_*^{3} - 0.00862 \; y_*^{2.5}; \; y* = \frac{yu_*}{\nu} \tag{4}$$

for the viscous sublayer ($y_* < 30$), and

$$\frac{u}{u_*} = 5.70 + 2.36 \ln y_*$$ (5)

for the logarithmic law region extending to the outer edge of the inner layer or $0.004\ e^{U/u_*/2.36}$ where U is the free stream velocity.

As shown in Figure 6, the average discharge within the inner-layer region is seen to be little less than 0.01 cfs/ft for the lower channel velocity (U = 9 fps) and to be about 0.01 cfs/ft for the higher channel velocity (U = 12 fps).   The drag reduction curves corresponding to these discharges are shown in Figure 5 to bear a close resemblance to the drag reduction curve obtained in

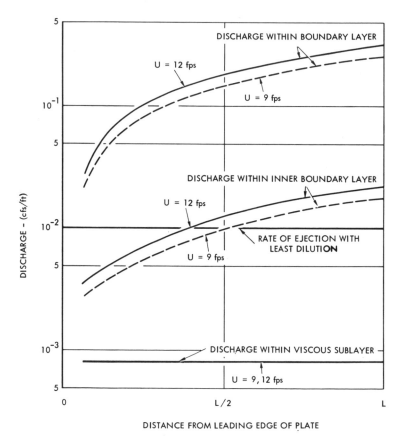

Figure 6 - Comparison Between Rate of Ejection with Least Dilution and Discharges within Viscous Sublayer, Inner Boundary Layer and Boundary Layer

the present experiment. These discharges are the rates of ejection with the least dilution. These discharges are also the
lowest rates of ejection with drag reduction peaked at the same
additive concentration as the present results obtained with homogeneous additive solutions. These facts seem to indicate that the
philosophy of ejection is to fill the inner boundary layer.

To demonstrate this point even further, calculations of drag
reduction for Love's experimental conditions can be made by
dividing the plate longitudinally into ten stations. For each
station, the ejected solution is assumed to be diluted within the
boundary layer according to a normal concentration curve (with the
maximum concentration at the wall and the boundary layer thickness
spanning some arbitrarily chosen standard deviation). Based on
the average concentration within the inner layer obtained from the
concentration curve at the middle length of the station, the drag
for that station can be determined from the present drag measurements. Summing up the drag determined at all stations, the total
drag reduction of the plate can be found. The results for the
case with the boundary layer thickness spanning five standard
deviations are plotted versus the initial concentration of the
ejected solution in Figure 7, and are in difference with Love's
results as follows:

(a) The calculated values are generally higher than the
measured values. This would be expected, since the sheet of
the ejected fluid must be reattached at some distance downstream from the slot which has not been considered in the calculation and which should result in less drag reduction for the
actual measurement.

(b) At higher concentrations, the calculation shows greater
drag reduction than Love's measurement. This fact indicates that
the mixing of the ejected fluid with surrounding pure water is
less than assumed. A better comparison between calculations and
measurements can be obtained by giving some consideration to suppression of turbulent mixing between the ejected additive solution
and surrounding pure water.

To consider the suppression of mixing, we suggest that the
adopted normal concentration curve reduces its span as the additive concentration of ejected solution increases. We assume that
the reduction ratio (the distance from the wall spanning five
standard deviations /the boundary-layer thickness) follows another
arbitrarily chosen normal distribution curve; for example, the
curve having a value of unity for ejecting in pure water, of
0.605 for ejecting 250 ppmw solution (for a span of one standard
deviation) and of 0.135 for ejecting 500 ppmw solution (for a span
of two standard deviations). We now repeat the previous calculation

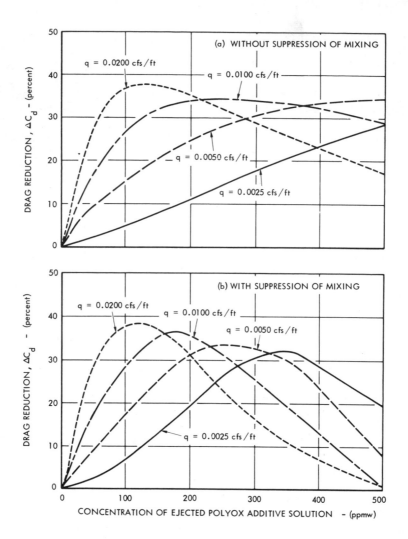

Figure 7 - Calculations of Drag Reduction for Love's Experimental
Conditions without and with Considering Suppression
of Mixing between Ejected Solution and Pure Water

and plot the new results in Figure 7, in which a closer resemblance
between this result and Love's data is demonstrated. An even
better comparison between calculation and measurement can be obtained by considering different concentration-distribution curves.

Optimum Additive Concentration for Boundary Layer Ejection

For external flow cases, it is commonly accepted to eject highly concentrated additive solution into the turbulent boundary layer and to let the turbulent mixing within the boundary layer dilute the ejected solution to an optimum concentration. As a result of this thinking, the required amount of additives for a desired drag reduction have been overestimated. The infeasibility of applying polymer additive to external flow cases due to this overestimate has discouraged serious ejection studies. Very few data have thus been published.

As discussed previously, the additive concentration of ejected solution should be dilute, because the drag reduction curves are peaked around these concentrations. For a longer plate (longer than Love's plate), the dilution is obviously greater toward the trailing end. However, we have not only verified the suppression of turbulent mixing with additive solutions, we can further argue that the flow at the upstream portion of the plate should dictate the choice of additive concentration, because the viscous drag of a smooth plate drops down rather sharply with the distance from the leading edge. In addition, for practical applications, although the plate is longer than Love's plate, the free stream velocity is much higher than in Love's experiments. With faster flow, less time is thus provided for turbulent mixing. Collectively, valuable information can be obtained from Love's experiment, as we base our discussion on the comparison between the ejection rate and the local inner-layer discharge.

The proposition of using dilute additive solution can be further substantiated by studies of Doherty (Ref. 10) and of Dove (Ref. 11), the only other ejection studies available. Relatively concentrated solutions have been ejected in these two experiments. Their experimental conditions as well as drag-reduction results are tabulated as follows:

Experiment	Model Length ft	Model Speed fps	Concentration of Ejected Solution ppmw	Drag Reduction %
Doherty (Ref. 10)	4	6.1	1000	15
		7.2	1000	20
Dove (Ref. 11)	16	5.4	387	8
		10.8	528	21
		5.4	407	16
		10.8	388	26

It is clear from these two studies conducted with a setup longer than Love's plate that less drag reduction results by ejecting relatively concentrated solutions.

Techniques of Applying Additive Solution to External Flow Cases

The addition of viscoelastic additive to water to reduce resistance has been utilized in practical problems for a number of years by chemical engineers. Their application, limited to internal pipe flow, include pumping of all sorts of mixtures and slurries. Based on the previous discussions, the following principles of ejecting the additive solution into the turbulent boundary layer for external flows are suggested:

(a) Fill up the inner boundary layer with additive solutions and minimize the velocity of ejection, especially the component normal to the wall, so that the additive solution will remain within the inner boundary layer. Within this layer, the shear stiffening effect of the additive halting the turbulence production occurs; the additive thus functions as a drag reducing agent. Beyond this region, not only the flow condition does not favor the shear-stiffening effect, but also very little turbulence is produced, and the additive is thus wasted.

(b) Eject dilute additive solution with its concentration being slightly more concentrated than the optimum concentration (the concentration producing the maximum drag reduction determined from studies with homogeneous additive solutions). The highly concentrated additive solution tends to remain concentrated; consequently, one not only wastes too much valuable additive, but more importantly, less drag reduction is obtained. Some dilution of the ejected fluid is inevitable, but the viscous drag along a plate is always greater near the leading edge, and, therefore, this is the exact place where the drag reduction is most needed and is precisely where the additive solution should have its most effective concentration.

For practical applications, these results thus modify the present philosophy of boundary-layer ejection of additive solutions, which was accepted without any analytical or experimental verification. Instead of ejecting a large rate (boundary-layer discharge) of concentrated additive solution (about 1000 ppmw), it is proposed to eject a small rate (inner-boundary-layer discharge which is less than 1/10 of the boundary-layer discharge) of diluted solution (about 100 ppmw). The amount of additive required is therefore about two orders of magnitude less than the common estimate.

CONCLUSIONS

A series of measurements of the drag on a flat plate in homogeneous solutions of high-molecular-weight additives, and a series of turbulent diffusion studies with submerged jets have been conducted. The drag reduction obtained in this experiment is generally lower than that for pipe flows, but the maximum reduction occurs at about the same concentrations in both cases. A comparison between the data compiled from ejection studies and the present results reveals that for a most efficient drag reduction, the ejected solution should be dilute and the rate of ejection should be comparable with the discharge within the inner boundary layer. These findings suggest that smaller amounts of additives are needed for ejection than are usually estimated for drag reduction in external flow cases.

ACKNOWLEDGMENTS

I am indebted to Mr. M. P. Tulin for his supervision of the work and review of this paper. The work was supported by the Office of Naval Research, under Contract Number 4181(00), NR 062-325.

REFERENCES

1. Hoyt, J. W. and Fabula, A. G., "The Effects of Additives on Fluid Friction," Proc. of 5th ONR Symposium on Naval Hydrodynamics, 1964

2. Love, R. H., "The Effect of Ejected Polymer Solutions on the Resistance and Wake of Flat Plate in a Water Flow," Hydronautics, Inc., Tech. Rep. 353-2, June 1965

3. Elata, C., "Reduction of Friction on Submerged Bodies by Polymer Additives," Proc. of 11th Intern. Towing Tank Conf. Japan, 1966

4. Tulin, M. P., "Hydrodynamic Aspects of Macromolecular Solutions," Proc. of 6th ONR Symposium on Naval Hydrodynamics, 1966

5. Levy, J. and Davis, S., "Drag Measurements on a Thin Plate in Dilute Polymer Solutions," J. of Intern. Shipbuilding Progress, Vol. 14, No. 152, April 1967

6. Wu, Jin, "Experiments on Free Turbulence in Viscoelastic Fluids," Hydronautics, Inc., Tech. Rep. 353-1, March 1965

7. Wu, Jin, "Viscoelastic Effect on Impact and Static Tube Readings," Hydronautics, Inc., Tech. Rep. 353-7 (in preparation)

8. Townsend, A. A., <u>The Structure of Turbulent Shear Flow</u>, Cambridge
    University Press, 1956

9. Landweber, L. and Siao, T. T., "Comparison of Two Analyses of
    Boundary-Layer Data on a Flat Plate," J. of Ship Research,
    Vol. 1, No. 4, March 1958

10. Doherty, B. J., "Investigation of Drag Reduction Obtained through
    Boundary Layer Injection of Dilute Solutions of Polyox," Report,
    U. S. Naval Academy, 1965

11. Dove, H. L., "The Effect on Resistance of Polymer Additives
    Injected into the Boundary Layer of a Frigate Model," Proc. of
    11th Intern. Towing Tank Conf. Japan, 1966

THE FLOW OF A DILUTE POLYMER SOLUTION IN A TURBULENT BOUNDARY
LAYER ON A FLAT PLATE

D. A. White

University College, London.

ABSTRACT

This paper outlines a method of interpreting boundary layer
behavior from data obtained from experiments in pipes, under conditions where turbulence is suppressed. The results show that,
for all except very slow flows, the whole of the turbulent boundary
layer will be suppressed, and that, for a particular case, very
significant drops in skin friction of the order of 30 percent may
be expected.

INTRODUCTION

Much work has been published in the past few years on the
turbulent flow of dilute polymer solutions; this work, mainly for
pipes, is reviewed in two recent papers (Refs. 1 and 2). Work on
the heat transfer aspect has been published (Refs. 3, 4, 5, 6).
One of the problems in understanding the flow of these solutions
through pipes has been the difficulty of correlating data under
conditions of suppressed turbulence. However an intuitive
suggestion by Gadd (Ref. 7), whose fundamental relevance has
been further explained by the present author, has provided a
basis for correlation of data that is of practical use due to
its simplicity, in contrast with the complex arguments advanced
in many previous papers.

Once the fundamental point of Gadd's correlation has been
grasped, the way is open for considering boundary layer flows.
This problem is of considerable potential importance in reducing
skin friction in ships and submarines, and a start will be made
by discussing flow in a turbulent boundary layer on a flat plate.

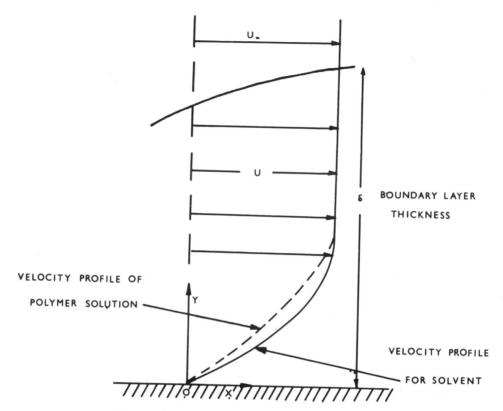

Figure 1   Structure of Boundary Layer

Consider the situation in Figure 7, in which we compare the velocity profiles at a point in the flat plate where the boundary layer thickness (δ) is the same and fluid is flowing past the plate at the same velocity (U_∞). In this case, there are several points of similarity between this flow situation and that in the pipe.

1.   In the turbulent layer the velocity profiles are unaltered.

2.   In the constant shear stress laminar sublayer, the velocity profile for polymer solution deviates from that for the solvent, and at the wall the shear stress for the polymer (T_p) is less than that for the solvent (T_s).

3.   It is also assumed, as in the case of pipe flow, that T_p is uniquely related to T_s, and drag reduction will occur only if T_s is greater than the critical shear stress (T_c).

The data for T_s and T_p can be obtained by simple experiment in a pipe. Results obtained for guar gum (Ref. 7) show that T_c is independent of concentration of polymer and that the results give a straight line on doubly logarithmic coordinates, as shown in Figure 2. This yields a simple relationship between T_P and T_S, namely

$$\frac{T_P}{T_C} = \left(\frac{T_S}{T_C}\right)^N \tag{1}$$

when the value of N depends on the concentration of the polymer in the solution. Of course, there are many other expressions that could be used to relate T_P and T_S, and another way of expressing Gadd's correlation is to say that the friction drag reduction T_P/T_S is uniquely defined by T_P or $\sqrt{\dfrac{T_P}{\rho}}$ the friction velocity (Ref. 8).

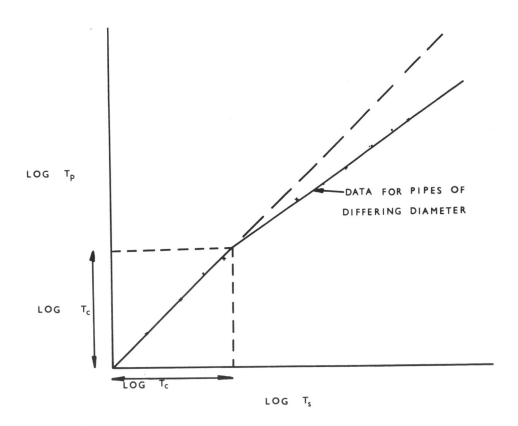

Figure 2   Drag Reduction Results From Pipe Flow Data

The flow of a Newtonian fluid past a flat plate has received quite a good deal of attention. One investigation of turbulent boundary layers is that of Falkner (Ref. 9), who proposes using the 1/5 power law for flow in the turbulent part of the boundary layer, i.e.,

$$\frac{U}{U_\infty} = (\frac{y}{\delta})^{1/5} .$$ (2)

Other formulas have been proposed, and it is easy to repeat the following calculations using a formula different from References 2 and 3. The boundary layer thickness and local wall shear stress T_S are given by the following formulas

$$\frac{\delta}{x} = 0.1285(Re_x)^{-1/7}$$ (3)

$$T_S = 0.0131\rho U_\infty^2 \ (Re_x)^{-1/7} ,$$ (4)

For a polymer solution, the form of the boundary layer complex on the flat plate will be given by Figure 3. The portion AB is the laminar boundary layer; transition is assumed to occur at B when $Re_x = 3 \times 10^5$ followed by a turbulent boundary layer until point C, where T_S exceeds T_C, and turbulence is suppressed. The positions of B and C depend on the free stream velocity U_∞.

One interesting case is the point where B and C coincide and all the turbulent boundary layer is suppressed. Substituting $Re_x = 3 \times 10^5$ in Equation (4) we obtain

$$T_C = 0.00211 \ U_C^2$$ (5)

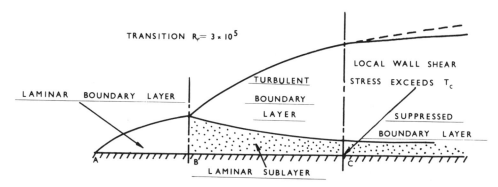

Figure 3   Structure of a Dilute Polymer Solution
Boundary Layer on a Flat Plate

Typical values of T_C are 0.4 N/m^2 for polyox WSR 301 and 2.4 N/m^2 for guar gum. For the guar gum U_C is just over one meter/second, which is of course an extremely low velocity and explains why the use of polymers is so beneficial in small craft and rowing boats. In the cases likely to be found in practice, therefore, the whole of the turbulent boundary layer is suppressed since $U_\infty > U_C$.

CALCULATIONS OF SHEAR STRESS AND THICKNESS IN A SUPPRESSED BOUNDARY LAYER

The calculation of boundary layer thickness and friction factor for a suppressed turbulent boundary layer of dilute polymer solution can readily be accomplished for the case where the whole boundary layer is suppressed, if it is assumed that the laminar boundary layer is small in comparison with the turbulent boundary layer that follows. For given δ and U_∞, T_S can be worked out and T_P, the actual shear stress, is calculated from Equation (1).

By rearranging Equations (3) and (4), we can obtain an expression for T_S in terms of $Re_\delta = \left(\dfrac{U_\infty \delta}{\nu}\right)$. From Equation (3)

$$x = 11.1 \, \delta^{7/6} U_\infty^{1/6} \nu^{-1/6}$$

substituting for x in Equation (4)

$$T_S = 0.0093 \, \rho \, U^2 \, (Re_\delta)^{-1/6}$$

Under conditions of suppressed turbulence T_P, the actual shear stress on the surface of the flat plate, is given by Equation (1). Hence

$$T_P = \left\{\frac{T_C}{\rho \, U_\infty^2}\right\}^{1-N} \rho \, U_\infty^2 (0.0093)^N (Re_\delta)^{-N/6} \tag{6}$$

If the von Karman integral momentum equation is now applied to the whole boundary layer

$$T_P = \frac{d}{dx} \rho \int_0^\delta U(U_\infty - U)\,dy \tag{7}$$

and substituting for U the 1/5 power law profile Equation (2), the integral on the right hand side of Equation (7) gives

$$T_P = \frac{5 \rho U_\alpha^2}{42} \cdot \frac{d\delta}{dx} \quad , \tag{8}$$

Combining Equations (6) and (8)

$$\frac{5}{42} \delta^{N/6} \cdot d\delta = \left\{ \frac{T_C}{\rho U_\infty^2} \right\}^{1-N} (0.0093)^N U_\infty^{-N/6} \nu^{N/6} dx \quad . \tag{9}$$

Integrating this equation with the boundary condition $\delta = 0$ when $x = 0$, we obtain the thickness of the boundary layer as

$$\frac{\delta}{x} = \left\{ \frac{T_C}{\rho U_\infty^2} \right\}^{\frac{6-6N}{6+N}} (0.0093)^{\frac{6N}{6+N}} \left[\frac{7}{5}(6+N) \right]^{\frac{6}{6+N}} Re_X^{\frac{-N}{6+N}} \quad . \tag{10}$$

With $N = 1$ Equation (10) becomes identical with Equation (3).

Consider a flat plate length L and breadth B. The total force on one side due to skin friction is given from Equation (8) by

$$B \int_0^L T_P \cdot dx = \frac{5}{42} \rho U_\infty^2 \int_0^{\delta_P} d\delta \tag{11}$$

where δ_P is the thickness of the boundary layer at the trailing edge of the plate. Integrating the right-hand side of Equation (11), the total force is given by

$$\frac{5}{42} \rho U_\infty^2 B . \delta_P \tag{12}$$

Considering the flow of solvent past the plate if δ_S is the boundary layer thickness at the trailing edge, from Equation (12) the total force will be given by

$$\frac{5}{42}\rho U_\infty^2 \ B.\ \delta_S \tag{13}$$

Hence the ratio of the drag forces is simply given by (δ_P/δ_S) and δ_P and δ_S are calculated by substituting $x = L$ in equations (10) and (3).   Hence

$$\delta_P / \delta_S = \left\{\frac{T_C}{\rho U_\infty^2}\right\}^{\frac{6-6N}{6+N}} \frac{(0.0093)^{\frac{6N}{6+N}}}{0.1285}$$

$$\left[\frac{7}{5}(6+N)\right]^{\frac{6}{6+N}} Re_L^{\frac{6-6N}{7(6+N)}} \ . \tag{14}$$

For a typical 120 ppm solution of guar gum in water pipe flow tests give $N = 0.92$, $T_C = 2.4 \ N/m^2$.   In this case Equation (14) becomes

$$\frac{\delta_P}{\delta_S} = 1.33\left\{\frac{T_C}{\rho U_\infty^2}\right\}^{0.069} Re_L^{0.010} \tag{15}$$

This shows the essential features of Equation (14); that the drag reduction increases with U_∞, decreases with increasing T_C, and, surprisingly, increases with length.   The following table gives more details of the ratio of skin drag with or without polymer.

TABLE 1 - VALUES OF δ_P/δ_S FROM EQUATION (15)

U, meters/sec	Length -10 meters	100 meters
2.5	0.93	0.95
5	0.85	0.87
10	0.77	0.79
20	0.70	0.72

(ρ taken as $10^3 k/m^3$ and $\nu = 10^{-6} m^2/sec$)

The table shows that skin friction drag reduction in excess of 30 percent may be expected in this particular solution.   Guar gum is one of many polymers in this class which will give drag reduction.

Guar gum is not believed to be the most efficient, but it is one of
the only polymer solutions that have been well characterized, so that
greater reductions in skin friction may be expected with polymers of
longer chain lengths than guar gum.

CONCLUSIONS

If it is assumed that a flat plate will show analogous behavior
to the boundary layer on the sides of a ship, then it is seen that
for all but the slowest vessels the whole of the turbulent portion
of the boundary layer is likely to be suppressed by injection of
polymer into the bows of a vessel providing, of course, that enough
is injected through the whole of the laminar sublayer. The resulting boundary layer is thinner everywhere than the analogous boundary
layer for the pure solvent, and the skin friction is reduced everywhere. The likely applications of this work would be for low speed
vessels where the Froude number is small and the effects of wave
drag are not predominant. It is not surprising to learn of its
application in sailing boats or rowing eights. It is clear that
more complex boundary layer flows can be dealt with in a similar
manner.

One practical problem in applying this to vessels is the existence
of surface roughness on the hulls of most vehicles. At the present
time the effect of a roughened surface can only be discussed
qualitatively. Recent results for pipes (Ref. 10) have shown that
roughness cuts down the effectiveness of a polymeric additive, and
this reduction of effectiveness is worse at higher wall shear
stresses until a point is reached where the polymer has no effect in
reducing drag. Since wall shear stresses on the hulls of most ships
are very large, it may be expected that the addition of polymer will
have little or no effect on the reduction of drag on a heavily
barnacle-encrusted hull.

NOMENCLATURE

B	Plate breadth
L	Plate length
N	Exponent defined by Equation (1)
T_C	Critical shear stress
T_P	Wall shear for polymer solution
T_S	Wall shear for solvent solution
U	Velocity

U_C	**Critical velocity (Equation 5)**
U	**Free stream velocity**
x, y	**Cartesian coordinates**
δ	**Boundary layer thickness**
δ_P	**Boundary layer thickness at trailing edge for polymer solution**
δ_S	**Boundary layer thickness at trailing edge for solvent**
ν	**Kinematic viscosity**
ρ	**Density**

REFERENCES

1. Virk, P. S., et al, "The Toms Phenomenon: Turbulent Pipe Flow of Dilute Polymer Solutions," Journ. Fluid Mech. 30, 305, 1967.

2. Patterson, G. K. and Z. L. Zakin, "Prediction of Drag Reduction with a Viscoelastic Model," A.I. Ch. E.J. 14, 435, 1968.

3. Poreh, M. and U. Paz, "Turbulent Heat Transfer to Dilute Polymer Solutions," Int. Journ. Heat & Mass Transf. 11, 805, 1968.

4. Wells, C. S., "Turbulent Heat Transfer in Drag Reducing Fluids," A.I. Ch. E. J. 14, 406, 1968.

5. Pruitt, G. T., N. R. Whitsitt, and H. R. Crawford, "Turbulent Heat Transfer to Viscoelastic Fluids," Western Co. Research Div., 1966.

6. Gupta, M. K., J. P. Hartnett, and A. B. Metzner, "Turbulent Heat Transfer Characteristics of Viscoelastic Fluids," Int. Journ. Heat & Mass Transf., 10, 1211, 1967.

7. White, A., "Turbulent Drag Reduction by Using Dilute Polymer Solution Instead of Water," Hendon Coll. Res. Bull., 3, 58, 1966.

8. Whitsitt, N. F., L. J. Harrington, and H. R. Crawford, "Effect of Wall Shear Stress on the Drag Reduction of Viscoelastic Fluids," Paper presented to Symposium on Viscous Drag Reduction, Dallas, 1968.

9. Falkner, V. M., "The Resistance of a Smooth Flat Plate with
    Turbulent Boundary Layer," <u>Aircraft Engng.</u>, <u>15</u>, 65, 1943.

10. Spangler, J. G., "Studies of Viscous Drag Reduction with Polymers
    Including Turbulence Measurements and Roughness Effects,"
    Paper presented at Symposium on Viscous Drag Reduction, Dallas,
    1968.

AN ANALYSIS OF UNIFORM INJECTION OF A DRAG-REDUCING FLUID

INTO A TURBULENT BOUNDARY LAYER

C. Sinclair Wells

LTV Research Center

ABSTRACT

The purpose of this analysis is to evaluate the mass flux requirements for drag reduction by uniform injection of a high molecular weight polymer solution into a turbulent boundary layer on a flat plate or slender body of revolution. This evaluation is necessary in order to determine the feasibility of using polymer solutions to reduce skin friction drag on marine vehicles. Uniform injection is chosen for analysis since it raises the additive concentration to the drag reducing level in the wall region only, where recent experiments have shown that it is needed. Calculations of skin friction reduction and mass flux required are plotted for conditions of interest for marine vehicles. Distributed injection is compared with slot injection and is found to require between 40 and 140 times less additive solution than does slot injection to maintain equivalent drag reduction. A "specific additive consumption" is defined and compared with specific fuel consumption of several underwater propulsion units. The comparison shows slot injection of a 1000 ppm solution to be of marginal value, while porous wall injection would give more performance increase than adding an equal amount of fuel. The point is made that there is considerably more performance advantage to be gained from a continuous ablating additive coating than from additional fuel, if it could be made to ablate at the optimum rate.

INTRODUCTION

The purpose of this paper is to analyze the effectiveness of distributed injection of a drag-reducing fluid into a turbulent hydrodynamic boundary layer flow. It has been well established that reduction of the drag of a body with an external turbulent boundary layer can be accomplished with additives (Ref. 1).   The question remains, however, as to the feasibility of getting the necessary additive into the boundary layer of the vehicle.

Efficiency of the additive is important since, obviously, a large volume of pre-mixed additive solution cannot be carried on board vehicles for which volume is limited, and equipment for mixing injected water with the additive to prepare a solution to be injected also may not be desirable because of volume limitations and mechanical complexity.   Therefore, the efficiency with which the additive is put into the boundary layer may determine the feasibility of its use.

Recent tests in this laboratory have shown that an additive is effective in reducing drag only when it is present in the region near the wall, either in the viscous sublayer or in the buffer region (Ref. 2).   A recent study by Webster and Keydel (Ref. 3) has indicated that raising the concentration of the additive to the drag-reducing level throughout the boundary layer by injection of a concentrated solution is of marginal value to torpedo performance. Therefore, a basic consideration in this analysis will be that of putting the additive into the wall region only.   Since the mass flow in this region is, in general, small compared to the mass flow in the total shear layer, a considerable saving of additive (or additive solution) can be made by putting it into the wall region only, as opposed to raising the concentration to the desired level throughout the shear layer.   An additional saving will be shown in the analysis, since one of the effects of the additive is to reduce the mass transport away from the wall.   This follows from the reduction of momentum and heat transport near the wall which has already been shown analytically (Refs. 4,5).

Practically speaking, this means addition of the material either by injection of a liquid solution through a porous wall (or closely spaced openings) or by ablation of a solid coating.   (Note: this is physically the case of continuously <u>putting</u> in the additive at the wall rather than depending on streamwise convection to carry it along).   The analysis is equally applicable to either technique.   The only difference is operational, since the porous-wall injection of a liquid solution permits easy control of injection rate while the solubility of a solid coating controls the ablation rate.   Therefore, this analysis should be useful for determining the feasibility of both types of systems.

The analysis by Meyer (Ref. 4) correlated the observed thickening of the viscous sublayer with the shear stress at the wall. This permitted the derivation of an analytical expression for the friction factor as a function of Reynolds number and two fluid parameters.   Data taken by Wells (Ref. 6), Ernst (Refs. 7,8) and

Elata and Tirosh (Ref. 9) confirmed this correlation. Recent discussions have brought the generality of the correlation into question for very effective additives; however, the pipe flow experiments which form the basis for the question are subject to question
because of other possible effects. In particular, the minimum
diameter effect shown by Granville (Ref. 10) and degradation of
certain additives such as poly(ethylene oxide) due to high shear
are limits on the correlation. Granville used this correlation to
develop a technique for predicting turbulent boundary layer flow
of a uniform solution of drag-reducing fluids.

A slightly different approach to the derivation for boundary
layer flow will be presented here, although the results are substantially the same. The diffusion of a drag-reducing fluid into
a Newtonian fluid is predicted by means of the Reynolds-Prandtl
analogy applied to fluids which have a thickened viscous sublayer.
The result is a means of predicting the skin friction on a flat
plate with zero pressure gradient, knowing only the mass flux of
a given additive at the surface of the flat plate. In addition,
some calculations are made for a specific additive which has been
used extensively in pipe flow drag reduction experiments.

BOUNDARY LAYER SKIN FRICTION

The assumptions which are made at the outset of the boundary
layer analysis are as follows:

1. Two-dimensional, zero-pressure gradient, turbulent
    boundary layer flow (this assumption is also a good
    approximation for a body of revolution if $R>>\delta$)

2. The similarity hypothesis of von Karman holds (this
    hypothesis deals with large-scale mixing, which has
    been shown to be unchanged for dilute solutions of
    drag-reducing fluids (Refs. 6,8)).

3. The mixing length constant, likewise, is the same
    as for Newtonian fluids.

4. The shift of the law-of-the-wall velocity profile
    is as predicted by the analysis of Meyer (Ref. 4)
    for pipe flow.

The case to be considered here is that of integrating the law
of the wall velocity profile for drag reducing fluids over the
surface of a flat plate, where the wall shear stress changes with
distance from the leading edge. The correlation of Meyer (Ref. 4)
for pipe flow of drag reducing fluids is consistent with a shift

in the Newtonian law of the wall profile which is a function of the wall shear stress. This case is analogous to the analysis of Fenter (Ref. 11) in which the law of the wall for rough surfaces was integrated for flat plate flow. The correlation for flow in rough pipes is also consistent with a shift in the law of the wall profile which is a function of wall shear stress. The reader can refer to Reference 11 for a complete bibliography on development and use of the law of the wall velocity profile.

The law of the wall profile for drag reducing fluids was given in Reference 4 as

$$\phi = \frac{2.303}{k} \log_{10} \eta + B + \alpha \log_{10} \frac{u_*}{u_{*_{cr}}} \qquad (u_* \geq u_{*_{cr}}) \qquad (1)$$

where ϕ and η are dimensionless velocity and length variables, respectively; α and $u_{*_{cr}}$ are properties of the drag reducing fluid; and u_* is the shear velocity.

Equation (1) is not valid within the viscous sublayer; however, the errors of applying it all the way to the wall can be shown to be negligible, even for drag reducing fluids. The momentum thickness for incompressible flow is defined by

$$\frac{\theta u_*}{\nu_w} = \int_0^{\eta_{max}} \frac{\phi}{\phi_1} \left[1 - \frac{\phi}{\phi_1} \right] d\eta \qquad (2)$$

which can be rewritten as

$$\frac{\theta u_*}{\nu_w} = \phi_1 \int_0^1 \frac{\phi}{\phi_1} \left[1 - \frac{\phi}{\phi_1} \right] \frac{d\eta}{d\phi} d\left(\frac{\phi}{\phi_1} \right) \qquad (3)$$

The derivative in Equation (3) can be evaluated from Equation (1) and Equation (3) can be integrated to give

$$\frac{\theta u_*}{\nu_w} = \frac{1}{k\phi_1} e^{k\phi_1 - kB} \left(\frac{u_*}{u_{*_{cr}}} \right)^{\frac{-\alpha k}{2.303}} \qquad (4)$$

The balance of momentum for a turbulent boundary layer with zero pressure gradient is given by

$$\tau_w = \rho u_1{}^2 \frac{d\theta}{dx} \qquad (5)$$

which can be written in terms of dimensionless variables as

$$\frac{dRe_\theta}{dRe_x} = \frac{1}{\phi_1{}^2} \qquad (6)$$

Equation (4) can be substituted into Equation (6) and the result integrated by parts to give

$$Re_x = \frac{1}{k} e^{-kB - k\alpha \log_{10} \frac{u_1}{u_{*cr}}} e^{k\phi_1} \left[\frac{\frac{\alpha k}{2.303} + 2}{\phi_1} \right.$$

$$- \text{ terms of order } \phi_1{}^{\frac{\alpha k}{2.303} + 1} \text{ or less}$$

$$\left. + \text{ constant} \right] \qquad (7)$$

The constant can be taken to be zero, since $\phi_1 = 0$ at $Re_x = 0$, in accordance with the discussion in Reference 11.

Since by definition,

$$\phi_1 = \sqrt{2/C_f} \qquad (8)$$

and since C_f is of the order 10^{-3} or less for Reynolds numbers above transition, all of the terms in Equation (7) other than the first can be neglected. Again, this is consistent with the procedure used in Reference 11 and others. The terms are not entirely negligible and will require a slight adjustment of the constants for experimental data. Thus Equation (7) can be rewritten,

$$Re_x = \frac{1}{k} e^{- kB - k\alpha \log_{10} \frac{u}{u_{*cr}}} \frac{e^{k\sqrt{2/C_f}}}{\left(C_f/2\right)^{-\left(1 + \frac{\alpha k}{4.606}\right)}} \qquad (9)$$

which can be written in the usual logarithmic form

$$\frac{1}{\sqrt{C_f}} = \frac{1}{\sqrt{2}} \left[\frac{2.303}{k} \log_{10} Re_x \, C_f + \alpha \log_{10} \frac{u_*}{u_{*_{cr}}} \right.$$

$$\left. + B - \frac{2.303}{k} \log_{10} \frac{2}{k} \right] \tag{10}$$

The constants are taken to be the same as for Newtonian fluids, which is also consistent with previous work,

$$k = 0.4 \tag{11}$$

$$B = 5.5 \tag{12}$$

which gives

$$\frac{1}{\sqrt{C_f}} = 4.08 \log_{10} Re_x \, C_f + \frac{\alpha}{\sqrt{2}} \log_{10} \frac{u_*}{u_{*_{cr}}} + 1.05 \tag{13}$$

Adjusting the constants to agree with ordinary incompressible boundary layer flow gives (Ref. 12)

$$\frac{1}{\sqrt{C_f}} = 4.15 \log_{10} Re_x \, C_f + 1.7 + \frac{\alpha}{\sqrt{2}} \log_{10} \frac{u_*}{u_{*_{cr}}} \tag{14}$$

This adjustment of constants will change the value of the dimensionless viscous sublayer thickness for Newtonian fluids ($\alpha = 0$) from 11.5 to 12.9, but this is not a significant difference in view of the relatively large changes in the dimensionless viscous sublayer thickness due to the drag-reducing fluid.

For cases where the additive solution viscosity is different from that of the solvent, Equation (14) can be written as

$$\frac{1}{\sqrt{C_f}} = 4.15 \log_{10} Re_{x_o} \, C_f + 4.15 \log_{10} \frac{\nu_o}{\nu_w} + 1.7$$

$$+ \frac{\alpha}{\sqrt{2}} \log_{10} \frac{u_*}{u_{*_{cr}}} \tag{15}$$

Equation (15) can also be written in a more convenient form for calculations

$$\log_{10} \text{Re}_{x_o} = \frac{1}{1 + 0.17\,\alpha} \left[\frac{1}{4.15\sqrt{C_f}} - (1 + 0.085\,\alpha)\,\log_{10}C_f \right.$$

$$\left. + 0.17\,\alpha\,\log_{10}\frac{\sqrt{2}\;x\;u_{*_{cr}}}{\nu_o} - 0.41 + \log_{10}\frac{\nu_w}{\nu_o} \right] \quad (16)$$

Equation (16) is a convenient form for calculating C_f for a given concentration of an additive (α and $u_{*_{cr}}$) and for a given freestream velocity, u_1, as a function of distance along the plate. Such a calculation has been made for the additive, POLYOX WSR-301, poly(ethylene oxide), a product of the Union Carbide Company. The calculations of C_f for a 30 ppm solution of POLYOX WSR-301, where $\alpha = 23.0$ and $u_{*_{cr}} = 0.068$ ft/sec, were used to graphically determine the total skin friction,

$$C_F = \frac{1}{L}\int_{x_o}^{L} C_f dx \quad (17)$$

where x_o is a very small distance from the leading edge compared to the length of the plate (Boundary layer transition was assumed to occur very near the leading edge due to the high Reynolds numbers of interest here). Values of α and $u_{*_{cr}}$ were determined from an analysis of Virk's data (Ref. 13). The results are shown in Figure 1, where C_F for various velocities are plotted versus Reynolds number based on the plate length, Re_L. C_F for the polymer solution is compared with the laminar and turbulent curves for Newtonian fluids. Also shown are the ranges of plate length for which the calculations are made. The plot shows that significant drag reduction should be attained by this concentration of the additive for this wide range of velocities and lengths.

In Figure 2, the percent total skin friction reduction, as compared with a standard skin friction correlation for water (Ref. 14), is shown versus distance from the leading edge, with freestream velocity as the parameter. It should be noted that the amount of drag reduction decreases somewhat as distance from the leading edge increases, although this is not a significant effect compared with the substantial drag reductions shown. This is certainly not an important effect at high velocities, e.g., above 50 feet per second.

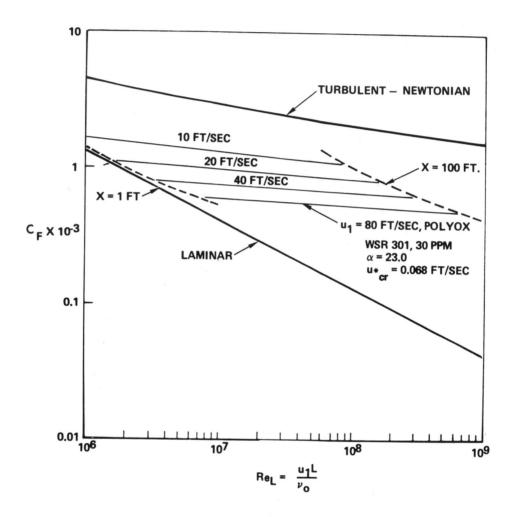

Figure 1   Total skin friction coefficient predicted by
Equation (16) for 30 ppm POLYOX WSR-301

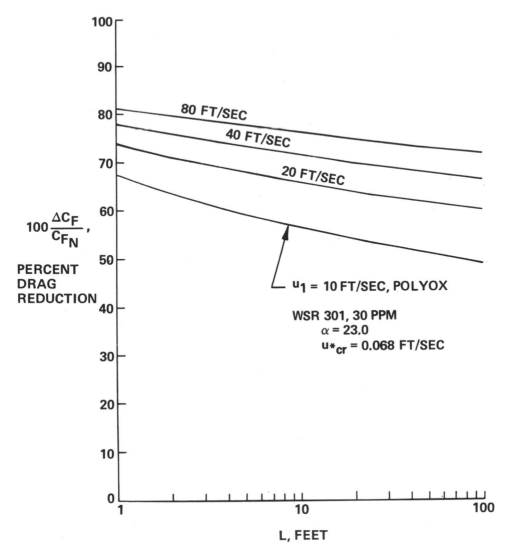

Figure 2   Percentage total skin friction reduction predicted
by Equation (16) for 30 ppm POLYOX WSR-301

DIFFUSION

The method of analysis of diffusion of an additive solution
from the wall into the boundary layer is to employ the analogy between momentum, heat and mass transfer. In particular, the
Reynolds-Prandtl analogy (Ref. 15) between the three types of
transfer is used, since it accounts for differences in the

dimensionless viscous sublayer thickness. The appropriateness of
the analogy between heat and mass transfer for high Prandtl and
Schmidt number fluids is discussed in Reference 16 . The analogy
was applied to drag-reducing fluids with a changing sublayer thickness in Reference 5 and was found to be very satisfactory in
predicting the results of several heat transfer experiments. The
analogy holds because of the identical forms of the three types of
turbulent transport equations, as will be shown below. The assumptions made in Reference 5 regarding the negligible effects of
dilute additive solutions on the shear flow away from the wall
region will also be employed here. That is, the usual assumptions
of Prandtl concerning turbulent mixing will be used.

The assumptions are as follows:

1. Two-dimensional, parallel flow

2. Small mass flux at the wall (See Reference 17 for
a discussion of this assumption which involves the
form of the mass flux term and neglecting the
velocity normal to the wall), uniform in the streamwise direction

3. Turbulent Schmidt number is unity

4. Uniform mass flux, constant in the turbulent core,
equal to the value at the wall

5. Dilute solution: $\nu_w = \nu_o$, $D_{AB} = D_{AB_o}$, $\dot{\omega}_{A_1} \doteq 0$

The expressions for mass and momentum flux are respectively:

$$j_{A_y}^{(t)} = j_{A_w}^{(t)} = -\rho k^2 y^2 \left| \frac{du}{dy} \right| \frac{d\omega_A}{dy} \tag{18}$$

$$\tau_y^{(t)} = \tau_w^{(t)} = -\rho k^2 y^2 \left| \frac{du}{dy} \right| \frac{du}{dy} \tag{19}$$

where: $j_{A_y}^{(t)}$ is the mass flux (mass per unit area per unit time)
of constituent A in the y - direction due to turbulent mass transport, j_{A_w} is the mass flux of A at the wall, k is the Prandtl mixing length coefficient, ω_A is the mass fraction of A, and τ is shear
stress. Equations (18) and (19) can be combined to give (where the
superscripts, t, have been dropped since only turbulent diffusion

is considered):

$$\frac{j_{A_w}}{\tau_w} = \frac{d\omega_A/dy}{du/dy} \tag{20}$$

On integrating from the edge of the viscous sublayer to the edge of the shear layer (given by subscripts L and m, respectively) the expression is found for the turbulent core,

$$\frac{j_{A_w}}{\tau_w} = - \frac{\omega_{A_m} - \omega_{A_L}}{u_m - u_L} \tag{21}$$

In the viscous sublayer, where transport of mass and momentum are on a molecular scale, expressions for mass and momentum transport are

$$\tau_w = \rho \nu_o \left(\frac{du}{dy}\right)_w \tag{22}$$

$$j_{A_w} = \rho D_{AB} \left(\frac{d\omega_A}{dy}\right)_w \tag{23}$$

where D_{AB} is the molecular diffusion coefficient of A into B. Integrating Equations (22) and (23) from the wall to the edge of the viscous sublayer and combining gives

$$\frac{j_{A_w}}{\omega_{A_w} - \omega_{A_L}} = \frac{D_{AB}}{\nu_o} \frac{\tau_w}{u_L} \tag{24}$$

Combining Equations (21) and (24) and eliminating ω_{A_L}

$$\frac{j_{A_w}}{\rho u_1 (\omega_{A_w} - \omega_{A_1})} = \frac{(u_*/u_1)^2}{1 + \dfrac{u_L}{u_*} \dfrac{u_*}{u_1} (Sc - 1)} \tag{25}$$

where $Sc = \nu_o/D_{AB}$. Metzner and Friend (Ref. 16) have found empirically that for large Schmidt numbers there is an additional term in the denominator of Equation (25) which correlates data for Newtonian and purely viscous non-Newtonian fluids. The additional Schmidt number effect arises because of the difference in momentum and mass flux sublayer thicknesses. Since it was assumed that the only effect of the polymer additive is to thicken the sublayer it should be appropriate to take the additional term directly into Equation (25), which becomes

$$
\frac{j_{A_w}}{\rho u_1 \left(\omega_{A_w} - \omega_{A_1} \right)} = \frac{(u_*/u_1)^2}{1 + \dfrac{u_L}{u_*} \dfrac{u_*}{u_1} (Sc - 1)(Sc)^{-1/3}}
\tag{26}
$$

Equation (26) describes diffusion in the boundary layer when conditions at the edge of the shear layer are taken to be freestream conditions. When the usual definition of skin friction coefficient is used; it can be written

$$
\frac{j_{A_w}}{\rho u_1 \left(\omega_{A_w} - \omega_{A_1} \right)} = \frac{C_f/2}{1 + \dfrac{u_L}{u_*} \sqrt{C_f/2} \, (Sc - 1) \, Sc^{-1/3}}
\tag{27}
$$

u_L/u_* can be determined as a function of flow conditions and the parameters of Meyer's correlation, α and $u_{*_{cr}}$; i.e.,

$$
\frac{u_L}{u_*} - 5.75 \log_{10} \frac{u_L}{u_*} = 5.5 + \alpha \log_{10} \frac{u_1}{u_{*_{cr}}}
$$

$$
+ \alpha \log_{10} \sqrt{C_f/2}
\tag{28}
$$

For the case of interest here, the constituent, B, is water and the concentration of the additive, A, is zero in the freestream, $\omega_{A_1} = 0$. If, in addition, the solution of additive is very dilute (<100 parts per million by weight) as is the case for drag reduction with very effective additives, the molecular transport coefficients are the same as for water. This has been shown for kinematic viscosity and recently for thermal conductivity Ref. 5, and will be assumed to be valid for diffusion. D_{AB} for water (or self-diffusion of most liquid solvents) is the order of 10^3. Therefore Equation (27) can be approximated by

$$\frac{j_{A_w}}{\rho u_1 \omega_{A_w}} \doteq \frac{\sqrt{C_f/2}}{\frac{u_L}{u_*}(Sc)^{2/3}} \tag{29}$$

MASS TRANSFER REQUIRED TO REDUCE SKIN FRICTION

Now, C_f for given flow conditions on a flat plate and a given uniform concentration throughout the boundary layer, i.e., a given α and u_{*cr}, can be calculated from Equations (15) or (16). However, recent experiments have shown that the additive need only be present in the region very near the wall in order for the drag to be reduced. Therefore, it is assumed that the effective concentration of additive for purposes of making the skin friction calculation is the average between the concentration at the wall and the concentration at the edge of the viscous sublayer. Now for dilute concentrations in the sublayer, the concentration in the turbulent core will be essentially zero. (This assumes essentially instantaneous mixing as the additive leaves the wall region, and no accumulation of concentration in the turbulent core). Therefore, the proper concentration for making the skin friction calculation is $\omega_{A_w}/2$, since a linear concentration profile in the sublayer is assumed. Once this calculation is done for a given flow condition, the mass flux of the additive required to achieve that concentration, j_{A_w}, can be calculated from Equation (29). This is the calculation procedure which would be used to determine the proper injection rate for an additive solution injected through a porous wall.

The same calculation could be made to determine the proper mass flux for a solid coating of an additive which ablates into the flow. However, it is not likely that a coating can be tailored to give exactly the optimum mass flux and the values of C_f and j_{A_w} must be evaluated by iterating between Equations (16) and (29), after measuring the ablation rate of the coating. Or, if a saturation concentration of the additive at the wall could be determined experimentally j_{A_w} could be calculated directly.

COMPARISON OF DISTRIBUTED INJECTION WITH SLOT INJECTION

It is of interest to calculate the relative mass flux requirements for distributed injection and slot injection. A slender body of revolution will be used for the calculation.

Equation (29) can be written, in terms of weight flux per unit time

$$\dot{w}_A \equiv j_A Ag$$

$$(\dot{w}_A)_{w\ dist} = \frac{2A\sigma\ u_\delta\ \omega_{A_{avg}}\ \sqrt{C_f/2}}{Sc^{2/3}\ (11.5 + \alpha\ \log_{10}\ \sqrt{C_f/2}\ \dfrac{u_1}{u_*})_{cr}} \tag{30}$$

where σ is the weight density of the fluid. An approximate form of Equation (28) has been used in the denominator of Equation (30).

For injection through a slot or for the total mass flow through a series of slots placed far enough apart so that transverse turbulent diffusion produces uniform concentrations in the boundary layer between slots, for a body of diameter, d,

$$(\dot{w}_A)_{slot} = \omega_{A_{avg}}\ \sigma u_1\ \delta_* \P d \tag{31}$$

Combining Equations (30) and (31) and using the total skin friction coefficient in Equation (30) because an integrated mass flux effect is desired

$$\frac{(\dot{w}_A)_{slot}}{(\dot{w}_A)_{dist}} = \frac{\delta_*}{L}\cdot\frac{Sc^{2/3}}{2}\ \frac{(11.5 + \alpha\ \log_{10}\ \sqrt{C_F/2}\ \dfrac{u_1}{u_*})_{cr}}{\sqrt{\dfrac{C_F}{2}}} \tag{32}$$

Figure 3 shows this comparison for the average concentration picked for δ_* at L/2 and for the 1/7-power velocity profile relation,

$$\frac{\delta_*}{L} = 0.046 \left(\frac{u_1 L}{\nu_w}\right)^{-1/5} \tag{33}$$

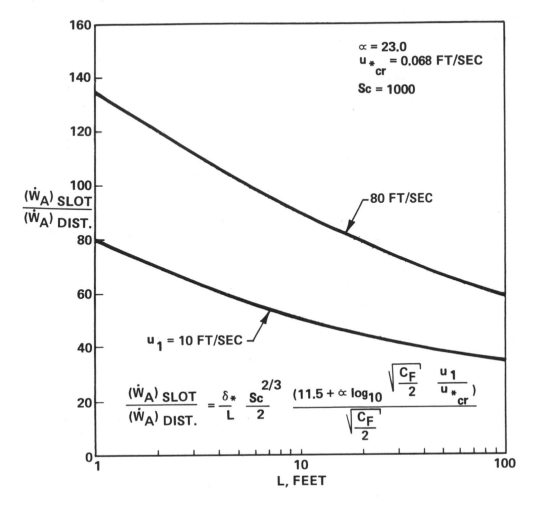

Figure 3. Comparison between mass flux requirements for slot
          and distributed injection; drag-reducing concentration
          is 30 ppm POLYOX WSR-301.

The figure indicates that distributed injection is between 40 and
140 times more effective in terms of additive mass flux than slot
injection. This is explained, physically, by the fact that the
distributed mass flux is required only to replenish the additive
diffused through the viscous sublayer into the turbulent core at a
rate sufficient to keep the sublayer concentration high, while the
slot injection must raise the concentration through the complete
boundary layer to a drag-reducing level.

Equation (32) assumes a comparison between two methods of

injecting a solution having a particular concentration. The ratio
becomes greater if an ablating coating (where the toal mass flux
away from the body is pure additive) is compared with a solution
injected through a slot. The ratio is increased by the inverse of
the solution concentration assumed; i.e., the ratio is between
40×10^3 and 140×10^3 for the case chosen for Figure 3 if an ablating coating is compared with slot injection of a 1000 ppm solution.

USE OF ADDITIVE FOR DRAG REDUCTION COMPARED WITH ADDITIONAL FUEL FOR THRUST INCREASE

One measure of feasibility of using additives for drag reduction is the amount of additive or additive solution required per
pound of drag reduced relative to the amount of power plant fuel
per pound of thrust produced. This is particularly true if vehicle
volume or range is to be traded off for drag. It may also be a
significant measure of feasibility for a trade-off of speed for
drag if specific fuel consumption of the power plant and propeller
effeciency do not change with speed.

The change in drag for the body of revolution considered earlier is

$$\Delta D = (\Delta C_F) (1/2 \rho u_1^2 \P dL) \tag{34}$$

The amount of additive solution per unit time required for a
given drag reduction is given by Equation (30) for distributed
injection and by Equations (31) and (33) for slot injection. Table
1 presents calculations for $\bar{w}/\Delta D$, pound of additive solution per
hour, per pound of drag reduced, for slot injection and distributed
injection. Calculations are made for an average concentration of
30 ppm of POLYOX WSR 301, given by an injected solution of 1000 ppm
for a freestream velocity of 80 feet per second and plate lengths
of 10 and 100 feet. The results show that the "specific additive
consumption" is almost two orders of magnitude less than for the
slot injection.

Also shown are calculations for an ablative coating with an
optimum ablation rate which reduces the specific additive concen-
tarion in the case of the porous wall, i.e., it is about five
orders of magnitude less than for slot injection.

Also of interest is the trend of the specific additive consumption to increase with plate length for distributed injection
and decrease with length for slot injection.

A typical specific fuel consumption is not available for
typical operational underwater vehicle propulsion units, but

Reference 18 gives a range of specific fuel consumptions for rocket engines of from 1 to 10 hr^{-1} and theoretical s.f.c. for certain heat engines and fuel cell engines of about 0.1 hr^{-1}. Thus the rocket engine has about the same order of magnitude s.f.c. as the additive consumption for slot injection. However, the porous wall injection case has less additive consumption than the most optimistic predictions of fuel consumption. And the ablative coating additive consumption is between 3 and 4 orders of magnitude less than the best fuel consumption.

Table 1   SPECIFIC ADDITIVE CONSUMPTION

$(\omega_{A_{avg}}$ = 30 ppm Polyox WSR 301

u_1 = 80 ft/sec)

	L, FT	$\dfrac{\dot{w}}{\Delta D}$, $\dfrac{LBS./HR}{LBS.\ DRAG\ REDUCED}$
CASE 1 - SLOT INJECTION OF	10	3.03
1000 PPM SOLUTION	100	2.83
CASE 2 - POROUS WALL INJECTION	10	0.053
OF 1000 PPM SOLUTION	100	0.075
CASE 3 - ABLATIVE COATING,	10	5.3×10^{-5}
WITH OPTIMUM ABLATION RATE	100	7.5×10^{-5}

DISCUSSION AND CONCLUSIONS

Three types of limitations on the application of this analysis should be discussed, two concerning the skin friction reduction and one concerning the mass flux required. The skin friction prediction depends on the appropriateness of the velocity profile assumed. If an appreciable part of the profile is not semi-logarithmic then the derived expression will not correctly describe the skin friction. This is a distinct possibility if the pipe diameter is too small for pipe flow experiments used to determine α, or if the boundary layer thickness is too small for flat plate boundary layer flow. In the former case, an incorrect value of α will result, and in the latter case an incorrect skin friciton prediction will result.

So that experiment and application may be evaluated, it is desirable to estimate the minimum pipe diameter or boundary layer thickness. This may be done with a method suggested by Granville

(Ref. 10), in which the inner limit of the logarthmic portion of
the velocity profile is calculated. This has been done for the
solution used in the example here, and is shown in Figure 4. The
minimum diameter, d_M, is plotted versus mean velocity $\bar{u}$. It is not
possible to say how much d_M must be exceeded for a valid experiment, since to the author's knowledge experiments have not been
done to determine this. Using $d = 2\delta$ and $\bar{u} = .8u_1$, it is possible
to estimate the minimum boundary layer thickness for boundary layer
flow. Using $\delta = 8\delta_*$ with Equation (33) it can be shown that $\delta > \delta_{,M}$
for distances greater than 6 inches from the leading edge for a
freestream velocity of 80 feet per second, for example. For values
of x<6 in. at that velocity, Equation (15) will yield predictions
of skin friction reduction which are too large. This would appear
to be a negligible effect in predicting skin friction for most
vehicles of interest, but the limitations placed on pipe diameter
for pipe flow experiments is significant.

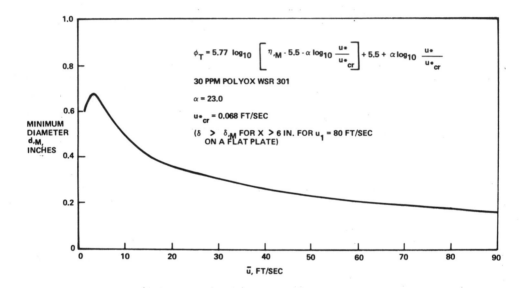

Figure 4   Minimum pipe diameter for valid use of the
            law-of-the-wall correlation. Calculations
            made for 30 ppm POLYOX WSR 301 according to
            the method of Reference 10.

        Another limitation is that of degradation due to shear. This
also may be a problem in either the determination of α and u_*
from pipe flow or the prediction of boundary layer skin friction.
This is a problem which is little understood and for which experimental data are needed.

The third possible limitation concerns the prediction of mass flux for distributed injection. The assumption was made for the calculations that the concentration in the viscous sublayer determines the drag reduction. This is inferred from the earlier experiments of Reference 2. If, instead, it is necessary to provide enough mass flux of additive to raise the concentration through the buffer or transitional layer, the required mass flux would increase by about the ratio of mass flow in the two layers. This would mean an increase of about an order of magnitude, which would still give the advantage to uniform injection over slot injection, although not as great. Further experimentation is needed here as well.

The primary conclusion of this study is that uniform injection of additive solution offers a significant saving in mass flux required for drag reduction over the case of injection through discrete slots. This saving would be even greater if a coating could be made to ablate at the optimum rate.

ACKNOWLEDGEMENT

This work was supported by Ling-Temco-Vought, Inc. as a part of its independent research program. The author would like to express particular appreciation to Dr. John Harkness for his encouragement and helpful suggestions.

NOTATION

A, wetted area

C_f, local skin friction coefficient, $\tau_w / 1/2 \rho u_1^2$

C_F, total skin friction coefficient, $D / 1/2 \rho u_1^2 A$

d, body diameter

D, drag

D_{AB}, molecular diffusion coefficient between species A and B

g, acceleration due to gravity

k, Prandtl's mixing-length constant, Equation (11)

L, plate or body length

Re_x, Reynolds number based on length from the leading edge, xu_1 / ν_w

Re_L, Reynolds number based on plate or body length, Lu_1/ν_w

Re_{x_o}, xu_1/ν_o

$Re_\theta = \theta u_1/\nu_w$

u, local velocity

$\bar{u}$, bulk average velocity

u_1, freestream velocity

u_*, shear velocity, $(\tau_w/\rho)^{1/2}$

$\dot{w}_A$, weight flux per unit time of species A

x, streamwise coordinate

y, coordinate normal to the wall

δ, boundary layer thickness

η, dimensionless coordinate normal to the wall, yu_*/ν_w

ϕ, dimensionless velocity, u/u_*

θ, momentum thickness, Equation (2)

ρ, density

τ, shear stress

ν_w, kinematic viscosity of the solution evaluated at the wall

ν_o, kinematic viscosity of the solvent

ω, mass fraction

σ, specific weight

δ_*, displacement thickness

Subscripts

N, for Newtonian fluids

w, wall conditions

A, species A

y, at a given y coordinate

l, conditions at the edge of the shear layer

L, conditions at the edge of the viscous sublayer

m, minimum

$()_{dist}$, injection distributed over area, A

$()_{slot}$, injection through discrete, separated slots

Superscript

(t), turbulent shear layer conditions

REFERENCES

1. Hoyt, J. W., "A Survey of Hydrodynamic Friction Reduction Tech-
    niques," AIAA Paper No. 67-431, presented at the AIAA 3rd
    Propulsion Joint Specialist Conference (1967).

2. Wells, C. S., and J. G. Spangler, "Injection of a Drag-Reducing
    Fluid into Turbulent Pipe Flow of a Newtonian Fluid," The
    Physics of Fluids, 10, 1890-1894 (1967).

3. Webster, W. C., and K. Keydel, "An Analysis of Some Recent
    Advances in Torpedo Design," AIAA Paper No. 64-464, pre-
    sented at the 1st AIAA Annual Meeting (1964).

4. Meyer, W. A., "A Correlation of the Frictional Characteris-
    tics for Turbulent Flow of Dilute Non-Newtonian Fluids in
    Pipes," AIChE Journal, 12, 522-525 (1966).

5. Wells, C. S., "Turbulent Heat Transfer in Drag Reducing Flu-
    ids," AIChE Journal, 14, 406-410 (1968).

6. Wells, C. S., "Anamalous Turbulent Flow of Non-Newtonian
    Fluids," AIAA Journal, 3, 1800-1805 (1965).

7. Ernst, W. D., "Investigations of the Turbulent Shear Flow of
    Dilute Aqueous CMC Solutions," AIChE Journal, 12, 581-586
    (1966).

8.   Ernst, W. D., "Turbulent Flow of an Elasticoviscous Non-Newtonian Fluid," AIAA Journal, 5, 906-909 (1967).

9.   Elata, C., and J. Tirosh, "Frictional Drag Reduction," Israel Journal of Technology, 3, 1-6 (1965).

10. Granville, P. S., "The Frictional Resistance and Velocity Similarity Laws of Drag-Reducing Dilute Polymer Solutions," Naval Ship Research and Development Center Hydromechanics Laboratory Report (1966).

11. Fenter, F. W., "The Turbulent Boundary Layer on Uniformly Rough Surfaces at Supersonic Speeds," Vought Research Center Report No. RE-E9R-2 (1959).

12. Goldstein, S. (Ed.), Modern Developments in Fluid Dynamics, Vol. 11, (Dover Publications, Inc., New York, 1965), p 364

13. Virk, P. S., "The Toms Phenomenon-Turbulent Pipe Flow of Dilute Polymer Solutions," Sc.D. Thesis, MIT (1966).

14. Schlichting, H., Boundary Layer Theory, (McGraw-Hill Book Company, Inc., New York, 1960) Chap. XXI, p 540.

15. Knudsen, J. G. and D. L. Katz, Fluid Dynamics and Heat Transfer, (McGraw-Hill Book Company, New York, 1958), p 407.

16. Friend, W. L. and A. B. Metzner, "Turbulent Heat Transfer Inside Tubes and the Analogy Among Heat, Mass, and Momentum Transfer," AIChE Journal, 4, 393-402 (1958).

17. Bird, R. B., W. E. Stewart, and E. N. Lightfoot, Transport Phenomena, (John Wiley & Sons, Inc., New York, 1962), Chap. 21, pp 637-646.

18. Greiner, L., "Theoretical Performances with Hydrogen-Oxygen as Propellant of Perfect Rocket, Heat, and Fuel-Cell Engines in Underwater Missiles," in Underwater Missile Propulsion, L. Greiner (Ed.), (Compass Publications, Inc., Arlington, Va.) pp 31-50.

VISCOUS DRAG REDUCTION EXAMINED IN THE LIGHT OF A
NEW MODEL OF WALL TURBULENCE

Thomas J. Black

Mechanical Technology Incorporated

ABSTRACT

The effect of soluble polymer additives on the structure of
wall turbulence is examined in the light of a new theoretical model
of wall turbulence, and explained in terms of the ability of the
polymer macromolecules to substantially increase the hydrodynamic
stability of the viscous sublayer flow. Drag reduction, increase
in sublayer thickness and apparent 'slip' of the velocity profile,
which have been observed experimentally are shown to result directly
from increased sublayer stability. Specific examples are presented
of the predicted effect of polymer additives on the distributions
of mean velocity, turbulent shear stress, turbulence production
and longitudinal velocity fluctuations. In particular, it is shown
that while turbulence intensity may decrease in dilute polymer
solutions, the overall longitudinal velocity fluctuations may be
greatly enhanced by increased (non-turbulent) time-dependent activity in the sublayer. It is consequently suggested that considerable
caution should be exercised in interpreting 'turbulence' measurements
in drag-reducing solutions. The effect of surface roughness on wall
turbulence and in particular on the flow of dilute polymer solutions
is also considered briefly.

INTRODUCTION

The phenomenon of drag reduction in turbulent flows of dilute
polymer solutions invokes two fundamental questions: first, how
does the presence of minute quantities of polymer additive affect
the flow at the macromolecular level; secondly, how do these
macromolecular effects result in substantial modification of the
overall structure of wall turbulence which involves length and time
scales many orders of magnitude larger than those which characterize

the polymer macromolecule and its behavior?

Most of the explanations of the drag-reducing properties of
polymers advanced to date have been concerned essentially with the
first of these problems. Thus, the phenomenon has been explained
either on the grounds of gross rheological changes in the solution
(e.g. viscoelasticity, effective wall slip, and other non-Newtonian
fluid properties) or in terms of discrete dynamical interaction
between the macromolecule and the small-scale turbulence present in
the flow. If, indeed, the effect of minute quantities of polymer
additive was to substantially modify the gross rheology of the
solution, then the observed changes in turbulent structure and skin
friction would not be difficult to explain, at least in principle.
Rheological measurements and experimental studies of laminar shear
flows of dilute polymer solutions, however, show little or no
evidence of such gross effects.

If, then, the essential interaction between the polymer macromolecules and the turbulence structure is of a dynamical rather
than rheological nature, we are forced to consider a problem which
is basic to the study of wall turbulence with or without polymer
additives: namely, the nature of the feed-back mechanism whereby
the large-scale structure of turbulence and such gross properties
as skin friction, rate of growth of the shear layer, etc., are
controlled by the small scale eddies within the structure (as evidenced, for example, by the observed effect of free-stream turbulence level on the development of turbulent boundary layers). We
are thus concerned with the very nature of wall turbulence itself,
and are consequently impeded by the continuing lack of an acceptable
physical model and understanding of turbulent shear flow.

This paper presents a new explanation of the drag-reducing
effects of dilute soluble polymer solutions which is based on a
physical model of wall turbulence developed recently by the author.
It attempts to describe the nature of the changes which occur in
the turbulence structure as a result of the addition of soluble
polymers and, furthermore, suggests a tentative explanation of these
effects in terms of the dynamic interaction between the polymer
macromolecules and characteristic eddies or vortices within the
proposed structure. Although the basic theory itself is controversial and far from general acceptance as yet, it is nevertheless
thought to provide an interesting interpretation of the observed
behavior of the turbulent flow of dilute polymer solutions and
therefore may hopefully contribute in some measure to the search for
a satisfactory solution of the drag-reduction phenomenon.

DISCUSSION

The Basic Theory of Wall Turbulence

The basic theory, which has already been described in some detail elsewhere (Ref. 1) asserts that the turbulent shear stress mechanism is generated and controlled by a powerful, repetitive, non-linear instability of the sublayer flow. The instability is assumed to occur in highly localized regions which are not fixed, but move downstream in a characteristic tempo-spatial array with a velocity, U_i, which approaches the freestream velocity in boundary layer flow, or the maximum (centerline) velocity in pipe flow. The individual instabilities throughout the array have characteristic mean longitudinal and lateral spacings over the wall of approximately 50 and 2 sublayer thicknesses respectively (for reasons which will become apparent, the sublayer thickness is defined herein as $\frac{\delta_s U_\tau}{\nu} = 50$). The instability pattern and motion is illustrated in Fig. 1 for the case of pipe flow (for simplicity pipe flow only will be considered throughout the remainder of the paper, although many of the concepts developed can be directly applied to the case of boundary layer flow).

At each moving point of instability, the sublayer flow breaks down continuously, thereby generating a series of ring vortices at the expense of sublayer flow energy. Each vortex may be considered to comprise outer and inner spanwise elements linked by two 'trailing' vortices. The inner spanwise elements remain close to the wall and are rapidly carried 'upstream'* from their point of origin. Since they play little or no role in the proposed shear stress mechanism, they can essentially be neglected; consequently, the vortices can be regarded as horseshoe vortices comprising a single (outer) spanwise element linked to the wall by two trailing vortex elements.

As the trailing vortices are stretched by the basic shear flow, the plane of the horseshoe vortex rotates so that in the moving axis system $(x-U_i t, y, z)$, the induced velocity field carries the spanwise element outwards from the wall along a characteristic curved path (Fig. 2a). The horseshoe elements thus move through and define a characteristic surface comprising a concave front and two sides, (Fig. 2b). It is important to note that while each vortex shed by the instability moves 'upstream' and outwards from it, the horseshoe-shaped surface thus defined is fixed relative to the instability and moves downstream with it with velocity U_i, thus

---

*Parentheses are used to denote motion relative to the moving array of instabilities i.e. in the axes-system $(x-U_i t, y, z)$.

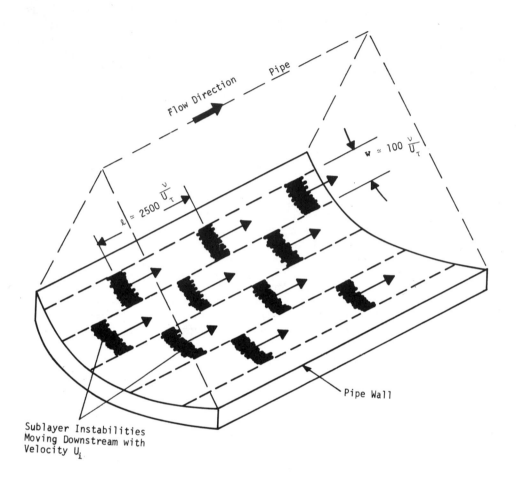

FIG. 1   SCHEMATIC ILLUSTRATION OF SUBLAYER INSTABILITY
            PATTERN

outpacing the basic flow throughout most or all of the shear layer.
Thus, an observer in the moving-axes system $(x-U_i t, y, z)$ would
see the basic flow moving 'upstream' through a stationary array of
vortex instability systems. This 'basic flow' comprises two component motions; namely,

(1)   an organized non-turbulent motion, which we define
      as the <u>primary</u> motion, and

(2)   a random, small-scale turbulent motion, (which we
      shall term the <u>secondary</u> motion) superimposed on
      the primary motion, and corresponding to the
      classically defined turbulent component motion.

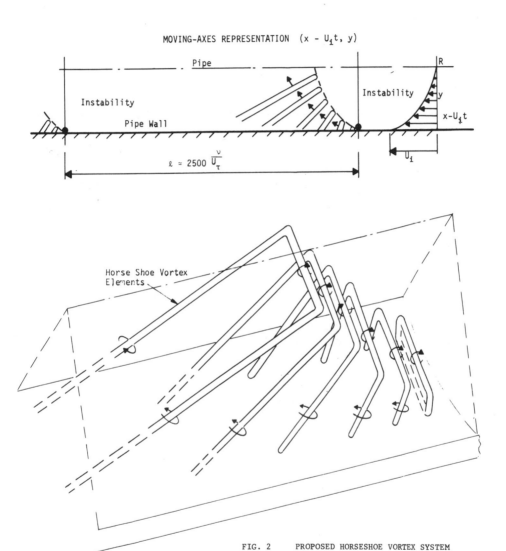

FIG. 2   PROPOSED HORSESHOE VORTEX SYSTEM

If we define the primary and secondary motions respectively in the fixed-axes system (x, y, z) as q^* and q' (where q may be identified with any one of the velocity components or with pressure), then we have that the instantaneous motion is

$$q(x, y, z, t) = q^* (x, y, z, t) + q' (x, y, z, t) \qquad (1)$$

Since, by definition, the mean value of q' is

$$\overline{q'} = 0 \qquad (2)$$

the mean motion $\overline{q}$ is given by

$$\overline{q} = \overline{q^*}. \qquad (3)$$

We shall see that in that <u>moving</u> axes system $(x-U_i t, y, z)$ the primary motion is <u>steady</u> and develops <u>spatially</u> between each successive pair of vortex systems, while in the <u>fixed</u>-axes system, it is <u>time-dependent</u> and undergoes a repetitive process of slow viscous development terminated by rapid breakdown, initiated by the passage of each instability/vortex system.

The Turbulent Shear Stress Mechanism

As illustrated in Fig. 3, the spanwise elements in the vortex front move outwards with induced velocity v_y, and 'upstream' relative to the instability with velocity u_y. Since the trailing vortex elements are rapidly rotated by the basic shear flow and quickly assume a near-horizontal attitude, they contribute little to the horizontal induced velocity u_y which is thus determined mainly by the spanwise elements themselves. It can be simply shown that the combined effect of these elements and their image system reflected in the wall is to induce a logarithmic or nearly-logarithmic velocity distribution, $u_y(y)$. The proposed turbulent shear stress hypothesis suggests that the primary flow passing 'upstream' through the vortex system is forced locally to 'adopt' this essentially logarithmic profile, irrespective of the nature of its velocity distribution immediately prior to entering the system.

This local and rapid 'remolding' of the primary velocity profile is achieved by the action of the trailing vortices which extract energy from, or feed energy into the primary motion, depending on the extent and sense of the local velocity mismatch between this motion and the induced motion of the spanwise vortex elements. If, for example, the primary motion enters the vortex system with

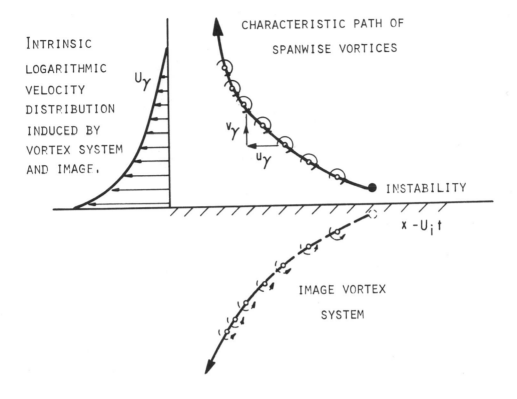

FIG. 3   CHARACTERISTIC LOGARITHMIC VELOCITY DISTRIBUTION
           INDUCED BY SPANWISE VORTEX ELEMENTS

'upstream' streamwise velocity $U_i - u*$ in excess of the induced velocity u_γ $(U_i - u*>u_\gamma)$, the trailing vortices are locally extended
('stretched') so that they gain energy at the expense of the primary motion. The effect is to create a local momentum 'sink',
(see Fig. 4a) so that the primary motion is decelerated and its
velocity reduced to the local induced value, u_γ. The effective
'drag' thus, imposed on the primary flow is equivalent to, and is
'seen' by the mean motion as the effect of a positive turbulent
shear stress gradient, though the 'stresses' involved are neither
turbulent, nor shearing in nature.

     Physically, the mechanism is closely akin to that responsible
for induced drag on airfoils of finite span.* In this case, how-

_____

The proposed shear stress mechanism was originally explained in
Reference 1 by analogy with the induced drag mechanism.

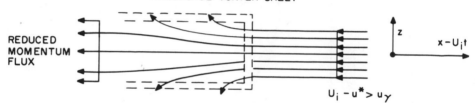

HORIZONTAL SECTION OF
HORSESHOE VORTEX 'SHEET'

REDUCED
MOMENTUM
FLUX

z

$x - U_i t$

$U_i - u^* > u_\gamma$

VORTEX STRUCTURE PROVIDES FLOW (MOMENTUM) 'SINK' AND
IMPOSES MOMENTUM DRAG ON PRIMARY MOTION, $U_i - u^*$

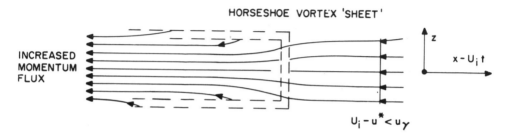

HORSESHOE VORTEX 'SHEET'

INCREASED
MOMENTUM
FLUX

z

$x - U_i t$

$U_i - u^* < u_\gamma$

VORTEX STRUCTURE PROVIDE FLOW (MOMENTUM) SOURCE AND
IMPOSES MOMENTUM <u>THRUST</u> ON PRIMARY MOTION, $U_i - u^*$

FIG. 4   'TURBULENT SHEAR STRESS' MECHANISM

ever, the energy absorbed by the trailing vortices is not immediately
and irretrievably lost to the primary motion since it is 'sorted' in
orderly fashion in the trailing vortices and is not subject at this
stage to degradation or (except within the vortex core) to viscous
dissipation. If, on the other hand, the velocity mismatch at another
(y) point in the vortex structure is negative (i.e. $U_i - u^* < u_\gamma$) the
trailing vortices behind the spanwise element are compressed and
shortened, so that energy is fed back into the primary motion, thus
accelerating it to the required value u_γ. In this case, the trailing vortices provide a momentum 'source' for the primary motion,
equivalent to the effect of negative turbulent shear stress gradient
(Fig. 4b).

Thus, depending on the form of its velocity distribution entering the vortex structure, the primary motion is accordingly accelerated or decelerated at each point across the shear layer so that it emerges 'upstream' from the system with the induced distribution $u_y(y)$. The associated process of reversible energy exchange between the trailing vortices and primary motion represents 'useful' work done on the primary (and hence on the mean) motion by the 'turbulent' shear stress gradient', and corresponds to the term $u \frac{d\tau}{dy}$ in the energy equation. At the same time, irrespective of whether velocity mismatch occurs or not, the trailing vortices are being continuously stretched by the primary velocity gradient, $\frac{\partial u^*}{\partial y}$, resulting in a continuous, one-way transfer of energy from the primary motion to the trailing vortices. The net amount of energy thus transferred to each horseshoe vortex in its lifetime, is ultimately lost to the primary motion, when the vortex finally breaks up into random turbulence and decays. This process provides the means of turbulence production and corresponds to the term $\tau \frac{\partial u}{\partial y}$ in the energy equation.

The Primary and Mean Motion

Viewed in the moving-axes system $(x-U_i t, y, z)$, the primary motion, $U_i - u^*$, emerges 'upstream' from the vortex system with essentially the induced logarithmic velocity distribution, whereupon the zero-slip condition immediately initiates a progressive viscous distortion of the profile close to the wall. This region of departure from the initial logarithmic distribution extends steadily outwards from the wall, as the primary motion develops 'upstream' towards the next vortex system, so that a growing viscous 'sublayer' is formed (Fig. 5). Within this sublayer, the primary flow is accelerated 'upstream' by the viscous shear stress gradient so that the 'upstream' momentum and energy flux is increased. Outside the growing sublayer, the primary motion is decelerated by the longitudinal pressure gradient in the pipe which opposes the 'upstream' flow.

At some characteristic distance, ℓ, 'upstream' from the first vortex system considered, the sublayer flow becomes unstable and breaks down, feeding its accumulated excess energy into the associated vortex system. This energy is transported out across the layer by the horseshoe vortex elements and subsequently fed back into the energy-depleted primary flow outside the sublayer (as described in the previous section) thus restoring it to its original initial condition and re-starting the cycle.

As indicated in the previous section the residual energy retained in each horseshoe vortex due to the net stretching which it

undergoes, eventually degrades to turbulence energy due to break-up
of the trailing vortices and is ultimately dissipated by the action
of viscosity.

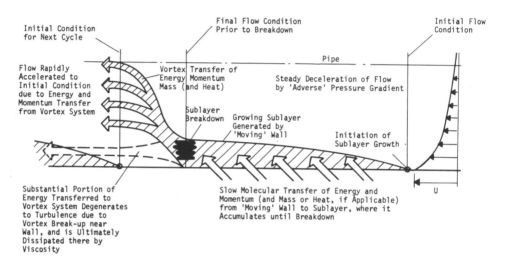

FIG. 5   CYLIC DEVELOPMENT AND BREAKDOWN OF PRIMARY
            MOTION

Apart from providing the source of turbulence production in the
flow, the trailing vortices may also play a major role in initiating
the hypothesized sublayer instability which terminates the development of the primary motion at the end of each growth cycle. Not
only do the vortices provide a source of high intensity turbulent
velocity fluctuations which may be required to trigger the instability;
they must also distort to some extent the developing primary motion
in which they are buried, and could therefore be responsible for
the development of inflexional instability in the primary velocity
profile. Whatever the precise nature of the instability mechanism
involved, it is assumed for present purposes that such an instability
exists and that it regularly limits the extent of the viscous development of the primary motion to a characteristic streamwise distance, ℓ, between successive vortex systems.

Transformed from the moving-axes system $(x-U_it, y, z)$ to the fixed axes system (x, y, z) the primary motion, u^*, takes the form of a time-dependent viscous motion initiated by the passage of one instability/vortex system and terminated by the arrival of the next, after a characteristic time T $(= \frac{\chi}{U_i})$. On the assumption that the initial velocity profile in each cycle is logarithmic and that the subsequent temporal development $(0 < \text{to} \leq T)$ of the primary motion is described adequately by the diffusion equation,

$$\frac{\partial u^*}{\partial t} = \nu \frac{\partial^2 u^*}{\partial y^2} - \frac{1}{\rho} \frac{dp}{dx} \tag{4}$$

A preliminary solution for u^* has been obtained (See Reference 1). The resultant time-dependent profiles $(\frac{u^*}{u_\tau}) = \frac{yu_\tau}{\nu}$ are replotted in Fig. 6, in the familiar semi-logarithmic form. The profiles display an increasing departure from the initial (logarithmic) condition with increasing time, with an associated growth of viscous sublayer.

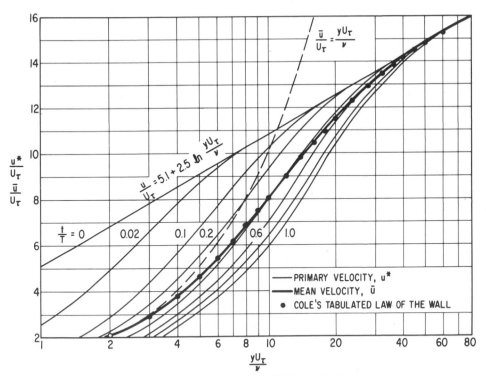

FIG. 6   SOLUTIONS FOR PRIMARY AND MEAN VELOCITY PROFILES

As discussed in Reference 1, the solution for u* contains two unknown constants of integration, one being related to the rate of transfer of energy from the sublayer to the vortex system, and the other being the sublayer stability parameter, $\frac{U_\tau^2 T}{\nu}$. These constants* are directly related to the empirical constants A & B in the experimentally observed logarithmic law of the wall,

$$\frac{\bar{u}}{U_\tau} = A + B \ell \frac{yU_\tau}{\nu} \tag{5}$$

and in the absence of a detailed sublayer stability analysis, have been empirically determined using Coles (Ref. 2) experimental values,

A = 5.1

B = 2.5

The resultant value of the stability parameter is

$$\frac{U_\tau^2 T}{\nu} = 116 \tag{6}$$

which yields the dimensionless (circular) frequency of passage of instability/vortex systems as

$$\frac{\omega\nu}{U_\tau^2} = \frac{2\pi}{U_\tau^2 \frac{T}{\nu}} = 0.056 \tag{7}$$

In Table 1, this empirically determined value is compared with direct measurements by several investigators of the frequency with which the sublayer has been observed to 'erupt' and breakdown. Also referenced in Table 1 is an analysis by the author of a considerable volume of subsonic and supersonic experimental wall pressure data in which evidence of a dominant frequency at or close to $\frac{\omega\nu}{U_\tau^2} = 0.06$ was found.

The mean motion $\frac{\bar{u}}{u_\tau}$, obtained by averaging the primary motion

---

*In practice, they may not be truly universal constants but may be weakly dependent on Reynolds number.

TABLE I

INVESTIGATOR	MEASUREMENT	ENVIRONMENT	$\dfrac{\omega \nu}{U_\tau^2}$
Einstein and Li (Ref. 5)	Autocorrelation of Wall Pressure Fluctuations	Oil – Pipeflow	.0585
Kline and Schraub (Ref. 6)	Visual Observation of Sublayer Bursting Rate Using Dye Injection	Water – B.L.	0.061
Kline, et. al (Ref. 7)	Same as above	Water – B.L.	0.061
Kim, et al (Ref. 3)	Visual Observation of Sublayer Bursting Rate using Hydrogen Bubble Technique	Water – B.L.	(1) .071 (3) .059
	Autocorrelation of Longitudinal Velocity Fluctuations in Sublayer	Water – B.L.	(1) .066 (2) .063 (3) .058
Black (Ref. 1)	Analysis of Subsonic and Supersonic Wall Pressure Spectra	Spectra of $\dfrac{\omega}{2}\,\dfrac{dp^2}{dx}\Big/\tau_o$ vs $\dfrac{\omega \nu^{*}}{U_\tau^2}$ Generally peak at or close to $\dfrac{\omega \nu}{U_\tau^2} = 0.06$	
Black (Present Theory)	Theory	A = 5.1 B = 2.5	.056
		A = 4.9 B = 2.45 (Kline's et al Values)	.059

* Value of Viscosity at Wall used in Analyzing Supersonic Data

over the dimensionless periodic time $\dfrac{U_\tau^2 T}{\nu} = 116$, is also shown in
Fig. 6, and is seen to provide good agreement with Coles' tabulated
(experimental) law of the wall. Some interesting supporting evidence
has recently been provided by Kim, Kline and Reynolds, (Ref. 3) in
the form of measured distributions of instantaneous velocity distribution in the sublayer, between successive observations of sublayer
breakdown or eruption. These are compared in Fig. 7, with corresponding distributions of the primary motion, u*, predicted by the
present theory.

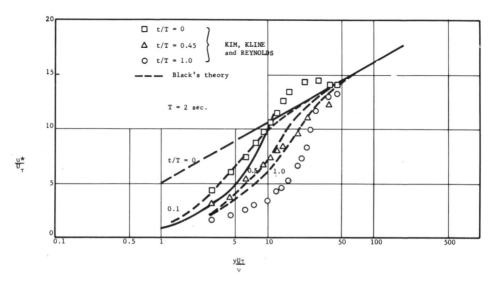

FIG. 7   COMPARISON OF PREDICTED PRIMARY VELOCITY
           DISTRIBUTIONS WITH MEASUREMENTS OF KIM,
           KLINE AND REYNOLDS.

The Effect of Polymer Additives on the Turbulence Structure

On further consideration of the proposed model of wall turbulence, it would seem that there are two fundamental ways in which the
addition of polymer macromolecules might significantly affect its
operation. First, it is conceivable that the macromolecules might
reduce the rate of energy transfer to the trailing vortices due to
stretching, by increasing the size of the vortex core and thus reducing the kinetic energy contained in unit length of the vortex
element for a given strength. Secondly, the macromolecules might

act to dampen and reduce in intensity the turbulence created by the breaking-up of the trailing vortex elements.

It is unlikely that the first of these possible effects would materially alter the proposed shear stress mechanism. According to the hypothesis advanced in an earlier section the reversible transfer of energy between the trailing vortices and the primary motion (corresponding to the useful work $u \frac{\partial \tau}{\partial y}$ performed by the 'shear stress' gradient) is determined by the extent of the velocity mismatch between the primary motion and spanwise vortex elements. Consequently, the total extent of stretching would merely increase to compensate for the reduced rate of energy transfer due to the presence of the polymer macromolecules. It is, however, reasonable to expect that reduction in the rate of energy absorption ($\tau \frac{\partial u}{\partial y}$) by the stretched trailing vortices close to the wall might enhance the stability of the primary sublayer flow by reducing the rate at which it is distorted (and hence distablized) by those vortices. Supression of the turbulence produced by trailing vortex break-up could also serve to increase sublayer stability, by reducing the intensity of turbulent fluctuations in the sublayer which may play a key role in triggering the instability.

There are, therefore, tentative grounds for examining the suggestion that polymer macromolecules fundamentally alter the structure of wall turbulence by significantly increasing the hydrodynamic stability of the sublayer flow, that is by increasing the magnitude of the stability parameter $\frac{U^2 T}{\nu}$, which, as we have seen, appears to have a universal, or near-universal value for normal turbulent shear flows. The solutions obtained in Reference 1 for the primary and mean motions as functions of this parameter, permit a simple study of the effects of increased sublayer stability on the mean motion and other time-averaged properties of the layer.

In particular, we can easily infer the general nature of the effect of increased stability on friction factor. Consider, for example, fully developed turbulent flow of a solvent in a pipe of fixed radius, R (Fig. 8a). The mean wall shear stress, τ_o, is determined by the pressure gradient $\frac{dp}{dx}$, since

$$\tau_o = \frac{R}{2} \frac{dp}{dx} \tag{8}$$

It thus follows that for a given pressure gradient, the velocity of the instability/vortex systems, U_i down the pipe, must be such that the mean value of the instantaneous wall shear stress, $\mu \frac{\partial u^*}{\partial y}$, taken over the non-dimensional periodic time of sublayer growth, $\frac{U^2 T}{\nu}$ (= 116)

must satisfy equation (8) as indicated in Fig. 8a. If we now in-
crease the sublayer stability, so that $\dfrac{U_\tau^2 T}{\nu} > 116$, while maintaining
the same pressure gradient and the same instability/vortex system
velocity, U_i, we find (Fig. 8b) that the sublayer growth is increased
and that, as a result, the mean value of wall shear stress
$\tau_o \; (= \mu \; \dfrac{\partial u^*}{\partial y})_{y = 0}$ is reduced, so that the requirement for steady
flow (Eq. (8)) is no longer satisfied. This dilemma can only be
resolved by a corresponding appropriate increase in U_i (Fig. 8c).

     Thus, the immediate effect of increasing sublayer stability is
to increase both the 'slip' velocity of the vortex systems over the
wall, and the sublayer thickness. The increase in U_i is entirely
legitimate, since the instability/vortex systems are in no way 'tied'
to the wall. According to this model, then, the effect of drag-
reducing polymers can be interpreted in terms of 'slip'; not, however, of fluid slip past the wall, but of increased slip of the
characteristic vortex systems.

     The effect of increasing sublayer stability is thus illustrated
in Fig. 9 first, in terms of increased vortex slip, U_i, in the moving
axes system, (Fig. 9a); and secondly in terms of increased mean flow
in the fixed axes system (Fig. 9b). This increase in mean flow for
a fixed value of wall shear stress yields reduced friction factors,
consistent with experimental observation. Thus, reduced friction
factor, increased sublayer thickness, and apparent slip of the logarithmic 'law of the wall' profile (i.e. increased value of constant
A in Eq. (5)) as observed by experimental investigators, are all
simply explained within the proposed theoretical framework by increased sublayer stability.

Mean Velocity Distribution Under Conditions of Drag Reduction

     As a specific example of the predicted effect of drag-reducing
additives on the mean velocity profile, a point on the asymptotic
drag reduction curve reported by Virk et al (Ref. 4) has been
selected corresponding to a pipe Reynolds' number of 26,000 and
friction factor $\left(f = \dfrac{\tau_o}{\frac{1}{2}\rho \bar{U}^2}\right)$ of 0.00144. As explained by Virk,
this value of friction factor is apparently the lowest which can be
attained at the Reynolds number chosen, irrespective of the nature
of polymer, or of the concentration employed. The value of stability
parameter, $\dfrac{U_\tau^2 T}{\nu}$, required to achieve this condition is easily found
from the analysis developed in Reference 1 and has the value 1380,
representing more than a 10-fold increase in stability over that of

MOVING-AXES SYSTEM ($x - U_i t$, y, z)

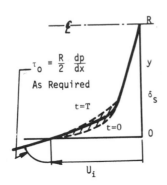

$$\tau_0 = \frac{R}{2} \frac{dp}{dx}$$

As Required

Normal Flow

$$\frac{U_\tau^2 T}{\nu} = 116$$

FLOW WITH INCREASED SUBLAYER STABILITY

$$\frac{U_\tau^2 T}{\nu} > 116$$

Convection Velocity Unchanged
$(= U_i)$

$$\tau_0 < \frac{R}{2} \frac{dp}{dx}$$

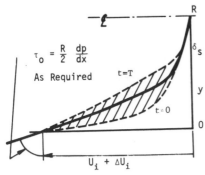

$$\tau_0 = \frac{R}{2} \frac{dp}{dx}$$

As Required

FLOW WITH INCREASED SUBLAYER STABILITY
AND CONVECTION VELOCITY

$$\frac{U_\tau^2 T}{\nu} > 116$$

(Note Increased Sublayer Thickness)

FIG. 8   EFFECT OF INCREASED SUBLAYER STABILITY ON
             INSTABILITY/VORTEX SYSTEM VELOCITY IN PIPE

THOMAS J. BLACK

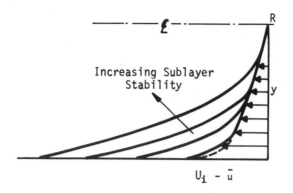

MOVING-AXES SYSTEM

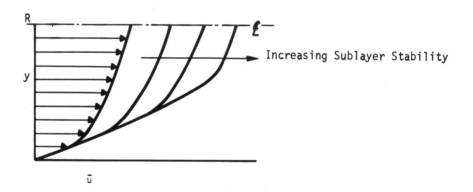

FIXED-AXES SYSTEM

FIG. 9   EFFECT OF INCREASED SUBLAYER STABILITY ON
         MEAN VELOCITY DISTRIBUTIONS IN PIPE

normal (solvent) pipe flow.

    The corresponding mean velocity distribution is shown in Fig. 10
where it is compared with the velocity distribution in normal flow
in the same pipe and with the same pressure gradient. We note that
the drag-reduction profile departs less rapidly from the linear

distribution, $\dfrac{\bar{u}}{U_\tau} = \dfrac{yU_\tau}{\nu}$, near the wall, and attains the logarithmic form

$$\frac{\bar{u}}{U_\tau} = 5.1 + 2.5 \ln \frac{yU_\tau}{\nu} \tag{9}$$

outside the sublayer, compared with standard logarithmic law

$$\frac{\bar{u}}{U_\tau} = 5.1 + 2.5 \ln \frac{yU_\tau}{\nu} \tag{10}$$

assumed for the solvent flow.

The dimensionless sublayer thickness $\dfrac{\delta_s U_\tau}{\nu}$, is likewise increased from 50 to 175.

Turbulent Shear Stress and Turbulence Production
Under Conditions of Drag Reuction

Distributions of turbulent shear stress and turbulence production determined from the analysis of Reference 1 are compared in Fig. 11 for the same cases of polymer solution and solvent consider- ed in the previous section. As might be expected both distributions for the polymer solution exhibit reduced magnitude and a shift of maxima away from the wall (relative to the solvent distributions) consistent with increased sublayer size and the corresponding in- crease in the role of viscosity.

Effect of Drag-Reducing Polymers on
Longitudinal Velocity Fluctuations

In contrast to the distributions of turbulent shear stress and turbulence production discussed above, the effect of drag-reducing polymers on the longitudinal velocity fluctuations is unexpected and consequently of particular interest. It has become accepted practice to refer to velocity fluctuations observed in wall turbu- lence as turbulent velocity fluctuations or turbulence intensities. However, if the present model is correct, a substantial portion of the measured longitudinal velocity fluctuations in and near the sub- layer is, in fact, contributed by the time-dependent primary motion and cannot be described as turbulent (i.e. random in nature). This

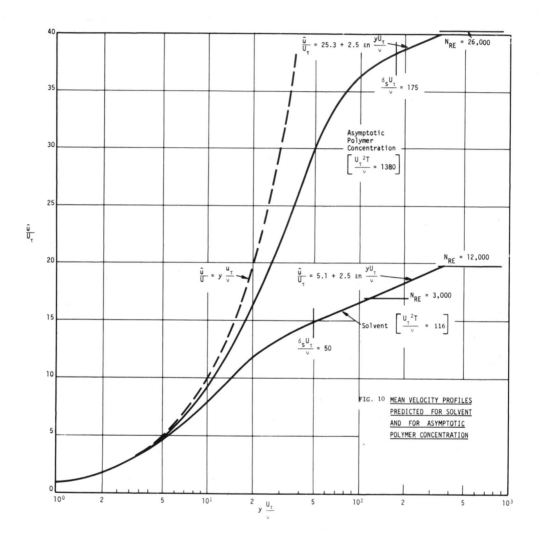

$$\frac{\bar{u}}{U_\tau} = 25.3 + 2.5 \ln \frac{yU_\tau}{\nu}$$

$N_{RE} = 26,000$

$$\frac{\delta_s U_\tau}{\nu} = 175$$

Asymptotic
Polymer
Concentration

$$\left[\frac{U_\tau^2 T}{\nu} = 1380 \right]$$

$N_{RE} = 12,000$

$$\frac{\bar{u}}{U} = y \frac{u_\tau}{\nu}$$

$$\frac{\bar{u}}{U_\tau} = 5.1 + 2.5 \ln \frac{yU_\tau}{\nu}$$

$N_{RE} = 3,000$

Solvent $\left[\frac{U_\tau^2 T}{\nu} = 116 \right]$

$$\frac{\delta_s U_\tau}{\nu} = 50$$

FIG. 10 MEAN VELOCITY PROFILES
PREDICTED FOR SOLVENT
AND FOR ASYMPTOTIC
POLYMER CONCENTRATION

$\frac{\bar{u}}{U_\tau}$

$y \frac{U_\tau}{\nu}$

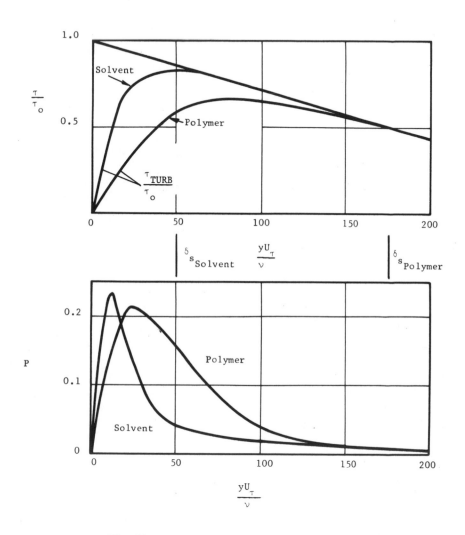

FIG. 11   DISTRIBUTIONS OF TURBULENT SHEAR STRESS AND
             TURBULENCE PRODUCTION FOR POLYMER SOLUTION
             AND SOLVENT

contribution is simply calculated, again on the basis of the analysis
presented in Reference 1, for we may write

$$\overline{(u-\overline{u})^2} = \overline{(u^*-\overline{u})^2} + \overline{u'^2}$$

| Total Measured Longitudinal Velocity Fluctuations | Contribution of Primary Motion | Contribution of Secondary (Turbulent Motion) |

$$= \overline{(u^*-\overline{u})^2} + \overline{u'^2} + \overline{2u'(u^*-\overline{u})}$$

$$= \overline{(u^*-\overline{u})^2} + \overline{u'^2} \tag{11}$$

Primary Velocity Fluctuations   Secondary (Turbulence) Velocity Fluctuations

since the primary and secondary (turbulent) motions are clearly un-
correlated.

The calculated contributions of the primary motion to the
longitudinal velocity fluctuations for the same cases of polymer
solution and solvent discussed above are shown in Fig. 12.   It is
seen that the contribution of the polymer solution is considerably
greater than that of the solvent in both magnitude and extent across
the shear layer.   Thus, even though the polymer solution may exhibit reduced turbulent velocity fluctuations, the total measured
longitudinal fluctuations would probably be considerably increased
over those measured in the solvent.   It is, therefore, evident
that considerable care should be exercised in interpreting fluctuating velocity data in dilute polymer solutions.

Surface Roughness Effects

The observed effect of surface roughness in increasing turbulent friction factors can also be simply explained in terms of
changes in sublayer stability, the effect in this case being to reduce rather than increase stability.   Recent experimental studies
of the turbulent flow of dilute-polymer solutions over rough walls
tentatively suggest that the individual effects of roughness   and
polymer additive may be simply compounded by 'adding' the individual effects of each with due attention to sign.   Such a conclusion
would tend to support the notion that the sublayer instability is
triggered and consequently controlled by the local intensity of

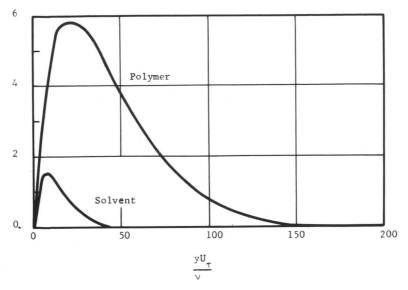

FIG. 12   CONTRIBUTION OF PRIMARY MOTION TO LONGITUDINAL
VELOCITY FLUCTUATIONS IN POLYMER SOLUTION AND
SOLVENT.

turbulence in the sublayer, so that the polymer macromolecules and
roughness elements compete directly against each other, the former
acting to dampen and lessen turbulence intensity, the latter acting
to generate and hence increase it. More experimental study is obviously required, however, before firm conclusions regarding the
precise nature of the interaction between these effects can be
reached.

Effect of Polymer Additives on Other Properties
of Turbulent Shear Layers

If accepted, the basic model of wall turbulence discussed
herein provides new and detailed insight into other processes and
phenomena which are characteristic of such flows. In particular,
it provides a new model for heat and mass transfer in turbulent
flows and affords a new interpretation and explanation of the
measured wall pressure field under turbulent layers. If these models
prove to be valid, for the case of normal turbulent flow, they can be
easily extended to include the effects of polymer additives on these
processes and mechanisms, thus providing a new approach to a number

of current practical problems involving various applications of
soluble polymers.

CONCLUSIONS

The effect of soluble polymer additives on wall turbulence and,
in particular in reducing turbulent friction has been examined in
the light of a new theoretical model of turbulent shear flow. The
tentative conclusions reached are:

1. that the effect of polymer additives on wall tur-
    bulence is to increase sublayer stability,

2. that the increase in sublayer stability results
    directly from the action of the polymer macromo-
    lecules in either (a) modifying the process of
    vortex-stretching which may be responsible for
    distablizing the sublayer flow, or (b) reducing
    the intensity of turbulence in the sublayer, which
    may be responsible for triggering the instability.

3. that the effect of soluble polymer additives may be
    to increase rather than decrease longitudinal
    velocity fluctuations, which increase should not,
    however, be attributed to increased turbulence in-
    tensities, but rather to increased viscous activity
    in the sublayer.

4. that, in view of 3 above, considerable caution may be
    needed in analyzing and interpreting fluctuating
    velocity data in dilute soluble polymer flows.

REFERENCES

1. Black, T. J. "An Analytical Study of the Wall Pressure Field
    Under Supersonic Turbulent Boundary Layers", NASA CR 888
    (1968).

2. Coles, D., "The Problem of the Turbulent Boundary Layer",
    ZAMP, 5, 3 (1954).

3. Kim, H. T., S. J. Kline and W. C. Reynolds, "An Experimental
    Study of Turbulence Production Near a Smooth Wall in the Tur-
    bulent Boundary Layer with Zero Pressure Gradient", MD-20,
    Thermosciences Div. Dept. of Mech. Engr., Stanford University
    (1968).

4. Virk, P. S., E. W. Merrill, H. S. Mickley, K. A. Smith,
    E. L. Mollo-Christiansen,"The Toms Phenomenon-Turbulent Pipe
    Flow of Dilute Polymer Solution", JFM, 30, 2, (1967).

5. Einstein, H. A., H. Li, "The Viscous Sublayer Along a Smooth
    Boundary", Proceedings of the ASCE, Journal of Engr., Mech. Div.
    82, EM2 (1956).

6. Kline, S. J. and F. A. Schraub, "A Study of the Structure of
    the Turbulent Boundary Layer With and Without Longitudinal
    Pressure Gradients,Rept. MD-12, Thermosciences Div., Dept.
    of Mech. Engr., Stanford University (1965).

7. Kline, S. J., P. W. Runstadler and W. C. Reynolds, "An Experi-
    mental Investigation of the Flow Structure of the Turbulent
    Boundary Layer", Rept. MD-8, Thermoscience Div., Dept. of Mech.
    Engr., Stanford University (1963).

THE THEORY OF SKIN FRICTION REDUCTION BY A

COMPLIANT COATING IN A TURBULENT BOUNDARY LAYER

Edward F. Blick

University of Oklahoma

ABSTRACT

The response of a compliant surface to pressure fluctuations is known to modify (sometimes decrease) the skin friction in a turbulent boundary layer. This paper develops the surface response (receptance) of a compliant coating to a pressure perturbation. The compliant coating was assumed to be composed of a thin membrane stretched over a shallow layer of liquid. This type of coating has been used successfully by several experimenters to reduce the skin friction. After the surface response equation was developed, the technique developed by Lin and Ffowcs Williams was utilized to determine the Reynolds stresses induced near the vibrating compliant surface. The technique is generalized to allow for random turbulent pressure fluctuations and surface motion, but it is restricted to two-dimensional surface oscillations. The interesting result is that certain combinations of the properties of the compliant coating may induce a negative Reynolds stress in the layer of fluid adjacent to the coating. This layer of fluid may then be responsible for starving the turbulent eddies of their energy supply and causing a reduction in turbulence intensity and skin friction.

INTRODUCTION

In the last few years there has been some interest generated in the area of drag reduction by compliant coatings. The originator of this idea was the German scientist Dr. Max O. Kramer (Refs. 1-3). According to Kramer, the flabby skin of the dolphin contributed to its high speed by retarding transition to turbulent flow of the boundary layer. Theoretical work by Benjamin (Ref. 4) indicated that the stability of the laminar boundary layer could indeed be affected by compliant coatings.

   Recent experimental work (Refs. 5-7) has shown that compliant
coatings affect the turbulent boundary layer by reducing the aerodynamic skin friction and air stream turbulence intensity.   The
effect of the compliant coating on the turbulent boundary layer has
led to the need of a theoretical explanation of how the compliant
coating can cause a reduction in skin friction.   As a first step
toward a more complete theoretical understanding of this phenomena,
this paper has undertaken the task of investigating a simplified two-
dimensional model of a compliant coating composed of a thin membrane
or sheet stretched over layer of incompressible damping fluid (Figure
1).   The compliant coating is assumed to extend to infinity in all
directions of the x-z plane.   The compliant coatings used in the
experimental work of References 5-7 are similar to the hypothetical
model proposed here, except the actual compliant coatings were not
infinite in length and width but were in fact rectangular in shape.

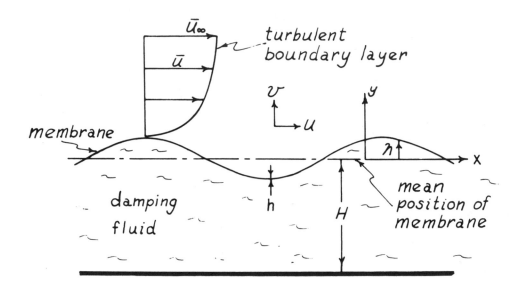

Figure 1   Model of the Compliant Coating

RESPONSE OF THE COATING

If the motion of the coating is confined to the x,y plane, the linearized Navier-Stokes equations (conservation of momentum equations) for the damping fluid become (Ref. 8)

$$\frac{\partial u}{\partial t} = -\frac{1}{\rho}\frac{\partial p}{\partial x} + \nu\left(\frac{\partial^2 u}{\partial x^2} + \frac{\partial^2 u}{\partial y^2}\right) \tag{1}$$

$$\frac{\partial v}{\partial t} = -\frac{1}{\rho}\frac{\partial p}{\partial y} + \nu\left(\frac{\partial^2 v}{\partial x^2} + \frac{\partial^2 v}{\partial y^2}\right) - g \tag{2}$$

The velocities of the damping fluid have been assumed to be very small and for this reason the Navier-Stokes equations could be linearized by omitting the convective terms.

The continuity equation (conservation of mass) for the incompressible damping fluid is

$$\frac{\partial u}{\partial x} + \frac{\partial v}{\partial y} = 0 \tag{3}$$

If functions Φ and Ψ are introduced, equations (1), (2), and (3) are satisfied by

$$u = -\frac{\partial \Phi}{\partial x} - \frac{\partial \Psi}{\partial y} \tag{4}$$

$$v = -\frac{\partial \Phi}{\partial y} + \frac{\partial \Psi}{\partial x} \tag{5}$$

and

$$\frac{p}{\rho} = \frac{\partial \Phi}{\partial t} - gy \tag{6}$$

provided that

$$\nabla^2 \Phi = 0 \tag{7}$$

and

$$\frac{\partial \Psi}{\partial t} = \nu \nabla^2 \Psi. \tag{8}$$

The perturbation portion of the atmospheric pressure in the boundary layer acting on the coating is assumed to be of the form of a traveling wave:

$$p' = P\, e^{ik(x-ct)}. \tag{9}$$

The response of the coating can be expressed in the same form:

$$\eta = N\, e^{ik(x-ct)},$$
(10)

The sheet covering the fluid substrate is assumed to have a flexural stiffness, D, and subject to a tension force in the x-direction, per unit width, of T. The fundamental displacement equation (obtained by Newton's second law) describing the motion of the sheet is given by

$$\sigma\, \frac{\partial^2 \eta}{\partial t^2} = -p' - p_{yy} - D\, \frac{\partial^4 \eta}{\partial x^4} + T\, \frac{\partial^2 \eta}{\partial x^2}$$
(11)

$(-p_{yy})$ is the stress exerted on the sheet in the positive y-direction by the damping fluid. Assuming that the damping fluid is a Newtonian fluid then (8),

$$p_{yy} = -p + 2\,\mu\, \frac{\partial v}{\partial y},$$
(12)

The solutions of equations (7) and (8) are

$$\Phi = (A \sinh ky + B \cosh ky)\, e^{ik(x-ct)}$$
(13)

$$\Psi = (F \sinh my + J \cosh my)\, e^{ik(x-ct)}$$
(14)

where

$$m^2 = k^2 - \frac{ikc}{\nu},$$
(15)

Thus, from equations (4), (5), (13) and (14),

$$u = -\,[ik(A \sinh ky + B \cosh ky + m(F \cosh my + J \sinh my)]\, e^{ik(x-ct)}$$
(16)

$$v = [-k(A \cosh ky + B \sinh ky) + ik(F \sinh my + J \cosh my)]\, e^{ik(x-ct)},$$
(17)

The problem now is to apply the boundary conditions (B.C.) in order to find N/P.

B.C. No. 1 & 2

At $y = -H$, $u = v = 0$.

From equations (16) and (17) and B.C. Nos. 1 and 2,

$$-ik\, A \sinh kH + ik\, B \cosh kH + m\, F \cosh mH - m\, J \sinh mH = 0 \quad (18)$$

$$-A \cosh kH + B \sinh kH - i\, F \sinh mH + i\, J \cosh mH = 0, \quad (19)$$

B.C. No. 3

At $y = \eta$, $u = 0$.

It is assumed that η is small and the condition $y = 0$, $u = 0$ will be used as an approximation. Subsequent solutions by the author (unpublished) and the experiments of Looney, Blick, and Walter, (Refs. 5, 6) have shown this to be a valid assumption. From equation (16) and B.C. No. 3.

$$ik\ B + m\ F = 0 \tag{20}$$

B.C. No. 4

At $y = \eta$, $\partial\eta/\partial t = v$

Again if one assumes η to be small, then this boundary condition can be approximated by

At $y = 0$, $\partial\eta/\partial t = v$

From equations (10) and (17) and B.C. No. 4,

$$N = -\frac{1}{c}\ (iA + J) \tag{21}$$

The damping fluid pressure in contact with the lower surface of the sheet $(y = \eta)$ is from Eq. (6)

$$(p)_\eta = \rho\ [\frac{\partial\phi}{\partial t}]_\eta\ \rho g\eta \tag{22}$$

By assuming η is small, then $\partial\phi/\partial t$ and $\partial v/\partial y$ at $y = \eta$ can be approximated by their values at $y = 0$. With this assumption, Eqs. (11), (12) and (22) combine to

$$N(\sigma k^2 c^2 - Tk^2 - Dk^4 - \rho g) + B(2\ \mu k^2 - ikc\rho) + F(-i\ 2\ \mu km) = P \tag{23}$$

Equations (18), (19), (20), (21), and (23) can be written in matrix form,

$$
\begin{bmatrix}
-ik \sinh kH & ik \cosh kH & m \cosh mH & -m \sinh mH & 0 \\
-\cosh kH & \sinh kH & -i \sinh mH & i \cosh mH & 0 \\
0 & ik & m & 0 & 0 \\
i & 0 & 0 & 1 & c \\
0 & 2\ \mu k^2 - ik\rho c & -i2\ \mu km & 0 & \sigma k^2 c^2 - Tk^2 \\
& & & & -Dk^4 - \rho g
\end{bmatrix}
\begin{bmatrix}
A \\ B \\ F \\ D \\ N
\end{bmatrix}
=
\begin{bmatrix}
0 \\ 0 \\ 0 \\ 0 \\ P
\end{bmatrix}
$$

Solution by Cramer's rule gives the sheet response equation,

$$\frac{N}{P} = \frac{1}{\sigma k^2 c^2 - Tk^2 - Dk^4 - \rho g + G(\rho,k,c,H,\nu)} \tag{24}$$

where

$$G(\rho,k,c,H,\nu) = \frac{\rho k c^2 (m \sinh mH \cosh kH - k \cosh mH \sinh kH)}{2k - 2k \cosh mH \cosh kH + (m + k^2/m) \sinh kH \sinh mH} \tag{25}$$

It is interesting to note the limit of N/P as $\nu \rightarrow 0$. The response for this case (inviscid damping fluid) is then

$$\lim_{\nu \rightarrow 0} \left(\frac{N}{P}\right) = \frac{1}{\sigma k^2 c^2 - Tk^2 - Dk^4 - \rho g + \rho k c^2 \coth(kH)} \tag{26}$$

By setting P equal to zero in Eq. (26), the free-surface wave speed of the sheet can be obtained,

$$c = \left[\frac{Tk/\rho + Dk^3/\rho + g/k}{\sigma k/\rho + \coth kH}\right]^{\frac{1}{2}} \tag{27}$$

Eq. (27) is equivalent to a similar equation derived by Basset (Ref. 9) for the free-surface wave of a layer of ice on water with T equal to zero.

For capillary waves on a free surface D and $\sigma = 0$, Eq. (27) reduces to

$$c^2 = (2\pi T/\lambda\rho + g\lambda/2\pi) \tanh(2\pi H/\lambda) \tag{28}$$

which is the same as an equation derived by Basset (Ref. 10).

For an inviscid free surface T, D, and $\sigma = 0$.

$$c^2 = \left(\frac{\lambda g}{2\pi}\right) \tanh\left(\frac{2\pi H}{\lambda}\right) \tag{29}$$

This is the same equation given in Basset (Ref. 11) for wave motion in two dimensions.

Another limiting case of equation (25) is when $\nu \rightarrow \infty$.

$$\lim_{\nu \rightarrow \infty} \left(\frac{N}{P}\right) = 0, \tag{30}$$

In other words the deflection of the membrane becomes zero as $\nu \rightarrow \infty$.

The compliant coating acts as a hard plate at this limit.

REYNOLDS STRESS REDUCTION

If the compliant coating is disturbed by the fluctuating pressures in a turbulent boundary layer, it will oscillate and induce velocity perturbations in the boundary layer. The velocity components of the turbulent boundary layer flow on top of the compliant coating will be denoted by $\bar{u} + u'$ and $\bar{v} + v'$, where u' and v' are perturbation velocities induced by the compliant wall. Assume that the perturbation velocities can be expressed as power series in y,

$$u'(x,y,t) = \sum_{n=0}^{\infty} a_n(x,t)y^n \tag{31}$$

$$v'(x,y,t) = \sum_{n=0}^{\infty} b_n(x,t)y^n \tag{32}$$

This technique of expanding the perturbation velocities in a power series in order to calculate the Reynolds stress is essentially that described by Lin (Ref. 12) and Ffowcs Williams (Ref. 13).

From the conservation of mass equation for an incompressible fluid,

$$\frac{\partial u'}{\partial x} + \frac{\partial v'}{\partial y} = 0 \tag{33}$$

one obtains from Eqs. (31) and (32),

$$b_n = -\frac{1}{n} \frac{\partial a_{n-1}(x,t)}{\partial x} \tag{34}$$

Therefore

$$v'(x,y,t) = b_0(x,t) - \sum_{n=1}^{\infty} \frac{1}{n} \frac{\partial a_{n-1}(x,t)y^n}{\partial x} \tag{35}$$

The no-slip boundary conditions are,

$$\bar{v}(\eta) + v'(x,\eta,t) = \frac{\partial \eta(x,t)}{\partial t} \tag{36}$$

$$\bar{u}(\eta) + u'(x,\eta,t) = 0 \tag{37}$$

Now take a Taylor expansion about $y = 0$, for $\bar{u}(\eta)$ and $\bar{v}(\eta)$

$$\bar{u}(\eta) = \bar{u}(0) + \left(\frac{\partial \bar{u}}{\partial y}\right)_{y=0} \eta + \cdots \doteq \left(\frac{\partial \bar{u}}{\partial y}\right)_{y=0} \eta \tag{38}$$

$$\bar{v}(\eta) = \bar{v}(0) + \left(\frac{\partial \bar{v}}{\partial y}\right)_{y=0} \eta + \cdots \doteq 0 \tag{39}$$

since $\bar{u}$ and $\bar{v}(0)$ are zero and by the continuity equation,

$$\left(\frac{\partial \bar{v}}{\partial y}\right)_{y=0} = -\left(\frac{\partial \bar{u}}{\partial x}\right)_{y=0} = 0$$

Substituting Eqs. (31) and (38) into (37) one obtains

$$a_o(x,t) + a_1(x,t)\eta + a_2(x,t)\eta^2 + \cdots = -\left(\frac{\partial \bar{u}}{\partial y}\right)_{y=0} \eta \qquad (40)$$

Keeping only the linear (first order) terms of wall displacement (terms like $a_1(x,t)\eta$ are regarded as second order), one obtains

$$a_o = -\eta\, \bar{U}' \qquad (41)$$

where

$$\bar{U}' = \left(\frac{\partial \bar{u}}{\partial y}\right)_{y=0}$$

Now substitute Eqs. (39) and (35) in Eq. (36),

$$b_o(x,t) - \frac{\partial a_o(x,t)}{\partial x}\,\eta - \frac{1}{2}\frac{\partial a_1}{\partial x}\,\eta^2 - \cdots = \frac{\partial \eta(x,t)}{\partial t} \qquad (42)$$

Again, neglecting the second order terms $\dfrac{\partial a_o}{\partial x}\,\eta$, etc., one obtains

$$b_o(x,t) = \frac{\partial \eta(x,t)}{\partial t} \qquad (43)$$

Now by substituting Eqs. (41) and (43) in Eqs. (31) and (35),

$$u'(x,y,t) = -\eta\bar{U}' + \sum_{n=1}^{\infty} a_n(x,t)y^n \qquad (44)$$

$$v'(x,y,t) = \frac{\partial \eta(x,t)}{\partial t} + \bar{U}'\,\frac{\partial \eta(x,t)}{\partial x}\, y \qquad (45)$$

$$-\sum_{n=2}^{\infty} \frac{1}{n}\frac{\partial a_{n-1}(x,t)}{\partial x}\, y^n$$

The vorticity perturbation, $\omega_3' = \dfrac{\partial v'}{\partial x} - \dfrac{\partial u'}{\partial y}$, must satisfy the diffusion equation near the wall

$$\frac{\partial \omega_3'}{\partial t} = \nu\, \nabla^2 \omega_3' \qquad (46)$$

This is just another way of requiring the perturbation velocities to satisfy conservation of momentum.

The generalized Fourier transform (Ref. 14) of the vorticity can be written as

$$\omega_3' (x,y,t) = \frac{1}{(2\pi)^2} \int_{-\infty}^{\infty} \int_{-\infty}^{\infty} \Omega_3 (k,\omega) \, e^{i(kx-\omega t)} \, e^{isy} \, dk d\omega$$

(47)

Now by substituting Eq. (47) into Eq. (46),

$$s = [\frac{i\omega}{\nu} - k^2]^{\frac{1}{2}}$$

(48)

where k = wave number and ω = frequency

$\Omega_3 (k,\omega)$ is the generalized Fourier transform of the vorticity at the surface.

Now expanding $e^{i[\frac{i\omega}{\nu} - k^2]^{\frac{1}{2}}y}$ in Taylor series about $y = 0$,

$$e^{i[\frac{i\omega}{\nu} - k^2]^{\frac{1}{2}}y} = 1 + \frac{i[\frac{i\omega}{\nu} - k^2]^{\frac{1}{2}}}{1!} y + \frac{i[\frac{i\omega}{\nu} - k^2]^{\frac{1}{2}}}{2!} y^2 + \cdots$$

Therefore

$$\omega_3' (x,y,t) = \frac{1}{(2\pi)^2} \iint_{-\infty}^{\infty} \Omega_3 (k,w) e^{i(kx-\omega t)} \sum_{n=0}^{\infty} \frac{y^n}{n!} \{i(\frac{i\omega}{\nu} - k^2)^{\frac{1}{2}}\}^n dk d\omega$$

(49)

But from the definition of vorticity and Eqs. (44) and (45),

$$\omega_3' (x,y,t) = \frac{\partial^2 \eta(x,t)}{\partial x \partial t} - a_1 (x,t) + \{\frac{\partial^2 \eta(x,t)}{\partial x^2} \bar{U}'$$
$$- 2a_2 (x,t)\}y + \cdots$$

(50)

The generalized Fourier transforms for η and a_n are,

$$\eta(x,t) = \frac{1}{(2\pi)^2} \iint_{-\infty}^{\infty} N (k,\omega) e^{i(kx-\omega t)} dk d\omega$$

(51)

$$a_n(x,t) = \frac{1}{(2\pi)^2} \iint_{-\infty}^{\infty} A_n (k,\omega) e^{i(kx-\omega t)} dk d\omega$$

(52)

By substituting Eqs. (51) and (52) into Eq. (50) one obtains,

$$\omega_3' = \frac{1}{(2\pi)^2} \int\int_{-\infty}^{\infty} [k\omega N(k,\omega) - A_1 - \bar{U}' k^2 N(k,\omega)y$$
$$- 2A_2 y] e^{i(kx-\omega t)} + \text{higher order terms} \tag{53}$$

Now by equating coefficients of y^n in Eqs. (49) and (53),

$$\Omega_3 (k,\omega) = k\omega N(k,\omega) - A_1(k,\omega) \tag{54}$$

$$\Omega_3 (k,\omega) [i(\frac{i\omega}{\nu} - k^2)^{\frac{1}{2}}] = - [\bar{U}'k^2 N(k,\omega) + 2A_2(k,y)] \tag{55}$$

From (54) and (55)

$$A_1(k,\omega) = \{i (\frac{i\omega}{\nu} - k^2)^{\frac{1}{2}}\}^{-1} \{\bar{U}' k^2 N(k,\omega)$$
$$+ 2A_2(k,y)\} + k\omega N(k,\omega) \tag{56}$$

The conservation of momentum equation close to the surface can be written as

$$\frac{\partial u'}{\partial t} + v'\bar{U}' = - \frac{1}{\rho_a} \frac{\partial p'}{\partial x} + \nu \nabla^2 u' \tag{57}$$

p' is the pressure perturbation. To zero order in y the pressure perturbation, p' can be expressed by the generalized Fourier transform

$$p'(x,t) = \frac{1}{(2\pi)^2} \int\int_{-\infty}^{\infty} P(k,\omega) e^{i(kx-\omega t)} dk d\omega \tag{58}$$

To zero order in y Eq. (57) can be expressed as

$$\frac{1}{\rho} ikP(k,\omega) = \nu [k^2 N(k,\omega)\bar{U}' + 2A_2(k,\omega)] \tag{59}$$

Therefore

$$A_2(k,\omega) = \frac{ikP(k,\omega)}{2\nu\rho_a} - \frac{k^2}{2} N(k,\omega)\bar{U}' \tag{60}$$

Now substitute Eq. (60) into Eq. (56), therefore

$$A_1(k,\omega) = [(\frac{i\omega}{\nu} - k^2)^{\frac{1}{2}}]^{-1} \frac{kP(k,\omega)}{\nu\rho_a} + k\omega N(k,\omega) \tag{61}$$

By writing the series expansions of u' and v' to order y and by substituting (61), (52), (51) into (44) and (45), one obtains,

$$u'(x,y,t) = \frac{1}{(2\pi)^2} \int\!\!\int_{-\infty}^{\infty} e^{i(kx-\omega t)} A(k,\omega) \, dk d\omega \tag{62}$$

where

$$A(k,\omega) = -\bar{U}'N + [\{(\frac{i\omega}{\nu} - k^2)^{\frac{1}{2}}\}^{-1} \frac{kP}{\nu\rho_a} + k\omega N]y + \text{higher order terms} \tag{63}$$

$$v'(x,y,t) = \frac{1}{(2\pi)^2} \int\!\!\int_{-\infty}^{\infty} e^{i(kx-\omega t)} B(k,\omega) dk d\omega + \text{higher order terms} \tag{64}$$

where
$$B(k,\omega) = -i\omega N(k,\omega) + \bar{U}'ikN(k,\omega)y \tag{65}$$

The perturbation Reynolds stress τ, near the mean position of the wall is defined by the following time average

$$\tau = -\rho_a \overline{u'v'}$$

or by assuming statistical stationarity in both time and space

$$\tau = -\rho_a \lim_{\substack{X\to\infty \\ T\to\infty}} \frac{1}{(2\pi)^4 XT} \int_{-X/2}^{X/2} \int_{-T/2}^{T/2} u'(x,y,t)v'(x,y,t)dxdt \tag{66}$$

Now by substituting (62), (63), (64) and (65) into (66) and keeping terms only to first order in y

$$\tau = -\rho_a \lim_{\substack{X\to\infty \\ T\to\infty}} \frac{1}{(2\pi)^4 XT} \int_{-X/2}^{X/2} \int_{-T/2}^{T/2} \int\!\!\int\!\!\int\!\!\int_{-\infty}^{\infty} \{\bar{U}'i\omega N(k,\omega)N(k',\omega')-i\omega N(k,\omega)$$

$$\cdot [\{(\frac{i\omega'}{\nu} - k'^2)^{\frac{1}{2}}\}^{-1} \frac{k'P(k',\omega')}{\nu\rho} + k'\omega'N(k',\omega')]y$$

$$-(\bar{U}')^2 yikN(k,\omega)N(k',\omega')\} e^{i[(k+k')x-(\omega+\omega')t]} dk dk' d\omega d\omega' dx dt \tag{67}$$

The crucial spot in the above integration are the integrals

$$\int_{-\infty}^{\infty} e^{i(k+k')x}dx = 2\pi\delta(k+k'); \quad \int_{-\infty}^{\infty} e^{-i(\omega+\omega')t}dt = 2\pi\delta(-\omega-\omega') = 2\pi\delta(\omega+\omega')$$

$$\int_{-\infty}^{\infty} f(k')\delta(k+k')dk' = f(-k); \quad \int_{-\infty}^{\infty} f(\omega')\delta(\omega+\omega')d\omega' = f(-\omega)$$

These are the property of e^{ikx} treated as a generalized function according to Lighthill (Ref. 14).

Accordingly, Eq. (37) can be reduced to

$$\tau = -\rho \lim_{\substack{X\to\infty \\ T\to\infty}} \frac{1}{(2\pi)^2} \iint_{-\infty}^{\infty} \{i\omega\bar{U}' \frac{N(k,\omega)N(-k,-\omega)}{XT} - \bar{U}'^2 iky \frac{N(k,\omega)N(-k,-\omega)}{XT}$$

$$- i\omega \frac{N(k,\omega)}{XT} [\{(-\frac{i\omega}{\nu} - k^2)^{\frac{1}{2}}\}^{-1} \frac{-kP(-k,-\omega)}{\nu\rho} + k\omega N(-k,-\omega)]y\} \, dkd\omega \tag{68}$$

Because of the assumption of statistical stationarity in both space and time, the first, second, and last integrations on the right-hand side of Eq. (68) will vanish because they are odd functions. The Reynolds stress is then,

$$\tau = -\lim_{\substack{X\to\infty \\ T\to\infty}} \frac{1}{(2\pi)^2} \int_{-\infty}^{\infty} \int_{-\infty}^{\infty} \frac{i\omega k}{\nu} \{(-\frac{i\omega}{\nu} - k^2)^{\frac{1}{2}}\}^{-1} \frac{N(k,\omega)P(-k,-\omega)}{XT} y \, dkd\omega \tag{69}$$

With a slight amount of rearranging it can be shown that

$$\{(-\frac{i\omega}{\nu} - k^2)^{\frac{1}{2}}\}^{-1} = \{[-\frac{i\omega}{\nu} (1 + \frac{1}{iR}]^{\frac{1}{2}}\}^{-1}$$

where R is the Reynolds number based on the wavelength $\lambda = 2\pi/k$ and the convective wave velocity, $c = \omega/k$

$$R = \frac{c\lambda}{\nu 2\pi} = \frac{\omega}{\nu k^2} \tag{70}$$

The term $(1 + 1/iR)^{-\frac{1}{2}}$ can be expanded in a Taylor expansion about $(1/R) = 0$, assuming R is large,

$$(1 + \frac{1}{iR})^{-\frac{1}{2}} = 1 + \frac{i}{2R} + \text{higher order terms}$$

Therefore

$$\{(-\frac{i\omega}{\nu} - k^2)^{\frac{1}{2}}\}^{-1} = \frac{1}{\sqrt{-i\omega/\nu}} [1 + \frac{i}{2R} + \cdots] \tag{71}$$

Now by substituting (71) into (69),

$$\tau = \lim_{\substack{X\to\infty \\ T\to\infty}} \frac{1}{(2\pi)^2} \int_{-\infty}^{\infty} \int_{-\infty}^{\infty} -\frac{i\omega k}{\nu} \frac{y}{\sqrt{-i\omega/\nu}} [1 + \frac{i}{2R} + \cdots]$$

$$\frac{N(k,\omega)P(-k,-\omega)}{XT} \, dkd\omega \tag{72}$$

For large values of Reynolds No., R, then $\dfrac{i}{2R} \ll 0$, then

$$\tau = \lim_{\substack{X \to \infty \\ T \to \infty}} \frac{1}{(2\pi)^2} \int_{-\infty}^{\infty} \int_{-\infty}^{\infty} \sqrt{-i} \sqrt{\frac{\omega k^2}{\nu}} \; y \; \frac{N(k,\omega)P(-k,-\omega)}{XT} \, dk d\omega \tag{73}$$

By substituting the sheet response equation, Eq. (24) into Eq. (73), one obtains,

$$\tau = \lim_{\substack{X \to \infty \\ T \to \infty}} \frac{1}{(2\pi)^2} \int_{-\infty}^{\infty} \int_{-\infty}^{\infty} \sqrt{-i} \sqrt{\frac{\omega k^2}{\nu}} \; y \; \frac{P(k,\omega)P(-k,-\omega)}{XT}$$

$$\cdot \frac{[\sigma\omega^2 - Tk^2 - Dk^4 - \rho g + G_r - iG_i]}{[(\sigma\omega^2 - Tk^2 - Dk^4 - \rho g + G_r)^2 + (G_i)^2]} \, dk d\omega \tag{74}$$

where, G_r and G_i are the real and imaginary parts of the complex term G (Eq. (25)),

$$G(\rho, k, c, H, \nu) = G_r + iG_i$$

Taking the real part of τ in Eq. (74),

$$\tau = \lim_{\substack{X \to \infty \\ T \to \infty}} \frac{(0.707)}{(2\pi)^2} \int_{-\infty}^{\infty} \int_{-\infty}^{\infty} \sqrt{\frac{\omega k^2}{\nu}} \; y \; \frac{P(k,\omega)P(-k,-\omega)}{XT}$$

$$\cdot \frac{[\sigma\omega^2 - Tk^2 - Dk^4 - \rho g + G_r - G_i]}{[(\sigma\omega^2 - Tk^2 - Dk^4 - \rho g + G_r)^2 + G_i^2]} \, dk d\omega \tag{75}$$

The spectral density, $S_p(k,\omega)$ of the perturbation pressure p' is defined as

$$S_p(k,\omega) = \lim_{\substack{X \to \infty \\ T \to \infty}} \left[\frac{1}{(2\pi)^2} \frac{P(k,\omega)P(-k,-\omega)}{XT} \right] \tag{76}$$

Therefore the perturbation Reynolds stress is

$$\tau = 0.707 \int_{-\infty}^{\infty} \int_{-\infty}^{\infty} \sqrt{\frac{\omega k^2}{\nu}} \; y \; S_p(k,\omega) \; \frac{[\sigma\omega^2 - Tk^2 - Dk^4 - \rho g + G_r - G_i]}{[(\sigma\omega^2 - Tk^2 - Dk^4 - \rho g + G_r)^2 + G_i^2]} \, dk d\omega \tag{77}$$

Eq. (77) is the Reynolds stress induced by the compliant coating in a thin layer adjacent to the coating. The equation is not valid far from the coating because terms of higher order than y were omitted in several steps leading up to Eq. (77).

The interesting thing to notice in Eq. (77) is that all terms
are positive except for the numerator (in brackets), which may be
positive or negative.   Hence there is the possibility that certain
combinations of the properties of the compliant coating may cause
the perturbation Reynolds to be negative. A negative Reynolds
stress might possibly reduce the total Reynolds stress throughout
the boundary layer, thus causing a reduction in wall skin friction.
This would also imply that a negative perturbation Reynolds stress
would tend to "starve" the turbulence energy throughout the boundary layer.   This possibility exists because the production of turbulence energy from the mean motion is proportional to the Reynolds
stress (production = $-\overline{u'v'}\,\partial u/\partial y$).   Unfortunately the two-dimensional nature of the current model plus the limitations imposed
by neglecting higher order terms of y do not allow a more rigorous
analysis of the entire turbulent boundary layer.

By examining the terms in the numerator of Eq. (77), it is
possible to see how they could cause the perturbation Reynolds stress
to become negative (Table 1).   The denominator of Eq. (77) is always
positive and will influence the magnitude of the perturbation
Reynolds stress but not the sign.   Notice that as any property of
the coating approaches a value of infinity, τ approaches the hard
plate of zero.

Table 1

Effect of Compliant Coating on Sign of Perturbation Reynolds Stress

Increasing Variable	Perturbation Reynolds Stress	
	Increase	Decrease
Skin mass/unit area, σ	X	
Skin flexural stiffness, D		X
Skin tension, T		X
Damping fluid density, ρ		X
Fluid layer thickness, *H	X	
Damping fluid kinematic viscosity, *ν		X

*The term $(G_r - G_i)$ was found to increase with H and decrease with ν

The experiments of Looney and **Blick** (Ref. 5) were checked to see if their measured values of skin friction correlated with Eq. (77) and Table 1. A correlation was found to exist with the variations of σ, T, ρ, and ν over the limited range that these parameters were varied. Thus Looney and Blick (Ref. 5) found in their experiments that the skin friction increased with increase in σ, but decreased with an increase in T, ρ, or ν. Hence the limited experimental evidence shows the same trends as predicted by this grossly simplified model of turbulent flow over a compliant surface.

ACKNOWLEDGEMENT

This work was sponsored by the U.S. Army Research Office, Durham, N.C. under Contract DA-31-124-ARO-D-349.

NOMENCLATURE

c	Wave velocity
D	Flexural stiffness = $Eh^3/12(1-\epsilon^2)$
E	Young's modulus of the membrane
h	Thickness of the membrane
H	Depth of the damping fluid
k	Wave number = $\omega/c = 2\pi/\lambda$
p	Pressure of the damping fluid
p'	Perturbation air pressure
$S_p(k, \omega)$	Pressure spectral density of the turbulent boundary layer
t	Time
T	Tension per unit length in x direction
u	Velocity in the x direction
v	Velocity in the y direction
ϵ	Poisson's ratio of the membrane
η	Amplitude of the compliant surface above the undisturbed position
λ	Wave length
μ	Viscosity of the damping fluid
ν	Kinematic viscosity of the damping fluid
ρ	Density of damping fluid

ρ_a Density of flowing fluid

σ Mass of the membrane per unit area

ω Frequency of the excitation pressure

ω'_3 Vorticity perturbation

τ Reynolds stress

REFERENCES

1. Kramer, M. O., "Boundary Layer Stabilization by Distributed Damping," J. Aero. Sci. 24, 459, 1957

2. Kramer, M. O., "Boundary Layer Stabilization by Distributed Damping," J. Am. Soc. Naval Engr. 72, 25, 1960

3. Kramer, M. O., "The Dolphins' Secret," J. Am. Cos. Naval Engr. 73, 103, 1961

4. Benjamin, T. B., "Effects of a Flexible Boundary on Hydrodynamic Stability", J. Fluid Mech. 7, 513, 1960

5. Looney, R. W., and Blick, E. F., "Skin Friction Coefficients of Compliant Surfaces in Turbulent Flow," J. Spacecraft & Rockets 3, 1562, 1966

6. Walter, R. R., and Blick, E. F., "Turbulent Boundary-Layer Characteristics of Compliant Surfaces," J. Aircraft 5, 11, 1968

7. Fisher, D. H., and Blick, E. F., "Turbulent Damping by Flabby Skins," J. Aircraft 3, 163, 1966

8. Lamb, H., Hydrodynamics, Dover Publications, Inc., New York, 1932, p. 626

9. Basset, A. B., Hydrodynamics, Dover Publications, Inc., New York, 1961, Vol. 2, p. 180

10. Ibid. p. 177

11. Ibid. p. 147

12. Lin, C. C., The Theory of Hydrodynamic Stability, Cambridge Univ. Press, Cambridge, Eng., 1955

13. Ffowcs Williams, J. E., "Reynolds Stress Near a Flexible
     Surface Responding to Unsteady Air Flow," Bolt Beranck and
     Newman, Inc., Report No. 1138, 3 June 1964

14. Lighthill, M. J., Introduction to Fourier Analysis and
     Generalised Functions, Cambridge Univ. Press, Cambridge,
     Eng., 1964

A MODEL FOR LARGE EDDY CONTRIBUTIONS IN

INCOMPRESSIBLE TURBULENT BOUNDARY LAYERS

J. L. Gaddis and J. P. Lamb

The University of Texas at Austin

ABSTRACT

Presented herein is an incompressible turbulent boundary layer analysis which is based on a two-region characterization for eddy viscosity. The eddy viscosity for the inner region is described with Spalding's generalized function whereas the outer region, which is characterized by large eddy scales, is treated through an application of Prandtl's eddy viscosity model for free shear flows. A similarity solution for the outer region is obtained for a linearized motion equation and suitably joined to the inner solution by requiring continuity of shear stress and eddy viscosity. The present matching criteria for the two regions result in the preservation of the velocity profile shape in the defect plane, while simultaneously yielding the correct longitudinal development of all layer parameters such as momentum thickness and wall shear stress. The present model is extended to the low Reynolds number regime where the wakestrength is greatly diminished. It is suggested that interfacial conditions are, collectively, the particular feature of incompressible flow which may serve as the point of reference for variable density transformations.

INTRODUCTION

Beginning with Prandtl's boundary layer concept which permitted a useful simplification of the differential equations of fluid motion, there has evolved a methodology of considerable proportions for obtaining solutions to laminar problems. The introduction by Boussinesq of an eddy viscosity to account for the Reynolds stresses in turbulent flow rendered the motion

equation for this flow regime in the same form as for laminar flow.
However, despite the similarity in appearance of the governing
equations, there is at present no universal specification of the
eddy viscosity so that the turbulent flow problem remains incomplete
from a mathematical standpoint. Prandtl and others have sought to
develop phenomenological descriptions of the eddy viscosity which
would close the formulation and permit a solution to the differential
equations.

   Because of the difficulties associated with the foregoing
approach, the integrated equations of the complete boundary layer
have been employed to achieve a large number of engineering
solutions. However, to use integral methods it is first necessary
to know (or imply) a velocity profile, although such specification
can be relatively crude without affecting the overall accuracy of
the results. Most of the velocity profiles in common usage are
composed of two essentially different distributions which are
suitably joined. One part of the profile describes details of the
flow near the wall while the other applies to the outer portion
of the layer. The primary disadvantages of the integral method
are that profile selection is based largely on experience and that
considerable ingenuity is required in the application of the computation technique, (Ref. 1). It is therefore considered
desirable that more perceptive, rational analyses be developed for
determining turbulent boundary layer parameters, especially velocity
profiles.

   The present analysis is based on the usual subdivision of
the turbulent layer into inner and outer regions; the former is
dominated by viscous stresses and small eddy scales, whereas the
latter is characterized by the occurrence of much larger eddy
sizes. This basic difference in the character of these regions
is demonstrated by the necessity of using a particular type of
graphical presentation for each portion of the velocity profile.
Furthermore, it has been found that there is a strong resemblance
between both the structure (Ref. 2) and mean motion (Refs. 3, 4)
of the outer portion of a turbulent wall layer and a free shear
region. Thus, it is possible to model the inner region with
strongly varying eddy viscosity and almost constant shear and
stress, and the outer zone with constant eddy viscosity.[1]

   The present approach incorporates, for the outer portion
of the layer, an eddy viscosity model which has heretofore been
applied successfully to free mixing zones. A similarity solution is obtained for the outer region, and the two solutions
are appropriately joined. The requirement of continuity of

------

[1]Both variations refer to the transverse direction only.

eddy viscosity and shear stress at the junction of the inner and outer regions permits proper longitudinal positioning of the velocity profiles without the use of an integral motion equation. Although the present results are confined to the incompressible flat plate case, it is believed that the model provides a rational basis for extending analytical boundary layer methods to compressible, diabatic, or nonisobaric flow situations. In addition, the present outer region analysis may be utilized in conjunction with various wall models, such as for rough or transpiring surfaces.

ANALYSIS

Previous attempts to obtain a single similarity solution for the complete turbulent layer have been generally unsuccessful. This is due principally to the inference that wall shear stress must be proportional to $x^{-1/2}$ in any single-layer model. Coles (Refs. 5,6) has noted previously the apparent mathematical futility of such an approach. On the other hand, it can be shown that multiple similarity solutions, within the framework of a multi-region model, do not possess the foregoing restriction on the shear stress variation and, therefore constitute a much more attractive approach.

The analytical description of the inner region is well developed, having originated with Prandtl's classical application of the mixing length hypothesis to a constant stress region. Taking the characteristic eddy size (i.e, mixing length) to be proportional to distance from the wall, one is led to the result that $u \sim \log(y)$ or, in implict form, that $y \sim \exp(u)$. In recent years this "law of the wall" has been widely investigated by Coles (Ref. 3), Kleinstein (Ref. 7), Tennekes (Ref. 8), and Spalding (Ref. 9). The latter author has expressed a generalized wall law in the form

$$y^+ = u^+ + E^{-1}\left[\exp(Z) - 1 - Z - Z^2/2 - Z^3/6 - Z^4/24\right] \quad (1)$$

where $Z = K_1 u^+$, and k_1 and E are constants. The significance of this expression is that it encompasses both the logarithmic asymptote and laminarlike region immediately adjacent to the wall. Because $\tau = \rho \nu \, \epsilon(\partial u/\partial y)$, which is almost constant near the surface, one obtains for the eddy viscosity of the inner region $\epsilon^+ = dy^+/du^+$. Upon substitution of Equation (1), it is found that

$$\epsilon^+ = 1 + (k_1/E)\left[\exp(Z) - 1 - Z - Z^2/2 - Z^3/6\right] \quad (2)$$

which, of course, approaches unity at the wall $(Z \to 0)$. This expression has been derived for a constant shear stress which is not strictly valid in any portion of the boundary layer. However, the use of this model for ϵ in a near-constant shear field is contemplated so that small deviations from Equation (1) will be permitted.

From the basic nature of its formulation, the law of the wall must eventually fail at increased distances from the surface because of its omission of the effects of variable shear and large-scale turbulence. This suggests that realistic results for the outer region should be obtained through the application of a model for free turbulence, which is dominated by large eddy scales. Such a procedure has been recently proposed by both Kline (Ref. 4) and Kovasznay (Ref. 10). In the present case, the Prandtl model, which has been widely applied (Ref. 11) in free layer analyses, is utilized. In this classic formulation, the eddy viscosity is taken to be proportional to the layer width (b) and to the difference in velocity across the layer. Thus

$$\epsilon = K\, b(u_{max} - u_{min}) \tag{3}$$

In the present development an approximate similarity solution for the outer region is obtained by utilizing the foregoing representation for ϵ. The following approximations, which are considered valid for the flat plate case, are involved in the analysis: (a) the motion equation is linearized by letting $Du/Dt \approx u_e\, \partial u/\partial x$, (b) the velocity u_i at the interface of inner and outer regions is considered to be nearly constant (i.e., $du_i/dx \approx 0$); and (c) the shape of the outer portion of the profile is similarly unaffected by development distance.

A solution can therefore be obtained in the form

$$\frac{u - u_o}{u_e - u_o} = f(\eta)$$

where $\eta = y/g$, $f(0) = 0$ and $f(\infty) = 1$. The linearized equation of motion $u_e\, \partial u/\partial x = \epsilon\, \partial^2 u/\partial y^2$ thus becomes

$$-u_e(u_e - u_o)\eta\,(g'/g)\,f' = (\epsilon/g^2)\,(u_e - u_o)\,f''$$

or

$$\left[\frac{u_e \, g \, g'}{2 \, \epsilon}\right] 2\eta f' + f'' = 0 \tag{4}$$

For similarity to be realized, the term in brackets must be a constant, which may be taken as unity. The resulting linear equation for f occurs frequently in viscous flow problems and its solution is f = erf η. The outer portion of the turbulent layer profile can therefore be written as

$$u = u_o + (u_e - u_o) \text{ erf } y/g \tag{5}$$

or in defect form as

$$u_e^+ - u^+ = (u_e^+ - u_o^+)(1 - \text{erf } \eta) \tag{6}$$

Turning now to the inner solution, we consider the equation of motion for zero pressure gradient with the transverse velocity neglected so as to yield

$$u \, \frac{\partial u}{\partial x} = \frac{\partial}{\partial y}\left[\epsilon(x, u) \frac{\partial u}{\partial y}\right] \tag{7}$$

For purposes of the present discussion it is assumed that the eddy viscosity can be represented by a product. Thus $\epsilon(x,u)$ = $\check{\epsilon}(x) \, \tilde{E}(u)$. Use of the Kirchoff transformation $V = \int \tilde{E} du$ then allows Equation (7) to be written as

$$\frac{u}{\check{\epsilon}} \, \frac{\partial V}{\partial x} = \frac{\partial^2 V}{\partial y^2} \tag{8}$$

where the shear stress is $\tau = \rho \, \epsilon \, \partial u / \partial y = \rho \, \tilde{\epsilon} \, \partial V / \partial y$. Solutions to modified diffusion equations such as (8) with $V_{y=0}$ = 0 exhibit a strong resemblance to the error function which yields a shear stress variation identical to that in the outer region (i.e., using Equation (5)). In view of this similarity, the inner solution is postulated to have essentially the same shear stress dependence on y as the outer solution would yield for the inner region. Continuity of the shear stress at the interface between the two regions thus implies that the outer solution may be used to evaluate the wall shear stress.

The differential equation for the inner region is

$$\frac{\tau}{\tau_w} \ \tau_w = \rho \nu \epsilon^+ \frac{du}{dy}$$

which, using $\tau_w = \rho v^{*2}$, implies that

$$\epsilon^+ du^+ = \frac{v^*}{\nu} \ \frac{\tau}{\tau_w} \ dy$$

However, $\tau/\tau_w = \exp (-y/g)^2$ from Equation (5), so that one may integrate to obtain the velocity profile for the inner region in the implict form

$$\int_0^{u^+} \epsilon^+ du^+ = \pi^{1/2} (2u_e^+)^{-1} (u_e g/\nu) \ \text{erf} \ \eta$$

Using the foregoing reasoning the wall shear stress may be written, using Equation (3), as

$$\tau_w = K \rho b (u_{max} - u_{min}) \left(\frac{\partial u}{\partial y}\right)_{y_o}$$

For the present let $u_{max} = u_e$, $u_{min} = u_o$, and define[2] the characteristic width b by

$$\left(\frac{\partial u}{\partial y}\right)_{y_o} = \frac{u_e - u_o}{b} \tag{9}$$

Thus the foregoing shear stress expression can be written in the form

$$u_e^+ - u_o^+ = K^{-1/2} \tag{10}$$

---

[2]This somewhat unorthodox definition of b is used primarily for convenience but is not considered to be inconsistent with more common formulations

This relationship indicates that $u_e^+ - u_o^+$ is independent of the ratio u_i/u_e and of the location y_i of the interface.

From Equations (3), (5), and (9), the value of eddy viscosity for the interface (and outer region) is given by

$$\epsilon_i = K(u_e - u_o)\, g\, \pi^{1/2}/2 \tag{11}$$

Using the value of g from the above expression, one can form a Reynolds number based on this scale factor as

$$Re_g = \frac{u_e g}{\nu} = \frac{2\epsilon_i^+ u_e}{K(u_e - u_o)\,\pi^{1/2}}$$

which, after substitution of Equation (10), becomes

$$Re_g = 2(\pi K)^{-1/2}\, \epsilon_i^+ u_e^+ \tag{12}$$

Recalling from Equation (4) that $(u_e g/2\epsilon)dg/dx = 1$, one can insert the value of Re_g from Equation (12) and obtain

$$\frac{dg}{dx} = \frac{(\pi K)^{-1/2}}{u_e^+} \tag{13}$$

One may now write
$$\frac{d\,Re_x}{d\,u_e^+} = \frac{d\,Re_x}{d\,Re_g}\,\frac{d\,Re_g}{d\,u_e^+}$$

The first ratio on the right side is merely equal to dx/dg, which is given in Equation (13), so that, using Equation (12), the foregoing relation may be written as

$$\frac{d\,Re_x}{d\,u_e^+} = \frac{2\,u_e^+}{\pi K}\frac{d}{d\,u_e^+}(\epsilon_i^+ u_e^+) \tag{14}$$

Using Equations (2), (10), and (18), one can show that the
quantity ϵ_i^+ is only a function of u_e^+. Thus Equation (14)
provides a unique relation between the local Reynolds number
and u_e^+ which therefore yields local wall shearing stress as
a function[3] of Re_x. For large values of u^+ the exponential
term in Equation[3] (2) becomes dominant so that a reasonable
approximation for Re_x can be obtained by utilizing this asymptotic variation to determine the integral required in Equation
(14). The result is

$$Re_x = \frac{2}{\Upsilon\,K\,k_1\,E}\,(1 - Z_e + Z_e^2)\,\exp(Z_i) \tag{15}$$

The final form of the outer portion of the velocity profile
can be expressed once the relation between g and δ is determined.
This can be seen from Equations (6) and (10) which yield

$$u_e^+ - u^+ = K^{-1/2}\left[1 - \mathrm{erf}\left(\frac{y}{\delta}\,\frac{\delta}{g}\right)\right] \tag{16}$$

The ratio δ/g depends upon the definition of boundary
layer thickness. For the present it is assumed[4] that $y = \delta$
when $u_e^+ - u^+ = 0.15$. From Equation (16) one thus obtains

$$1 - \mathrm{erf}\,(\delta/g) = 0.15\,K^{1/2} \tag{17}$$

which is an implicit expression for δ/g as a function of K. The
outer portion of the velocity profile is thus expressed by
Equations (16) and (17).

The position of the interface is determined by the quantity
y_i/g which is a constant whose value can be found from the
relations

---

[3]This shear stress variation obviously does not include any
transitional effects.

[4]The more common definition of δ at $u/u_e = 0.995$ is not
employed here primarily because it would not produce an
absolutely constant defect profile.

$$\frac{y_i}{g} = \frac{Re_{y_i}}{Re_g} = \frac{(\pi K)^{1/2}}{2} \frac{y_i^+}{\epsilon_i^+} \approx \frac{(\pi K)^{1/2}}{2k_1} \qquad (18)$$

DISCUSSION OF RESULTS

The only free parameter in the present analysis is the constant K occurring in the Prandtl eddy viscosity model, Equation (3). The value of this constant establishes the absolute magnitude of the intensity of the large-eddy turbulence; it is directly analogous to the spread-rate parameter which occurs in free-layer analyses wherein the similarity variable or homogeneous space coordinate is written as $\sigma y/x$. To graphically illustrate this analogy Fig. 1 presents a schematic representation of the juxtaposition of these two types of velocity profiles. For proper comparison of such different types of flow, the mean velocity profiles must coincide so that, for the hypothetical free layer, there is a secondary velocity given by $u_s = 2u_o - u$. If the various turbulence parameters, such as eddy viscosity, are indeed dependent only upon the local mean velocity field, the values of K for free and boundary layer must be identical.

Studies (Refs. 12, 13) of free layers with finite secondary velocity u_s have suggested that the value of σ is highly dependent upon u_s and varies according to $\sigma = \sigma_{ref} F(u_s)$ where $\sigma_{ref} = \sigma_{u_s} = 0 \approx 11$ or 12 from (Ref. 14). Although the exact form of the function $F(u_s)$ has not yet been well established, one expects from Equation (3) that K will be independent of u_s. Using an error function profile similar to Equation (5) for the free layer, one may show that with consistent definitions of width and velocity difference, the relation between σ_{ref} and K is $K = 2\pi^{1/2}\sigma_{ref})^{-1}$. For the above values of σ_{ref} the values of K are 0.103 and 0.094, respectively. These typical values for free layers may be compared with that obtained by bringing

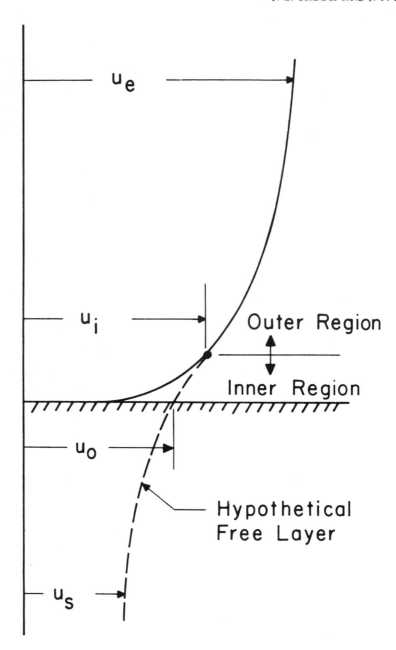

Figure 1   Schematic Comparison of
           Velocity Profiles for Boundary
           Layer and Hypothetical Free
           Layer

into congruence the present prediction with well-known experimental profiles (Ref. 15) in the defect plane as in Figure 2. It is observed that excellent agreement is obtained with a K value of 0.01, thus indicating that the large-eddy structure in

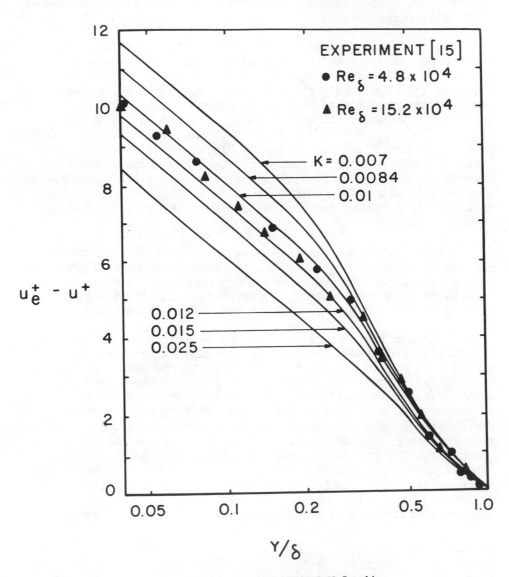

Figure 2 Comparison of Predicted Velocity Profile for Outer Region with Experimental Data, Showing Effect of K in Eddy Viscosity Model, Equation (3)

boundary layer and free layer results in eddy viscosity values differing by a factor of about 10 when the mean velocity profiles are related as in Figure 1. This ratio is comparable to the ratio of general turbulence levels for the free and boundary layers which were observed in the experiments in (Ref. 14) and (Ref. 16), respectively.

It is instructive to examine the effect of the velocity difference and width definitions on the value of K. For example, one could assume that the definitions of b and Δu in Equation (3) should be pertinent to the region in which the large eddies predominate (i.e., the outer region). If one chooses the velocity difference as $u_e - u_i$ and the width as $(u_e - u_i)(\partial u / \partial y)_i$, the value of K which yields the correct defect profile (Figure 2) is found to be 0.0165. It is therefore clear that, although the definitions can affect K somewhat, there appears to be no specification of velocity and width which yields a universal value of K for all flows.[5] In addition, the value of K for the boundary layer is sensitive to effects of free-stream turbulence.

It is also significant to note that the predicted profile remains constant with u_e^+ (or Re_θ). This invariance of the profile in the defect plane is taken to be a primary confirmation of the present formulation because any essentially different large-eddy model for ϵ would not preserve the defect representation.

Although the foregoing theory is satisfactory for the large Re_θ range, it does not predict the experimentally observed decrease (Ref. 6) in the relative strength of the wake component for Re_θ less than 4000. Rather, the present wake strength is constant.[6] For the wake to decrease, the eddy viscosity must be larger than that predicted by Equation (3), thus confirming the existence of a portion of the flow in which the large eddy contribution is not dominant. Similar conclusions have been drawn (Ref. 17) from free layer investigations where parallel streams have only a small difference in velocity. In such cases there exists a substantial shear layer even though Equation (3) would predict a vanishing ϵ. The development of a model which incorporates a variable wake component must therefore include

---

[5] A similar conclusion for free shear flows was given by Kline (Ref. 4).

[6] This implies that, for Coles wake expression in which $u^+ = A + B \log y^+ + B\pi(x)\omega(y/\delta)$, the value of π is predicted to be essentially constant.

the contributions of both large and small eddy sizes in outer
region.

The present theory provides a basis for estimating the
relative contributions of various eddy scales. Using Equation
(3) and Figure 2 one may relate the wake component strength to
the parameter K, which is permitted to vary for small Re_θ (less
than 4000). Utilizing the variations of wake component with
Re_θ presented in Figure 11 of Reference 6, one may determine a
unique relation for K (Re_θ). Then, in lieu of experimental
data, the tabulation of (Ref. 18) can be used to relate u_e^+ and
Re_θ. This permits the establishment of a relation between K
and u_e^+ which, with Equation (10), enables one to plot u_i/u_e as
a function of u_e^+. This significant relationship, shown in
Figure 3, exhibits a well-defined inflection point. Although
the line representing a variable-strength wake is subject to
some uncertainty, it is believed to be essentially correct.

Also shown in Figure 3 is the variation of u_i/u_e implied
by a constant wake component (or constant K); this does not lead
to any inflection point. It is therefore obvious that the
sizable differences between these two variations of u_i/u_e could
lead to significant errors, especially when the use of a compressibility transformation is contemplated.

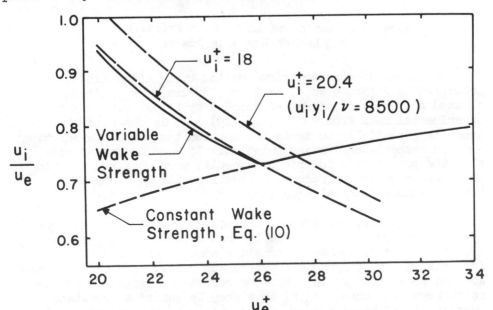

Figure 3   Predicted Variation of Interfacial
           Velocity Illustrating the Effect of
           Various Joining Schemes between
           Inner and Outer Regions

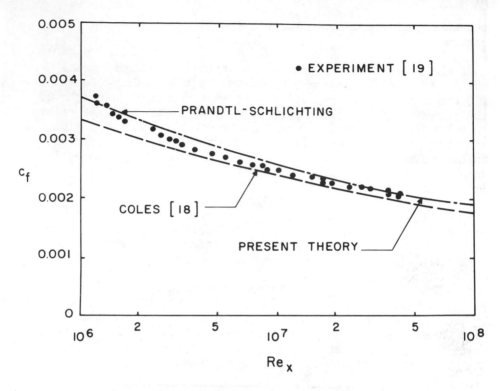

Figure 4   Variation of Local Skin Friction
with Length Reynolds Number

The shear stress variation implied by Equation (15) is presented in Figure 4 as c_f $(= 2/(u_e^+)^2)$ versus Re_x. Also plotted are the variations recommended by Coles (Ref. 18) and experimental data from Smith (Ref. 19). It is observed that there is essentially no deviation between the present prediction and the Prandtl-Schlichting relation. It should also be noted that the predicted skin friction results were obtained through integration of the differential equation <u>without</u> recourse to the von Karman integral equation.

In the pursuit of a more rational description of the turbulent boundary layer, especially when estimating compressibility effects, it is desirable to consider some alternate criteria for patching or joining in a two-region model. Two such possible schemes would require (a) that the regions be merged at a constant Reynolds number or (b) that they be joined at constant velocity. If Re_i $(= u_i^+ y_i^+)$ is constant, the regions must

---

[7]The present theory requires only that du_i/dx be small.

be joined at a constant value of u_i^+.. Equation (2) then forces ϵ^+ (and hence ϵ) to be constant with development length. Clearly, this requires that the wake component grow without limit as τ_w decreases, an obvious violation of experimental observations for the large Reynolds number regime.[8]

In the other aforementioned alternative, the interface velocity u_i is constant; as a consequence, Equation (5) shows that the velocity profile will be similar in the physical plane (u/u_e vs. y/δ) rather than in dimensionless defect plot (Figure 2). Although this is not a poor description,[9] the defect plot has been shown by many experiments to be the pre-served characterization for a large range of Reynolds numbers. On the other hand, the present requirement of interfacial continuity of τ and ϵ in a two-region model results in a nearly constant interface velocity, which is equivalent to an absolutely constant defect velocity, $u^+ - u_i^+$. Therefore, over a small range of Reynolds numbers, the constant-velocity joining scheme and the present model are nearly equivalent, as can be seen in Figure 3.

In summary, the predicted location of the "edge of the wake," is given by $u_i^+ \approx 18$ up to $u_e^+ \approx 26$ after which it is expressed as $u_i^+ \approx u_e^+ - 7.6$ from Equations (16) and (18). It is significant to recall that Coles' substructure hypothesis (Ref. 5) led to the identification of a line given by $uy/\nu = 8500$ as being the point of reference for compressibility transformations. However, after considerable study of available experimental results Coles was unable to discern any significant feature of the incompressible flow which was represented by this line. However, if it is remembered that compressible flow experiments are usually run with values of u_e^+ less than 30, it is found that $u_i y_i/\nu = 8500$ corresponds to a line of $u_i^+ \approx 20.4$. Therefore the present two-layer representation does in fact yield a feature of the incompressible flow near a point in the layer which had been anticipated previously.

---

[8]For extremely small Reynolds numbers such a criterion is quite accurate. For example, the predicted variation in Figure 3 for $u_e^+ < 26$ is well represented by $u_i^+ \approx 18$.

[9]This is evidenced by the widespread use of power-law profiles.

CONCLUDING REMARKS

The present paper has presented an incompressible turbulent boundary layer analysis which is based on a two-region characterization for eddy viscosity. The inner region is described with Spalding's generalized law of the wall whereas the outer region, which is characterized by large eddy scales, is treated through an application of Prandtl's eddy viscosity model for free shear flows.

A similarity solution for the outer region is obtained for a linearized motion equation and suitably joined to the inner solution by requiring continuity of shear stress and eddy viscosity. The present matching criteria for the two regions result in the preservation of the velocity profile shape in the defect plane while simultaneously yielding the correct longitudinal development of all layer parameters such as momentum thickness and wall shear stress.

It is shown that the present model can be extended to the low Reynolds number regime where the wake strength is greatly diminished. The predicted location of the interface between inner and outer regions (i.e., between small and large eddy sizes) is shown to be in general agreement with the requirements of Coles' compressibility transformation, thus suggesting that interfacial conditions are, collectively, the particular feature of incompressible flow which may serve as the point of reference for variable density transformations.

NOMENCLATURE

b $\qquad$ = effective width of outer region

c_f $\qquad$ = skin friction coefficient, $2\,\tau_w / \rho\, u_e^2$

E $\qquad$ = constant in equation (1), taken as 10.1

f $\qquad$ = outer region profile function, equation (4)

g $\qquad$ = width scale factor for outer region, equation (4)

K $\qquad$ = constant in eddy viscosity model, equation (3)

k_1 $\qquad$ = constant in equation (1), taken as 0.407

Re_g = Reynolds number, $u_e g / v$

Re_x = Reynolds number, $u_e x / v$

Re_θ = Reynolds number, $u_e \theta / v$

x = longitudinal coordinate

y = transverse coordinate

y^+ = $v^* y / v$

u = longitudinal velocity

u^+ = u / v^*

v^* = friction velocity, $(\tau_w / \rho)^{1/2}$

Z = $k_1 u^+$

δ = boundary layer thickness

ϵ = eddy kinematic viscosity

ϵ^+ = dimensionless eddy viscosity, $1 + \epsilon / v$

η = similarity parameter y/g

v = kinematic viscosity

ρ = fluid density

τ = shear stress

Subscripts

i = designation of interface between inner and outer regions

e = designation of free stream edge of boundary layer

o = designation of outer solution evaluated at wall $(y = 0)$

w = designation of wall conditions

REFERENCES

1. Spence, D. A., "Development of Turbulent Boundary Layers,"
    J. Aeronautical Sciences, 23, 3-15 1956

2. Townsend, A. A., The Structure of Turbulent Shear Flow, 246
    Cambridge University Press, 1956

3. Coles, D. E., "The Law of the Wake in the Turbulent Boundary
    Layer," J. Fluid Mechanics, 1, 191-226 1956

4. Kline, S. J., "Some Remarks on Turbulent Shear Flows,"
    Proc. Inst. of Mech. Engrs., 180, 222-244 1965

5. Coles, D. E., "The Turbulent Boundary Layer in a Compressible
    Fluid," Physics of Fluids, 7, 1403-1423 1964

6. Coles, D. E., "The Turbulent Boundary Layer in a Compressible
    Fluid," RAND Report, R-403-PR, 1962

7. Kleinstein, G., "Generalized Law of the Wall and Eddy Viscosity
    Model for Wall Boundary Layers," AIAA J. 5, 1402-1407

8. Tennekes, H., "Law of the Wall for Turbulent Boundary
    Layers in Compressible Flow," AIAA J. 5, 489-492, 1967

9. Spalding, D. B., "A Single Formula for the 'Law of the
    Wall,'" Trans., ASME, 83, Series E, 455-467 1961

10. Kovasznay, L. S. G., "Structure of the Turbulent Boundary
    Layer," Boundary Layers and Turbulence, Physics of Fluids
    Supplement, S25-S30 1967

11. Schlichting, H., Boundary Layer Theory, (McGraw-Hill,
    New York, 1968) 6th Ed.

12. Korst, H. H. and W. L. Chow, "Non-Isoenergetic Turbulent
    Jet Mixing Between Two Compressible Streams at Constant
    Pressure," NASA CR-419, 1966

13. Sabin, C. M., "An Analytical and Experimental Study of
    the Plane, Incompressible Turbulent, Free-shear Layer
    with Arbitrary Velocity Ratio and Pressure Gradient,"
    Trans. ASME, 87, Series D, 421-428 1965

14. Leipman, H. W., and J. Laufer, "Investigations of Free
     Turbulent Mixing," NACA TN 1257 1947

15. Klebanoff, P. S. and Z. W. Diehl, "Some Features of
     Artificially Thickened Fully Developed Turbulent Boundary
     Layers with Zero Pressure Gradient," NACA Report 1110, 1957

16. **Klebanoff, P. S., "Characteristics of Turbulence in a**
     Boundary Layer with Zero Pressure Gradient, "NACA Report
     1274 1955

17. Peters, C. E., "A Model for the Free Turbulent Eddy
     Viscosity," Arnold Engineering Development Center Report,
     AEDC TR-65-209, 1965

18. Coles, D. E., "Measurements in the Boundary Layer on a
     Smooth Flat Plate in Supersonic Flow," Ph D Thesis,
     Cal. Inst. of Tech., 1953

19. Smith, D. S. and J. P. Walker, "Skin Friction Measurements
     in Incompressible Flow," NASA TR R-26, 1959

AN EXPERIMENTAL STUDY OF THE EFFECTS OF DILUTE SOLUTIONS OF POLYMER
ADDITIVES ON BOUNDARY LAYER CHARACTERISTICS

John M. Killen and John Almo

St. Anthony Falls Hydraulic Laboratory

University of Minnesota

ABSTRACT

Experimental measurements of drag, root mean square surface
pressure fluctuation, surface pressure fluctuation spectrum, and
radiated flow noise on a rotating cylinder in water are described.
It was found that the addition of the dilute solution of polymer
additive would reduce drag, surface pressure fluctuation, and also
high frequency radiated flow noise.

The polymer additives used were Polyox WSR 301, Separan, and
JP 2 polymer in concentrations of 10 to 1000 ppmw.

INTRODUCTION

The work reported here is an effort to show from laboratory
experiments the effect of various concentrations of water soluble
polymers on the surface pressure fluctuations, radiated noise,
and drag on a surface in relative motion with water.

The effectiveness and benefits of polymers as drag reducers
are now well recognized. However, their parallel effect on surface
pressure fluctuations and radiated flow noise remains partly in the
realm of speculation.

The root mean square (rms) values of the surface pressure
fluctuations integrated over the band of frequencies present have
been shown to be closely related to the wall shear (Ref. 1)

$$P'/\tau_o = K$$

where the constant K has been given values from 1.0 to 4.0 (Ref. 2), depending on the experimenter.

The use of polymer additives as a drag reducer would be expected from the relationship given above to reduce surface pressure fluctuations. The experiments to be reported here show this to be only partly true depending also on the frequency spectrum distribution. The average rms value of the pressure integrated over the whole band tends to be greater than expected. A recent paper by F. White (Ref. 3) suggests the observations reported here. The explanation is offered that the addition of a polymer produces a reduction in the integrated rms pressure and also a shift in the pressure spectrum, which can with some types of polymers offset the benefit of the part due to shear reduction. The three polymers used here — guar gum, Polyox WSR 301, and Separan — seemed to produce the same result, a reduction in rms level only partly correlated with shear. The polymer CMC, which White estimated would produce a greater effect on pressure fluctuation, was not used as it requires rather large quantities for comparable drag reduction as compared with the Polyox and Separan.

Measurements of radiated flow noise with the addition of polymer were also made. The addition of a polymer produces a marked reduction in flow noise in the high frequency range. The integrated flow noise over the spectrum is reduced in the same order as the drag reduction.

EXPERIMENTAL EQUIPMENT

A rotating cylinder test facility was chosen in preference to a towing tank or water tunnel for the following reasons: it has the smallest mass for the active area, it has a minimum of moving parts to generate unwanted noise, and it has a naturally rigid structural form. The rotating cylinder was positioned on the axis of a steel tank 6 ft in diameter and 6 ft high. The tank was supported on three I beams. A cork pad was installed between the I beams and the concrete floor of the laboratory for sound isolation. Sandbags were placed against the exterior walls of the tank to provide additional damping of the tank wall as well as some isolation from sound transmitted through the air.

The tank capacity was 1260 gallons. It was filled to a 5-1/2 ft depth from the municipal water supply or the contents of the St. Anthony Falls Hydraulic Laboratory's 6 in. water tunnel. The water tunnel is also filled from the municipal water supply, which is processed river water. The water tunnel is equipped with an air separator and pressure control and thus provides a simple and rapid means of removing dissolved and free air from the water

to the concentration level required. Diversion of water from the
water tunnel to the tank enabled tests to be conducted with various
dissolved air contents. A steam heat exchanger was also installed
in the tank to permit adjustment or control of the water temperature.

The rotating cylinder was supported on a hollow stainless steel
shaft mounted in water-lubricated rubber bearings. The cylinder
itself was 1 ft long with an external diameter of 1 ft. Its
top was submerged 2 ft below the static water surface in the tank.
The cylinder was hollow to provide space for instruments and was
constructed of a synthetic wood material (Renwood) with brass end
plates 1/4 in. thick. Renwood cones were attached to both end
plates. A wall thickness of 3 in. was selected to reduce cylinder wall vibrations. This type of construction has proved to be
free of any detectable resonant peak in the noise spectrum. The
cylinder and end cones were finished with a heavy coat of epoxy
paint. The surface was machined to a 0.001 in. "runout" dynamically
balanced and polished to a high gloss. It was waxed frequently
during the test program to assure that the cylinder surface approached
a hydraulically smooth surface.

The cylinder shaft was supported by a wood framework attached
to the laboratory floor and wall, avoiding contact with the tank.
A water-lubricated rubber bearing and thrust washer connected
the cylinder, drive shaft, and pulleys to the support frame. A
second rubber guide bearing mounted on a cross frame inside the
tank was necessary to hold the cylinder in an axial position. The
cross frame also supported a 2 ft diameter disk immediately above
the cylinder to prevent air from being drawn down the vortex core
which occurred in the tank during operation. The cylinder was
driven by a 20 hp, 3500 rpm induction motor through a "V" belt
drive. Speed changes were effected by various combinations of
pulleys on the motor and cylinder shaft. Figure 1 shows a drawing
of the tank and cylinder.

A set of strain gages was mounted on the drive shaft of the
rotating cylinder and served to measure total torque exerted by
the fluid on the cylinder and end cones. A second dynamometer was
mounted in one of the end cones to measure the drag on the cone
separately for purposes of correction of the total drag for end
effects.

The acoustical pressure in the tank was sensed by a USRL H17
hydrophone. The hydrophone was supported on a strut mounted mid-
way between the rotating cylinder and the tank wall. Its active
surface was located on a horizontal plane passing through the
lower edge of the rotating cylinder. The calibrations supplied by
USRL were used as a reference.

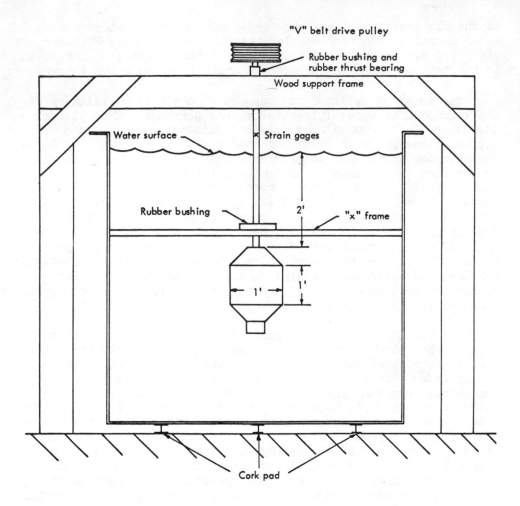

Figure 1 - Sketch of Test Tank with Rotating Cylinder in Place

    The signal from the hydrophone was amplified by a Sensonic model SE 140 preamplifier. A Panoramic model Sb-7b2 frequency analyzer was used above 10 kHz and a Hewlett Packard model 300 frequency analyzer was used below 10 kHz to measure sound intensity in discrete frequency bands.

    The fluctuating pressure on the surface of the rotating cylinder was measured by a flush-mounted hydrophone 1/8 inch in diameter obtained on loan from NSRDC and described in Reference 4. The signal from the hydrophone was amplified by a low noise preamplifier before transmission by slip rings to the remainder of the signal processing equipment.

The rms pressure was measured by a Ballentine 300 true rms voltmeter. The power spectrum was measured by a Quan-Tech frequency analyzer. The surface pressure hydrophone and preamplifier low frequency rolloff began at 200 Hz (3 Db point).

EXPERIMENTAL PROCEDURE

The test tank was surveyed with a hydrophone to determine the presence of standing waves. Those measurements indicated a nearly uniform pressure field throughout the liquid in the tank when excited with a random noise source or flow noise from the rotating cylinder. This fact made possible the measurement of sound power from a pressure measurement at an arbitrary point without the necessity of providing a means for averaging the standing wave pressure.

To relate the power input to the tank to the pressure measured by the hydrophone, a procedure similar to that of Reference 5 was followed. A source of acoustical energy was installed in the tank. The proportionality constant relating the acoustical energy introduced into the tank to the resulting pressure was determined at discrete frequencies. The acoustical source referred to above was a 1/4 in. copper pipe flattened near one end. The pipe was connected to a constant pressure water supply. As water flowed through the flattened part of the pipe, cavitation occurred, creating essentially a point source of intense noise.

The energy output of the source was determined by measuring the pressure at a known distance from the cavitating source with a standard hydrophone. The intensity $(P')^2/\rho c$ was then integrated over a spherical surface surrounding the source.

It was known from previous work that the air would be released from the water as tiny bubbles in regions of high shear near the rotating cylinder surface. As an air bubble diffused away from the surface into the liquid of the reverberant chamber it would produce greater attenuation of the sound, destroying the tank calibration. An effort was made to reduce this effect by filling the tank with water of low dissolved air content so that the released air bubbles would redissolve quickly. The test water was deaerated in the St. Anthony Falls Hydraulic Laboratory's 6 in. water tunnel described previously. Air contents as low as 7 ppmw were used. The water was discarded at approximately 15 ppmw. The total air content of the test water was monitored by a Van Slyke apparatus. It was found to remain constant for several days. It was learned in previous work that this procedure would eliminate the effect of air bubbles on measurements.

RESULTS

The cylinder rotating in a large tank gives rise to two
dominant motions: (1) a free vortex where the product of velocity
and radius equals a constant Vr = C, and (2) an approximately
logarithmic velocity distribution near the cylinder (Ref. 6).
Flow no doubt occurred along the axis of the cylinder, although
it was hoped a brief operating period would reduce this effect.

Velocity profiles were measured on the rotating cylinder with
a Pitot tube for velocities of 25 and 38 fps. These results are
shown in Figure 2 in comparison with the data of Tsai, (Ref. 7),
taken in a gravity flow water tunnel with flow velocities of
4 to 8 fps.

Measurements closer to the wall were prevented by the small
eccentricity of the cylinder shaft in its guide bearings.

The drag coefficient of the rotating cylinder in tap water and
in polymer was measured for a speed range of 12 to 100 fps. The
drag coefficient C_d is defined according to the following equation
from Reference (8):

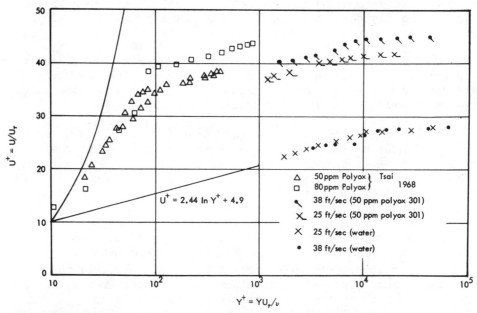

Figure 2 - Velocity Profile near Rotating Cylinder

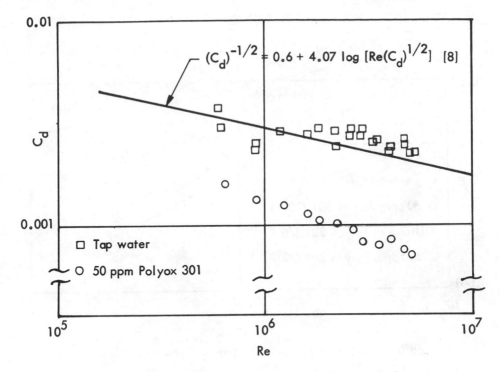

Figure 3 - Drag Coefficient for a Rotating Cylinder

$$C_d = \frac{M}{qsa} = \frac{M}{\pi \rho a^4 \omega^2 \ell}$$

The measured drag coefficient is shown in Figure 3 in comparison
with the extrapolation of the hydraulically smooth cylinder data
of Theodorsen and Regier (Ref. 8). The moment coefficient C_m for
a cone is shown in Figure 4. The moment coefficient in Figure 4
is for two cones, which was convenient for the purposes of this
investigation.

The surface hydrophone was calibrated in place by exciting the
tank with a cavitating source as described previously for the
tank calibration. The voltage output was compared with an H17 USRL
hydrophone in the same tank.

A comparison is made in Figure 5 of the surface fluctuations
on a rising cylindrical body as measured by Nisewanger and Sperling
(Ref. 9) and as found in the present study. Only one size of
microphone (1/8 in.) was used on the rotating cylinder. This

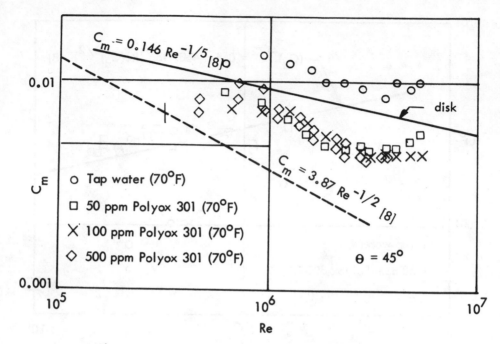

Figure 4 - Moment Coefficient for a Rotating Cone

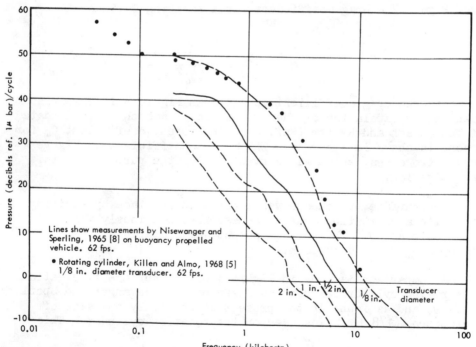

Figure 5 - Comparison of Surface Pressure Fluctuation on a Rotating
Cylinder and Buoyant Body

comparison is presented as further evidence of the usefulness of the rotating cylinder in flow noise studies.

Figures 6 and 7 show the root mean square pressure integrated over the range of frequencies present as a function of Reynolds number. In Figure 6 the rms pressure is divided by the wall shear, while in Figure 7 the rms pressure is divided by the dynamic pressure. The rms values have not been corrected for hydrophone size, as appropriate correction with polymer will have to wait for more information on the correlation of pressure fluctuation. Correlation measurements are contemplated very soon under the present investigation program.

The polymer produces a reduction of pressure in level with the addition of polymer but not as much as the reduction in shear, as can be noted from Figure 6. This is in accord with White's prediction (Ref. 3) that for a given velocity the addition of a polymer will cause a reduction in surface pressure fluctuation, but for a given shear an expected increase in surface pressure fluctuation will result. It was also found in some instances that the ratio

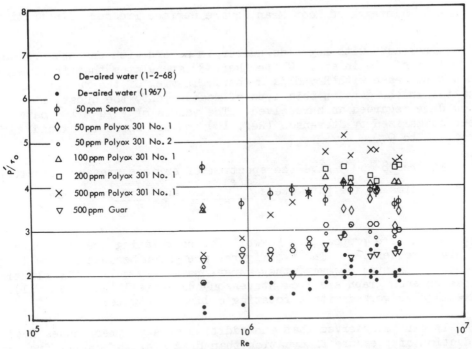

Figure 6 - Integrated Root Mean Square Surface Pressure Fluctuation

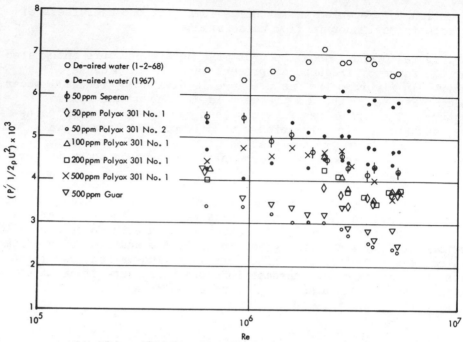

Figure 7 - Integrated Root Mean Square Surface Pressure Fluctuation

P'/τ_0 increased with Reynolds number in accord with the measurement of Bull (Ref. 2) in air. White (Ref. 3) speculates that the P'/τ_0 should decrease with Reynolds number. In view of the rather large scatter in the data in this type of measurement, the question should be regarded as unresolved. The values of $P'/q \times 10^3$ have been summarized by Stevenson (Ref. 10) and are shown to extend from 4.2 to 9.0.

Figures 8 and 9 give the spectrum of surface pressure fluctuation in terms of the parameters $\dfrac{\phi(f) \, U_\infty}{\tau_0^2 D}$ and $\dfrac{fD}{U_\infty}$. These parameters were proposed by Foxwell for correlating pressure data at high frequencies. The two figures are given because of the large number of points; however, they superimpose very well. The slanting lines on each graph are from Stevenson and Foxwell (Refs. 10, 11). Foxwell also worked with a rotating cylinder in water.

It can be observed that the addition of a polymer causes less reduction of pressure fluctuation than drag over the entire fre-

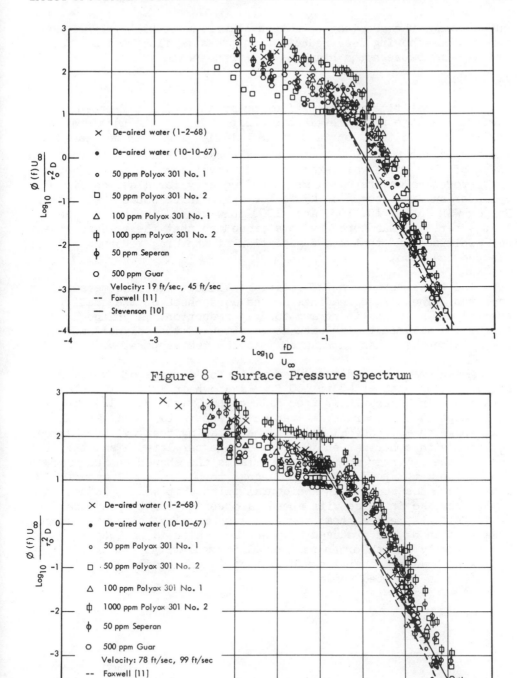

Figure 8 - Surface Pressure Spectrum

Figure 9 - Surface Pressure Spectrum

quency band, the greatest deviation occurring at high polymer concentrations showing less reduction in pressure fluctuation. A
break point between the high and low frequencies at $\log \frac{fD}{U_\infty} \approx -0.5$
is evident.

A typical time record of flow noise at a single frequency indicated that the noise level rose sharply during the acceleration
period, dropped to a constant value briefly, and then decreased as
the vortex built up in the tank and air was released. The recorded
level of flow noise was taken from the level portion of the record.
This procedure was repeated at each frequency for a series of
cylinder surface speeds of 45 to 102 fps. Three concentrations of
Polyox WSR 301 of 10, 100, and 1000 ppmw were dissolved in the
test water. It was hoped by this procedure that the release of air
was minimized and that the degradation of the drag reducing polymer
was reduced also.

The total torque on the rotating cylinder was also measured at
each run. The torque readings served as a check on the quality of
the polymer solution in regard to drag reduction. A change in
torque was assumed to indicate degradation of the polymer and a
new solution was then introduced into the test apparatus.

Measurement of radiated flow noise for a range of cylinder
surface velocities of 40 to 100 fps is shown in Figure 10. The
data shown in Figure 10 is from Killen and Crist (Ref. 12) with
the exception of two runs, in tap water and in 1000 ppmw Polyox
301, in which the conical ends on the rotating test cylinder were
replaced with spherical ends. This change permitted a smooth joint
between the cylinder and its end surfaces and showed an increase in
flow noise with speed more nearly equal to U^0. A small amount of
added roughness such as an accidental paint chip would produce the
rapid increase in noise with speed as observed on the previous data.
It is felt, therefore, that the increases in flow noise with speed
greater than U^0 are produced by a surface which is no longer
hydraulically smooth or an accidental irregularity. It is significant, however, that the addition of Polyox produced a sizable
reduction in radiated noise.

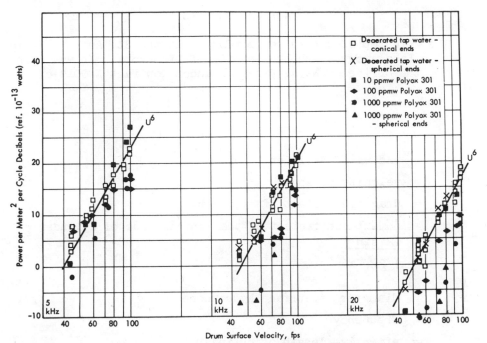

Figure 10 - Radiated Flow Noise from Rotating Cylinder

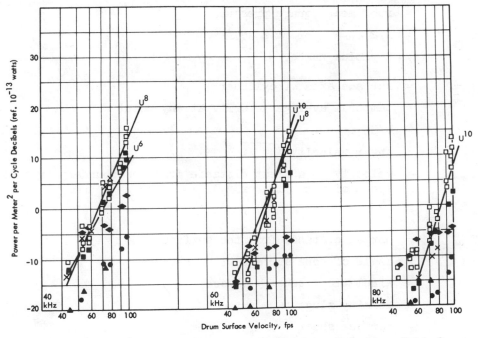

Figure 10 (Cont.) - Radiated Flow Noise from Rotating Cylinder

ACKNOWLEDGMENTS

    The work reported here was performed at the St. Anthony Falls
Hydraulic Laboratory of the University of Minnesota. It was sponsored by the Office of Naval Research under Contract N00014-67-0113-
0003.

NOMENCLATURE

a	=	radius of cylinder
c	=	velocity of sound
C_d	=	drag coefficient of cylinder
C_m	=	moment coefficient of the conical ends of cylinder = $\dfrac{2M \sin \theta}{1/2 \rho \omega^2 a^5}$
D	=	diameter of surface hydrophone
f	=	frequency
ℓ	=	effective length of cylinder
M	=	moment
P'	=	root mean square pressure
q	=	$1/2\, \rho \omega^2 a^2$ or $1/2\, \rho U_\infty^2$
Re	=	Reynolds number = $\dfrac{\omega a^2}{v}$
S	=	surface area of cylinder
U	=	temporal average velocity at any point
U^+	=	U/U_τ
U_τ	=	shear velocity $\sqrt{\tau_o/\rho}$
U_∞	=	velocity at a great distance from the boundary or surface speed of the cylinder
Y^+	=	$\dfrac{Y U_\tau}{v}$
Y	=	normal distance from the surface
θ	=	angle of cone surface with the axis
v	=	kinematic viscosity f^2/sec
ρ	=	density slugs
τ_o	=	surface shear
$\phi(f)$	=	pressure squared per cycle

REFERENCES

1. Kraichnan, R. H., "Pressure fluctuations in turbulent flow over a flat plate," Jour. Acoustical Soc. of Am. 28, p. 378 (May 1956).

2. Bull, M. K., J. F. Willy and D. R. Blackman, "Wall Pressure Fluctuation in Boundary Layer Flow and Response of Simple Structures to Random Fields," University of Southhampton Astronautic and Aeronautics Report 243, AD 631-521.

3. White, F. W., "An analysis of the effect of polymer additives on boundary layer noise," AIAA Paper No. 68, p. 642 (June 1968).

4. Franz, G. J., "Flow noise measurement in water," 72 Meeting of the Acoustical Soc. of Am. (Nov. 2-5, 1968).

5. Fitzpatrick, H. M. and R. Lee, "Measurement of Noise Radiated by Subsonic Air Jets," David Taylor Model Basin Report 835, November 1952.

6. Skudrzyk, E. and G. Haddle, "Noise production in a turbulent boundary layer by smooth and rough surfaces," Second Symposium on Naval Hydrodynamics 1958, pp. 75-103.

7. Tsia, F. Y., "The Turbulent Boundary Layer in the Flow of Dilute Solutions of Linear Macromolecules," P.H.D. Thesis, University of Minnesota, 1968.

8. Theodorsen, T. and A. Regier, "Experiments on Drag of Revolving Disks, Cylinders, and Streamline Rods at High Speed," NACA Report 793, 1944.

9. Nisewanger, C. R. and F. B. Sperling, "Flow Noise Inside Boundary Layers of Buoyancy-Propelled Test Vehicles," U.S. Naval Ordnance Test Station, China Lake, Calif., NOTSTp3511.

10. Stevenson, M., The Wall Pressure Spectra in a Thick Turbulent Boundary Layer, Robert Taggart Report RT 15101, April 1967.

11. Foxwell, J. H., "The Wall Pressure Spectrum Under a Turbulent Boundary Layer," Admiralty Underwater Weapons Establishment, August 1966.

12. Killen, J. M. and S. D. Crist, "The Effect of Dilute Solutions of Drag Reducing Polymers on Radiated Flow Noise," St. Anthony Falls Hydraulic Laboratory Project Report No. 90, University of Minnesota, July 1967.

NORMAL-STRESS EFFECTS IN DRAG-REDUCING FLUIDS

R. I. Tanner

Brown University

ABSTRACT

It is shown that some viscoelastic fluid theories show an increased "resistance" to nonviscometric (or nonshearing) deformations due to "normal-stress effects," but no upper limit on stretch rate is discernible. Using this fact in a one-dimensional Burgers-type model of "weak turbulence," drag reduction is predicted.

Some observations on transition in solutions of polyethylene-oxide (Polyox) were made using a water-table. The main findings are not discordant with the idea of extra difficulty in setting up nonviscometric motions. It was found that (1) the rate of spread of turbulent "spots" is reduced; (2) a fine-grained wavy structure convered the surface; waviness increased with concentration; and (3) turbulent spot generation at sharp edges was reduced.

RHEOLOGICAL PRELIMINARIES

The phenomenon of turbulent drag reduction has brought forth several explanations which may be roughly classified in categories as follows:

1. Slip at the wall
2. Viscoelastic effects of the linear type, leaning on reduction of dynamic viscosity
3. Nonlinear viscoelastic phenomena
4. Special effects occurring on a molecular scale.

The first explanation seems highly unlikely to be literally correct, particularly in view of the experiments of Goren and Norbury (Ref. 1) who showed that a uniform concentration of additive existed throughout a circular tube. The second explanation has not been supported by an analytical study (Ref. 2) nor does it seem very plausible since the effective viscosity cannot be reduced below the solvent viscosity; this leaves very little room for reduction in dilute solutions. Lumley (Ref. 3) has considered the problem of matching time scales and was led to some hypotheses about molecular behavior (Category 4), but these ideas require experimental verification before acceptance.

In **Category** 3 some much more attractive ideas have been proposed by, e.g., Metzer and Astarita (Ref. 4). The basic idea is that a non-Newtonian elastic fluid possesses a maximum stretch rate, usually a fraction of $1/\lambda$, where λ is a relaxation time. The reasoning behind this idea involves the use of several constitutive relations which show such a maximum stretch rate in certain homogeneous flows; e.g., simple extension of rods and sheets. It is then argued that the nonviscometric motion (turbulence) is also governed by a maximum rate of deformation. This reduces dissipation and, hence, drag reduction occurs.

In support of this idea, Astarita (Ref. 5) has stated that "fluids for which the rate of stress relaxation is essentially exponential may flow at any value of $\lambda \sqrt{II_d}$ without developing infinite stresses, but cannot flow at values of $\lambda \overline{\sqrt{II_d - II_\omega}}$ exceeding some critical upper limit of the order of unity." Here II_ω is the second invariant of the vorticity tensor and II_d is the second invariant of the rate of deformation tensor. It is not difficult to find numerous examples not obeying the above statement. For example, some versions of the Kaye-Bernstein-Kearsley-Zapas (KBKZ) theory (Refs. 6,7) can relax exponentially and yet show no critical upper limit for the quantity stated. A concrete example is provided by the so-called network-rupture theory (Ref. 8) using the following relation between the stress matrix ($\underline{\underline{T}}$), the pressure p, the unit matrix ($\underline{\underline{I}}$), the relative (Finger) strain matrix $\underline{\underline{B}}$ and a memory function $\mu(t-t')$:

$$\underline{\underline{T}} = -p\underline{\underline{I}} + \int_{t-\tau_R}^{t} \mu(t-t') \; \underline{\underline{B}}(t') \; dt' \tag{1}$$

where t is the present time, $t > t'$ and τ_R is the network lifetime. τ_R depends in general on the flow at the point being considered and on the time. For simple shearing it is found that $\tau_R = B/|\gamma|$ where γ is the shearing rate and B is a "rupture strain magnitude" (a material constant). Consider the case when the memory function μ has only a single relaxation time λ; i.e.,

$$\mu = \frac{\eta}{\lambda^2} \exp \{-(t-t')/\lambda\}$$
(2)

where η is the zero-shearing-rate viscosity. It is readily shown (Ref. 8) that the simple shearing viscosity η_s at a shear rate γ is given by

$$\eta_s(\gamma) = \eta\left[1 - \left(1 + \frac{B}{\lambda|\gamma|}\right) \exp - \left(\frac{B}{\lambda|\gamma|}\right)\right]$$
(3)

and the tensile (Trouton) viscosity η_T at an extension rate G is given by

$$\eta_T(G) = \frac{\eta}{\lambda G} \left[\frac{1 - \exp(2\bar{B} - \frac{B}{\lambda G})}{1 - 2\lambda G} - \frac{1 - \exp - (\bar{B} + \frac{B}{\lambda G})}{1 + \lambda G}\right]$$
(4)

where $\bar{B}$ is related to the rupture strain B by the relation

$$B^2 = \exp 2\bar{B} + 2 \exp(-\bar{B}) - 3$$
(5)*

(In a tensile flow we recall that the velocity field is of the form $\underline{V} = (Gx, -\frac{G}{2} y, -\frac{G}{2} z)$.)

Equation (1) also yields the following result for shear stress relaxation following the sudden cessation of motion at t = 0 in a sample that was undergoing steady shearing at a shear rate γ (Ref. 9).

$$\frac{\tau}{\gamma} = \eta_s(\gamma) \exp(-t/\lambda)$$
(6)

where $\eta_s(\gamma)$ is given by equation (3). Thus the rate of stress relaxation is essentially exponential. For arbitrarily large values of stretching rate G, which gives arbitrarily large values of $\lambda\sqrt{II_d - II_\omega}$, we find no singular behavior in the tensile stress and no critical upper stretch rate exists. However, a finite maximum does appear in the tensile viscosity curves. Figure 1 shows the type of result obtained for a single time constant and various values of the rupture parameter $\bar{B}$. Clearly, if a "solvent" viscosity η_∞ is also considered (simple adding η_∞ to (3) and 3 η_∞ to (4)), then we may have a large ratio of maximum tensile/shear viscosity while the shear viscosity is relatively constant. With many time constants a broad maximum of η_T/η_s is obtained, and this

---

*This formula corrects that given by Tanner and Simmons (Ref. 8).

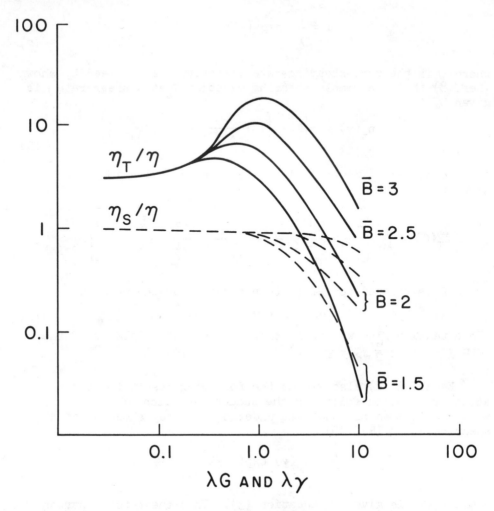

Figure 1   Typical Calculated Tensile and Shearing Viscosities

seems to be characteristic of the (scanty) data on polymer melts
(Ref. 10).   More relevant to the drag reduction problem is the
evidence which is becoming available on the behavior of climbing
"ropes" or threads of dilute polymer solutions. Although exact
quantitative analysis of the rope "trick" is difficult, it becomes clear from recent data of our own that the tensile viscosity
of such ropes can at least be $10 - 10^2$ times the shear viscosity.
For example, with a 400 ppm Polyox solution, we found that the
tensile viscosity was apparently of the order of 10^2 times the

shear viscosity. Considering the value of the tensile viscosity (from equation (4)) at $\lambda G = 1/2$, we find, for large $\bar{B}$,

$$\left. \eta_T/\eta \right|_{\lambda G = 0.5} = 4\bar{B} \tag{7}$$

Thus for η_T/η of order 10, we require that $\bar{B}$ is about 2 to 3, which has been found to be a reasonable value for polysytrene melts (Ref. 11). Larger values of $\bar{B}$ may be appropriate for dilute solutions but exact values are not yet available.

In summary, we see that the idea of an absolute maximum of stretch rate does not seem to be rigorously demonstrable, and thus, some doubt is cast upon theories of drag reduction which appeal to a maximum stretching rate. However, the idea that resistance to motion ("viscosity") in a nonviscometric non-Newtonian flow exceeds that in a Newtonian fluid whose viscosity is equal to the shear viscosity, seems to be fruitful. This idea is explored below in a Burgers-type model of turbulence.

MODEL TURBULENCE CALCULATIONS FOR A SHEAR FLOW

Because of the sheer difficulty of turbulent flow analyses, the present paper uses a one-dimensional model of turbulent shear flow (Ref. 2) of the Burgers (Ref. 12) type. If the turbulence "velocity" is split into the steady part $(U(x))$ and the fluctuating part $(u(x,t))$, then the turbulence dynamics is modelled by the following equations:

$$\tau = \nu_s \frac{dU}{dx} + \overline{u^2} \tag{8}$$

where τ is the local (kinematic) "shear stress" and ν_s is the mean shear (kinematic) viscosity; and

$$\frac{\partial u}{\partial t} + 2u \frac{\partial u}{\partial x} = u \frac{\partial U}{\partial x} + \frac{\partial \sigma}{\partial x} \tag{9}$$

where σ is the turbulent "shear stress" to be calculated from an equation similar to (1). For a "Newtonian" flow $\sigma = \nu_s \frac{\partial u}{\partial x}$. The calculation of σ for general (three-dimensional) nonviscometric flows is very difficult. If we consider weak "turbulence," then we may appeal to the results of Pipkin and Owen (Ref. 13) for nearly viscometric flows, finding σ as a linear functional of the (small) deviation of the flow from a shear flow. This process yields, in principle, a form for σ which may be simplified for the one-dimensional calculation. A process of solution similar to

that used previously (Ref. 2) may then be attempted, but in general
this does not result in a closed set of equations. Instead of this
approach we will assume that the nonviscometric response ("turbulent" part of the motion) can be represented satisfactorily by
an effective tensile viscosity (v_T) greater than v_s, so that
equation (8) is unchanged, but in equation (9) we replace σ by
$v_T \frac{\partial u}{\partial x}$. If one considers that the relative motion of neighboring
particles in a turbulent medium (Ref. 14) leads, on average, to
particle separation much as occurs in the tensile flow, then the
above hypothesis appears to be reasonable. The idea of taking
$v_T > v_s$ represents a useful way of building the physical concept
of extra resistance to nonviscometric motion into our one-dimensional
model, which concept is strongly suggested by the available evidence.
We emphasize the difficulties attending the exact three-dimensional
calculation and more complex versions of the one-dimensional calculation. Following our previous analysis (Ref. 2) with the constant
effective tensile viscosity v_T, we find that the model equations
may be solved as before to yield the following result for the turbulent friction factor c_f (assuming "weak turbulence")

$$\frac{\tau}{\frac{1}{2}U^2} = \frac{v_s}{v_T} c_f(Rv_T/v_s) \tag{10}$$

where R is the Reynolds number based on the zero-shear viscosity
defined by

$$R = 4b^2\tau/v_s^2 \tag{11}$$

and where 2b is a characteristic dimension ("channel width"). In
a laminar flow the familiar form for the friction factor results
$(c_f = 2/R)$ and the result is no different with or without viscoelastic effects. At a value of $R = v_T\pi^2/v_s$, "transition" occurs,
and the result for c_f may be expressed in terms of Jacobian elliptic
functions (Ref. 2). For various values of v_T/v_s $(\equiv \eta_T/\eta \equiv \epsilon)$,
the friction factor curves are shown in Figure 2. Thus drag re-
duction is predicted and the transition Reynolds number is raised.

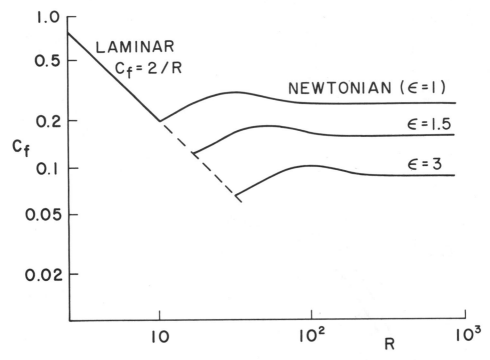

Figure 2   Friction Factor in Model Shear Flow for Various

$$\epsilon(= \nu_T / \nu_S)$$

In Couette flow, such observations on transition have been reported
by Karlsson and Griem (Ref. 15) so that the above arguments may be
applicable to that case also. Figure 3 shows the change in the
"velocity profiles" which, incidentally, are remarkably similar
to experimentally measured curves (Ref. 2). Regarding the
practical application of the relevant form of equation (10) to
real shear flows, the difficulty lies in estimating ν_T / ν_S which
in the real three-dimensional case probably depends on the local
turbulent intensity as well as rheological parameters. Further,
since the derivation is based on the notion of weak turbulence,
equation (10) is probably only indicative of direction of change
far from transition. (Attempts to include triple correlations in
the model need further unattractive assumptions.) With these reservations, it is hoped that the analysis shows that an upper
critical stretching rate for nonviscometric motions is not necessary
for the prediction of drag reduction; it is only necessary that
nonviscometric motions be more difficult to maintain. Thus a
plausible modification of the maximum stretch rate type of theory
(Category 3 above) is proposed, whereby nonviscometric motions
are constrained but not prohibited.

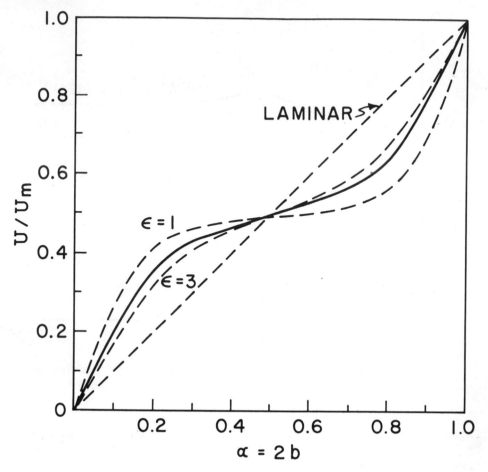

Figure 3   Calculated "Velocity" Profiles (ϵ = 1 and 3 - - -) compared

with an experiment (_____) at 9 X (critical R)

SOME OBSERVATIONS ON THE TRANSITION MECHANISM IN POLYOX SOLUTIONS

The classical observations on transition in boundary layers were made by Emmons (Ref. 16) using a nearly horizontal glass plate with water flowing over it in a layer about 1/4 inch deep. He observed "spots" or bursts of turbulence which spread from an initial point of disturbance to "contaminate" the whole flow with turbulence. Figure 4 shows a sketch of the situation. The sharp edges of the plate are a prolific and continuous source of spots (Ref. 18) and the angle α is about $\tan^{-1}$ 1/6. We have repeated these

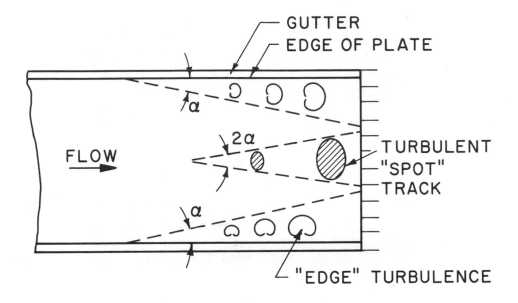

Figure 4   Areas of Turbulent Spot Growth

observations and the angles are reproduced closely on our own
sloping glass plate; the spot shapes are a little different (Fig.
6). The addition of Polyox causes three major changes: (1) A
narrowing of the angle of spreading as the concentration of Polyox
(Grade WSR-301 from Union Carbide) increases. At about 100 ppm the
flashes of turbulence are scarcely able to spread at all (Fig. 5)
and look very elongated. (2) A **fine-grained** wave structure appears
to cover the surface. This is completely absent from the Newtonian
case (compare Figs. 5 and 6) and may possibly imply that the mechanism
of transition is vastly different in polymer solutions. (The transfer
of energy by waves has been foreseen by Tulin (Ref. 17).) (3) Most
surprisingly the edge "spots" are eliminated (Fig. 5). Accepting
Elder's (Ref. 18) arguments that edges generate secondary flows, which
in turn generate edge "spots," then it is tempting to believe that the
inhibition of nonviscometric motions (secondary flows in this case)
is the reason for the apparent lack of edge spots.

   In conclusion, we see that the idea of increased resistance
to nonviscometric motions is useful in drag reduction and transition
studies. A short motion picture has been made of some of the
transition phenomena and will be reported on later.

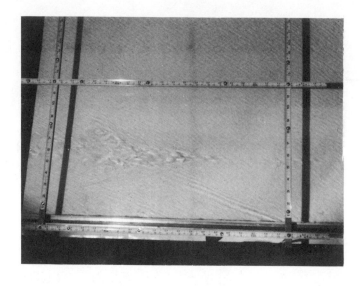

Figure 5   A Turbulent Spot in 100 wppm Polyox Solution.   Note
wavy surface and absence of strong edge spots.

Figure 6   A Turbulent Spot in Water.   Note smooth surface outside
spot and strong edge growth.

ACKNOWLEDGMENTS

This study was supported by the National Aeronautics and Space Administration under the Multidisciplinary Space-Related Research Program (Grant NGR-40-002-009) at Brown University. This support is gratefully acknowledged. The help of G. Williams and T. A. Raso of the Division of Engineering is also acknowledged with thanks.

REFERENCES

1. Goren, Y. and J. F. Norbury, "Turbulent Flow of Dilute Aqueous Polymer Solutions," Trans. ASME Paper No. 67 - WA/FE-3

2. Tanner, R. I., "Drag Reduction in a Model of Shear-Flow Turbulence," I. & E. C. Fundls. 7, 32-38, 1968

3. Lumley, J. L., "The Toms Phenomenon: Anomalous Effects in Turbulent Flow of Dilute Solutions of High Molecular Weight Linear Polymers," Appl. Mech. Rev. 20, 1139-1149, 1967

4. Metzner, A. B. and G. Astarita, "External Flows of Viscoelastic Materials: Fluid Property Restrictions on the Use of Velocity-Sensitive Probes," A.I. Ch. E. J. 13, 550-555, 1967

5. Astarita, G., "Two Dimensionless Groups Relevant in the Analysis of Steady Flows of Viscometric Materials," I. & E. C. Fundls. 6, 257-262, 1967

6. Kaye, A., "Non-Newtonian Flow in Incompressible Fluids: Part I, A General Rheological Equation of State; Part II, Some Problems of Steady Flow; Part III, Some Problems of Transient Flow," College of Aeronautics, Cranfield, Note No. 134, 1962

7. Bernstein, B., E. Kearsley, and L. Zapas, "A Study of Stress Relaxation with Finite Strain," Trans. Soc. Rheol. 7, 391-410, 1963

8. Tanner, R. I. and J. M. Simmons, "Combined Simple and Sinusoidal Shearing in Elastic Liquids," Chem. Eng. Sci. 22, 1803-1815, 1968

9. Tanner, R. I., "Comparative Studies of Some Simple Viscoelastic Theories," Trans. Soc. Rheol. 12, 155-182, 1968

10. Ballman, R. L., "Extensional Flow of Polystyrene Melt," Rheol. Acta 4, 137-140, 1965

11. Tanner, R. I. and R. L. Ballman, "Prediction of Tensile Visco-
     sity for a Polystyrene Melt," (to appear 1969)

12. Burgers, J. M., "A Mathematical Model Illustrating the Theory
     of Turbulence," Adv. in Appl. Mech. 1, 171-196, 1948

13. Pipkin, A. C. and D. R. Owen, "Nearly Viscometric Flows,"
     Physc. Fluids 10, 836-843, 1967

14. Batchelor, G. K. and A. A. Townsend, Surveys in Mechanics
     (ed. G. K. Batchelor and R. M. Dvaies, Cambridge University
     Press, Cambridge 1956, pp. 352-399

15. Karlsson, S. K. F., and J. M. Griem, "Hydrodynamic Stability
     Behavior of a Viscoelastic Fluid in Couette Motion," Bull. Am.
     Phys. Soc. 11, 616, 1956

16. Emmons, H. W., "The Laminar-Turbulent Transition in a Boundary
     Layer - Part I," J. Aero. Sci. 18, 490-498, 1951

17. Tulin, M. P., "Hydrodynamic Aspects of Macromolecular Solutions,"
     preprint of lecture given at 6th Naval Hydrodynamics Symposium,
     Washington, D. C., September 28, 1966

18.   Elder, J. W., "The Flow Past a Flat Plate of Finite Width,"
     J. Fluid Mech. 9, 133-153, 1960

RELATIONSHIP BETWEEN FLOW PATTERN,

CONSTITUTIVE EQUATION AND MOLECULAR STRUCTURE

Fitzhugh W. Boggs

Ordnance Research Laboratory
The Pennsylvania State University

ABSTRACT

In developing the constitutive equation for an arbitrary
fluid on a purely phenomenological basis, it has been shown
that the stress tensor can be represented as a generalized functional depending on a Finger rate of strain tensor. If only
the first derivative with respect to time and only a single
quadratic term are retained in the general equation, then the
second-order fluid results.

From the phenomenological point of view, there is no a
priori reason why the coefficients in the second-order fluid
should be related to each other. However, it has been found
experimentally that, for the second-order fluid, the two second-
order coefficients can, to a good approximation, be expressed
in terms of one of them. This has been shown to lead to equations
which differ from the Navier-Stokes equation by a term which
depends only on the Weissenberg number.

To assist us in choosing a constitutive equation, we have
turned to the theory of viscosity of polymeric solutions as
developed by Kirkwood. This theory, or theories closely related
to it, have been able to explain the linear viscoelastic properties
of polymeric solutions quite well.

It is shown that it is possible to develop a constitutive
equation from these same assumptions which includes nonlinear as
well as viscoelastic terms. The coefficients of the acceleration
tensors are found to depend only on the concentration and intrinsic
viscosity for a wide variety of polymers. It suggests, as does
the Weissenberg conjecture, that in dilute polymer solutions,

nonlinearity and viscoelasticity are always present together.
Their relative importance will depend on the nature of the flow.

INTRODUCTION

Considerable attention has been devoted to analyzing the
influence of the consititutive equation on the pattern of flow
of dilute polymer solutions. It is apparent from these studies
that the nature of the flow can change substantially as the
constitutive equation is varied.

For example, Boggs and Thompsen (Ref. 1) showed by an approximate calculation that in a shear flow in a second-order fluid, a
vortex having its axis in the direction of flow was highly damped.
The Weissenberg (Ref. 2) conjecture was accepted in their treatment. Further work (Ref. 3) showed that an array of vortices
rotating in alternating direction provides an exact solution.
The relaxation time of this exact solution was identical with the
one obtained by the approximate treatment. The radii of the
vortices were found to be proportional to the square root of the
product of the concentration intrinsic viscosity and relaxation
time of the polymer. Since the relaxation time of the polymer
(not necessarily of the fluid) is proportional to the intrinsic
viscosity (for the free draining molecule), one expects the dimensions of the vortices to be proportional to the intrinsic
viscosity and to the square root of the concentration.

More recent work (Ref. 4) has shown that, if the constitutive
equation is assumed linear in Lagrangian coordinates (but not
necessarily in Eulerian coordinates), the time-dependent behavior
will not be purely a relaxation; instead, damped oscillations
appear. Thus, in this case, the rigidity of the fluid plays a
more important role. This assumption of linearity is, however,
inconsistent with what is usually found in a polymer solution in
which it is usually found that if the viscoelastic terms do not
vanish, then the quadratic terms will also not vanish.

If we consider terms which are linear in the shear stress
but of any order in the Rivlin Ericksen tensors, then the result
will be similar to what is obtained for the second-order fluid.
However, instead of a single relaxation time, there will be a
distribution of relaxation times. If quadratic terms in the shear
stress are included, then the relaxation time will depend upon
the shear. Finally, if more terms than this are included, the
simple type of solution is no longer possible.

It is apparent from the discussion of the previous paragraphs
that the nature of the constitutive equation will influence the
flow pattern in the neighborhood of the wall. It follows that

the appropriate choice of a constitutive equation is important in
the development of an understanding of the flow of dilute polymer
solution. The principal objective of this paper is to outline
a theory which may assist in this choice.

Theory of Non-Newtonian Fluids

There has been extensive work on the linear viscoelastic
properties of polymer solution. Theories have been developed
which calculate (Refs. 5, 6) the mechanical properties in terms
of a distribution of relaxation times. The results are in reasonable accord with experimental fact. Basic to this work were the
pioneering papers of Kirkwood (Refs. 7, 8, 9) and several of his
students. They assume that the polymer is a long chain immersed
in a fluid supposed, on the microscopic scale, to obey the Navier-
Stokes equations. They attempted to solve for the shear stress
in the flow by calculating the modification of the flow induced
by the polymer. Their approach was very general. They assumed
that the configuration of the molecule could be expressed in its
Gaussian coordinates and that its internal motions would be
governed by the internal diffusion equation in the space of all
of the dimensions of the molecule. Interactions between different
polymer molecules were neglected.

The portions of the equation relevant to flow are:

$$\sum_{\substack{\alpha,\beta \\ =1}}^{\nu} \frac{1}{\sqrt{g}} \frac{\partial}{\partial q^{\beta}} \left[\sqrt{g} \left(D^{\alpha\beta} \frac{\partial}{\partial q^{\alpha}} + \frac{D^{\alpha\beta}}{kT} \frac{\partial W_{o}}{\partial q^{\alpha}} \right) f \right] - \frac{\partial f}{\partial t}$$

$$= \sum_{\substack{\alpha,\beta \\ =1}}^{\nu} \frac{1}{\sqrt{g}} \frac{\partial}{\partial q^{\beta}} \left[\sqrt{g} \ g^{\alpha\beta} \ v_{\alpha}^{o} \ f \right] \ , \qquad (1)$$

where f is the distribution function expressing the probability
of finding the molecule in a given configuration, q^{α} are the
contravariant Gaussian coordinates in the space of the internal
degrees of freedom of the molecule, $g^{\alpha}{}_{\beta}$ is the metric tensor,
g the corresponding determinant, and $D^{\alpha}{}_{\beta}$ is the rotatory diffusion
tensor.

Kirkwood and his students met great difficulties in deriving numerical results from these equations. More restricted but related theories were developed by Rouse (Ref. 5) and by Zimm (Ref. 6) from which detailed calculations could be made. These calculations provide a successful theory of the linear visco-elastic properties of dilute polymer solutions. However, in all of them, the response is a linear function of the force. Conse-quently, it has often been assumed that only linear results could be derived from this model. This assumption is erroneous for, in a frequently neglected paper, Kirkwood shows how quadratic terms in the constitutive equation in Lagrangian coordinates can be derived from his theory. We will show that the theory yields the series development of a functional for the relationship between the stress and the rate of strain.

Usually, it is assumed that, in convected (Lagrangian) coordinates, the stress is a functional of the rate of strain tensor. This is often expressed as follows:

$$\underset{\sim}{\sigma} = \underset{s=-\infty}{\overset{s=t}{\underset{\sim}{F}}} [\underset{\sim}{e}(t - s)] - p\underset{\sim}{I} \quad . \tag{2}$$

It is then assumed that the functional (Ref. 10) can be developed in a series

$$-p\underset{\sim}{I} \quad + \quad \int_{-\infty}^{t} \underset{\sim}{\phi}_1(t - s) \; \underset{\sim}{e}(s) \; ds$$

$$+ \quad \int_{-\infty}^{t} \int_{-\infty}^{t} \underset{\sim}{\phi}_2(t - s_1, \; t - s_2)\underset{\sim}{e}(s_1)\underset{\sim}{e}(s_2)ds_1 ds_2$$

$$+ \quad \ldots \ldots \quad . \tag{3}$$

It has been shown that, in transforming to Eulerian coordinates, the constitutive equation becomes a series in certain accelera-tion tensors, named after Rivlin and Erickson (Ref. 11). The coefficients of these tensors tend asymptotically to the moments of the independent variables averaged over the functions ϕ_n appearing in the development of the functional (Ref. 10). Our objective

must be to show how the functions ϕ_n can be derived from the
assumptions made in the theory of dilute polymer solution which
have been used to explain viscoelasticity.

General Perturbation of Rotatory Diffusion Equation

Kirkwood (Ref. 9) was able to develop an equation relating
the distribution in configuration space to the forces. We will
now show how similar methods can be used to develop Equation (3).
We suppose that the polymer molecule, a single isolated one, is
governed by the linear differential equation of diffusion given
in Equation (1) which is rewritten in the simplified form,

$$L\rho - \frac{\partial \rho}{\partial t} = -\gamma\, h_{(t)}\, Q\, \rho \qquad . \qquad (4)$$

Here L is the diffusion operator in the configuration space of
a single polymer molecule. The operator was shown to be second
order and self-adjoint. The quantity of the right-hand side of
Equation (4), exclusive of the dependent variable ρ, represents
the forcing function. This time-dependent function is proportional
to the constant γ, which we will use in the development of the
solution.

Before we undertake a solution of the differential equation
given in Equation (4), we will, for convenience, put it in
dimensionless form. The operator L is given by the expression

$$\sum_{\alpha\beta} \frac{1}{\sqrt{g}} \frac{\partial}{\partial q^\beta} \left\{ \sqrt{g}\, D^{\alpha\beta} \frac{\partial}{\partial q^\alpha} \right\} f \qquad . \qquad (5)$$

We have omitted the intermolecular forces. Had we retained them,
a more complex expression would have been obtained. The general
nature of the reasoning would still be valid, but the dimensionless form would be somewhat modified. We have not carried out
this work in all its generality because, even as simplified, the
mathematics is complex enough. In addition, although the more
general expressions can be carried further than we have carried
them, simplifying assumptions have to be made ultimately to
obtain numerical results.

In addition to the operator given in Equation (5), we must
express the operator of the perturbing forces

$$\sum_{\alpha\beta} \frac{1}{\sqrt{g}} \frac{\partial}{\partial q^\beta} \left\{ \sqrt{g}\; g^{\alpha\beta}\; v_\alpha^{\;o}\; f \right\} \qquad . \tag{6}$$

The quantity $v_a^{\;o}$ is the covariant component of the velocity unperturbed by the presence of the molecule. If we neglect the hydrodynamic interaction expressed by the Oseen interaction tensor, then it is shown (Ref. 9) that the diffusion tensor and the metric tensor are related through

$$D^{\alpha\beta} = \frac{kT}{\xi}\; g^{\alpha\beta} \qquad , \tag{7}$$

where ξ (the friction constant of the polymeric units) will be proportional to a characteristic length R_1, and to the viscosity of the solvent. We will express the components q^a in terms of the same characteristic length. Again, we could have included the hydrodynamic interaction terms in $D^{\alpha\beta}$. This would have led to a different dimensionless form, but the general results would have been similar.

We can now write the operator in the form

$$L = \frac{kT}{\xi R_1^{\;2}}\; \mathcal{L} \qquad . \tag{8}$$

The new operator $\mathcal{L}$ is dimensionless. We define the parameter τ_o as

$$\tau_o = \frac{\xi R_1^{\;2}}{kT} = \frac{n_o R_1^{\;3}}{kT} \tag{9}$$

which has the dimension of time.

Let us now consider the eigenvalue problem,

$$\mathcal{L}\; \psi_j = \frac{v_j\; \psi_j}{\tau_o}$$

or

$$L \, \psi_j = \nu_j \psi_j \quad . \tag{10}$$

We know from the properties of the operator L that the eigenfunctions will form a complete set and that, therefore, a solution of Equation (4) may be developed in terms of them.

Let us suppose further that the solution of Equation (4) can be developed in a series in γ of the form

$$\rho = \sum_{n=0}^{\infty} \gamma^n \rho_n \quad . \tag{11}$$

and let us suppose also that the functions ρ_n in which ρ is developed are in turn developed in terms of the eigenfunctions of Equation (10). This will lead to the expression

$$\rho_n = \sum_i f_{ni}(t) \, \psi_i \quad . \tag{12}$$

If we substitute into Equation (4) expressions given in Equation (11) and Equation (12), and if we further identify to zero the coefficients of τ, we will obtain the recursion relationship

$$\sum_i \psi_i \left[\frac{\nu_i}{\tau_o} f_{ni}(t) - \frac{\partial f_{ni}(t)}{\partial t} \right]$$

$$= \frac{1}{\tau_o} h(t) \, Q \sum_i f_{n-1,i}(t) \, \psi_\alpha \quad . \tag{13}$$

This equation allows us to obtain the solution of Equation (4) in powers of the scalar quantity γ by successive solution of Equation (13). We will suppose that the solution ρ_o is independent of the time and that when it is developed in terms of the eigenfunctions, we can define a set of quantities (a vector in Hilbert space) such that

$$f_{oi} = a_i \tag{14}$$

is satisfied. Let us now multiply through Equation (13) by ψ^*_{nj} and integrate over configuration space. Because of the orthogonality of the eigenfunctions, we will obtain the set of ordinary differential equations.

$$\frac{\nu_j}{\tau_o} f_{nj}(t) - \frac{df_{nj}(t)}{dt} = \frac{1}{\tau_o} h(t) \sum_i A_{ij} f_{n-1,i}(t) \tag{15}$$

where the elements of the infinite matrix A_{ij} are given by the expression

$$A_{ij} = \int \cdots \int \psi^*_j \, Q \, \psi_i \, dq_1 \cdots dq_n \qquad . \tag{16}$$

Up to now, we have not departed in any substantial way from Kirkwood's development. From here on, it is convenient to proceed differently so that a generalized solution can be obtained rather than the somewhat complicated step-by-step solution which appears in the original work. Let us make the substitution

$$f_{n,i}(t) = e^{\frac{\nu_i}{\tau_o} t} \phi_{ni}(t) \qquad . \tag{17}$$

Then, after some elementary manipulation, Equation (15) will become

$$e^{\frac{\nu_j t}{\tau_o}} \frac{d\phi_{nj}}{dt} = \frac{1}{\tau_o} h(t) \sum A_{ji} \, e^{\frac{\nu_i t}{\tau_o}} \phi_{n-1} \, h(t) \qquad . \tag{18}$$

This in turn can be rearranged to give

$$\frac{d\phi_{nj}(t)}{dt} = \frac{1}{\tau_o} h(t) \sum_i A_{ji} \, e^{\frac{(\nu_i - \nu_j)t}{\tau_o}} \phi_{n-1} \, h(t) \qquad . \tag{19}$$

If we integrate Equation (19) with respect to time, we will obtain

$$\phi_{nj}(t) = \frac{1}{\tau_o} \int_{-\infty}^{t} h(\tau) \sum_i A_{ji} e^{\frac{(\nu_i - \nu_j)\tau}{\tau_o}} \phi_{n-1} h(\tau) d\tau \quad .$$

(20)

If we resubstitute in terms of the function f, then Equation (20) will become

$$f_{nj}(t) = e^{\frac{\nu_j t}{\tau_o}} \frac{1}{\tau_o} \int_{-\infty}^{t} h(\tau) \sum_i A_{ji} e^{\frac{(\nu_i - \nu_j)\tau}{\tau_o}} \phi_{n-1,i}(\tau) d\tau$$

$$= \frac{1}{\tau_o} \int_{-\infty}^{t} \sum_i A_{ji} e^{\frac{\nu_j}{\tau_o}(t-\tau)} h(\tau) f_{n-1,i}(\tau) d\tau \quad . \quad (21)$$

We have developed a Green's Function for the recursion relation, and the successive members of the series can be developed by the successive application of the Green's Function. This Green's Function is an infinite matrix, and it operates on a vector in Hilbert space which is dependent on the time.

Up to now, we have used a notation for the matrix which includes subscript. This was to clarify the calculation. However, to retain it further would vastly complicate our task without assisting comprehension. We will, therefore, drop the subscripts. Let us define the scalar matrix.

$$\sigma \frac{t}{\tau_o} = \delta_{ji} e^{\frac{\nu_j t}{\tau_o}} \quad . \quad (22)$$

Equation (21) will then become

$$\frac{1}{\tau_o} \int_{-\infty}^{t} g(\tau)\, \sigma^{\frac{t-\tau}{\tau_o}}\, A\, f_{n-1}(\tau)\, d\tau \;=\; f_n(t) \qquad . \qquad (23)$$

Equation (23) expresses a recursion relation between vectors in Hilbert space, which we can now apply successively, starting with the first one.

$$f_1(t) \;=\; \frac{1}{\tau_o} \int_{-\infty}^{t} \sigma^{\frac{(t-\tau_1)}{\tau_o}}\, A\, a\, h(\tau_1)\, d\tau_1 \qquad . \qquad (24)$$

This equation defines the first function which is dependent upon the time. The next one is:

$$f_2 \;=\; \frac{1}{\tau_o^2} \int_{-\infty}^{t} \sigma^{\frac{t-\tau_2}{\tau_o}}\, A\, h(\tau_2) \int_{\infty}^{\tau} \sigma^{\frac{\tau_2-\tau_1}{\tau_o}} \cdot A\, g(\tau_1)$$

$$a\, d\tau_1\, d\tau_2 \quad . \tag{25}$$

We notice that in Equation (25) the upper limit of the first integral is not the same as in the second. In the development of a functional governing the relationship between the deformation and the forces, one usually finds that the upper limit is the same for all variables. This result can be achieved by introducing the unit step function $S(\tau_2 - \tau_1)$ into Equation (25) which will then become

$$f_2(t) \;=\; \frac{1}{\tau_o^2} \int_{-\infty}^{t} \int_{-\infty}^{t} \sigma^{\frac{t-\tau_2}{\tau_o}}\, A\sigma^{\frac{\tau_2-t}{\tau_o}}\, \sigma^{\frac{t-\tau_1}{\tau_o}}\, A\, a\, S(\tau_2-\tau_1)$$

$$h(\tau_2)h(\tau_1)d\tau_2 d\tau_1 \quad . \tag{26}$$

Equation (26) in turn can be rewritten as follows:

$$\frac{1}{\tau_o^2} \int_{-\infty}^{t} \int_{-\infty}^{t} \sigma^{\frac{t-\tau_2}{\tau_o}} \cdot A\sigma^{\frac{\tau_2-t}{\tau_o}} S[(\tau_2-t)-(\tau_1-t)]\sigma^{\frac{t-\tau_1}{\tau_o}} A\,a\,h(\tau_2)$$

$$h(\tau_1)d\tau_2 d\tau_1 \quad . \tag{27}$$

Having developed these relations, we can carry out the integration to give us

$$f_n = \frac{1}{\tau_o^n} \int_{-\infty}^{t} \cdots \int_{-\infty}^{t} \sigma^{\frac{t-\tau_n}{\tau_o}} \sigma^{\frac{\tau_n-t}{\tau_o}} S[(\tau_n-t)-(\tau_n-t)]\sigma^{\frac{t-\tau_{n-1}}{\tau_o}} A$$

$$\cdots \sigma^{\frac{t-\tau_2}{\tau_o}} A\sigma^{\frac{\tau_2-t}{\tau_o}} S[(\tau_2-t)-(\tau_1-t)]\sigma^{\frac{t-\tau_1}{\tau_o}} A\,a\,h(\tau_n)h(\tau_{n-1})$$

$$\cdots h(\tau_2)h(\tau_1)d\tau_n \cdots d\tau_1 \quad . \tag{28}$$

Let us turn to the problem of calculating some average property. This property may be a scalar, a vector or, in our case, a tensor quantity. The specific nature does not matter. Let us suppose that the general distribution function has the form

$$\rho = \sum_n \left[\gamma^n \sum_i (f_{ni}\ \psi_i) \right] \quad . \tag{29}$$

If we have a function B of which we wish to calculate the average, we will multiply by ρ and integrate over all configuration space;

$$\overline{B} \ = \ \int \rho \ B \ dv \qquad . \tag{30}$$

It will be convenient to express the quantity B in terms of the eigenfunctions of the operator which appears in Equation (4). This requires us to define

$$\int B \ \psi_i \ dv \ = \ b_i \quad or \quad b \qquad . \tag{31}$$

The quantity b is a vector in Hilbert space, but it may also be a scalar vector or tensor in ordinary Cartesian space. Having defined b, the average quantity will be given by

$$\overline{B} \ = \ \sum_n \gamma^n \ b \ f_n \ (t) \qquad . \tag{32}$$

This average is obtained by forming the scalar product of b with a vector obtained by successive operations on a with A.

Now, we wish to develop a succession of functions having the same properties as $\phi_n(\eta_1 \ ... \ \eta_n)$ in Equation (3). Such a development would have the form

$$\overline{B} \ = \ \int_{-\infty}^{t} \phi_1(t-\tau_1)h(\tau_1)d\tau_1 \ + \ \int_{-\infty}^{t}\int_{-\infty}^{t} \phi_2(t-\tau_1,t-\tau_2)h(\tau_1)$$

$$h(\tau_2)d\tau_1 d\tau_2 \ + \ \cdots \ + \ \int_{-\infty}^{t} \cdots \int_{-\infty}^{t} \phi_n(t-\tau_1,t-\tau_2$$

$$\cdots \ t-\tau_n) \ \prod_{k=1}^{n} h(\tau_k)d\tau_k \qquad . \tag{33}$$

The integrands appearing in Equation (28) do not have the symmetry which would be required to identify them with ϕ_n. We will now show how this symmetry can be achieved. The inter-change in Equation (28) of the τ's in any two of the functions $h(\tau)$ without any other change is equivalent to interchanging these same τ's everywhere except in the functions $h(\tau)$. In the same instance, it is obvious that the values of the integral will not be changed and, hence, it will remain unchanged in the second. It follows that if we interchange two of the τ's every-where except in the function $h(\tau)$, and if we add the integral so obtained to the original integral and divide by two, then the value of the integral will be unchanged. Hence, if we perform all possible permutations of the τ's in the kernels without interchanging them in the function $h(\tau)$, and if we add together all these permuted functions and divide by n! (the number of possible permutations), we will obtain a function multiplying the $h(\tau)$, which is symmetric with respect to the interchange of the variables. The value of the integral, however, will be no different from the one given in Equation (28). Let us, there-fore, define the set of functions

$$\phi_n(n_1 \cdots n_n) = \frac{\gamma^n}{\tau_o^n n!} \sum_{\substack{\text{all permutations} \\ \text{of } n_s}} b\sigma^{\frac{n_n}{\tau_o}} A\sigma^{\frac{-n_n}{\tau_o}} S(n_n-n_{n-1})$$

$$\sigma^{\frac{n_{n-1}}{\tau_o}} A\sigma^{\frac{-n_{n-1}}{\tau_o}} \cdots \sigma^{\frac{n_2}{\tau_o}} A\sigma^{\frac{-n_2}{\tau_o}} S(n_2-n_1)\sigma^{\frac{n_1}{\tau_o}} A \, a \, .$$

$$(34)$$

These functions will be symmetrical with respect to interchange of the variables on which they depend, and when substituted into Equation (33), they will yield the average quantity. Thus, we have shown that an average quantity will be a functional of the applied deformation and that the memory functions (or kernels) ϕ will not be independent of each other, but will be related since they all derive from the linear operator given in Equation (4).

Relation to Constants of Constitutive Equation

The various constants of the constitutive equation are obtained from the moments of the functions ϕ_n. Instead of calculating the moments separately, it is convenient to find the generating function by taking the Laplace transform of Equation (20) for all the n variables on which it depends. For the sake of simplicity, we will consider only the matrix terms.

$$
\int_0^\infty \cdots \int_0^\infty \left[\sigma^{\frac{\eta_n}{\tau_o}} A\, S(\eta_n - \eta_{n-1}) \sigma^{-(\eta_n - \eta_{n-1})\frac{1}{\tau_o}} A\, S(\eta_{n-1} - \eta_{n-1}) \right.
$$

$$
\sigma^{-(\eta_{n-1} - \eta_{n-2})\frac{1}{\tau_o}} A \cdots A\, S(\eta_2 - \eta_1) \sigma^{-(\eta_2 - \eta_1)\frac{1}{\tau_o}}
$$

$$
\left. e^{-(\lambda_n \eta_n + \lambda_{n-1}\eta_{n-1} + \cdots \lambda_2 \eta_2 + \lambda_1 \eta_1)} d\eta_n \cdots d\eta_1 \right]
$$

$$(35)$$

Let us make the substitution

$$
\eta_n = -\tau_o \xi_n
$$

$$
\eta_{n-1} = -\tau_o (\xi_n + \xi_{n-1})
$$

$$
\eta_{n-2} = -\tau_o (\xi_n + \xi_{n-1} + \xi_{n-2})
$$

$$
\cdots\cdots
$$

$$
\cdots\cdots
$$

$$
\eta_1 = -\tau_o (\xi_n + \xi_{n-1} + \cdots \xi_2 + \xi_1) \qquad . \qquad (36)
$$

The Jacobian of this transformation is equal to $(-\tau_o)^n$. Consequently, the expression in Equation (35) will become

$$b \int_0^\infty \sigma^{-\xi_n} e^{-(\lambda_n + \lambda_{n-1} + \cdots + \lambda_2 + \lambda_1)\tau_o \xi_n} A \, d\xi_n$$

$$\times \int_0^\infty \sigma^{-\xi_{n-1}} e^{-(\lambda_{n-1} + \lambda_{n-2} + \cdots + \lambda_2 + \lambda_1)\tau_o \, \xi_{n-1}} A \, d\xi_{n-1}$$

$$\times \cdots \cdots \cdots \cdots$$

$$\times \int_0^\infty \sigma^{-\xi_2} e^{-(\lambda_2 + \lambda_1)\tau_o \xi_2} A \, d\xi_2 \int_0^\infty \sigma^{\xi_1} e^{-\lambda_1 \tau_o \xi_1} A \, d\xi_1 \, a \tag{37}$$

The proper symmetry can be obtained by interchanging the λ's, adding and dividing by n!.

The various coefficients in the constitutive equations will be the terms in a development of the expressions in Equation (37) in a Taylor series in $\lambda_1 \ldots \lambda_n$. A detailed study of the properties of these generating functions is now in progress. Although this work is far from complete, some conclusions can already be drawn. Suppose that we write the constitutive equation in the form given by Metzner, White, and Denn (Ref. 10)

$$\sigma = -P \underset{\sim}{I} + \sum_n \underset{\sim}{M}_n \tag{38}$$

where

$$\underset{\sim}{M}_1 = (\eta_o + \omega_1) B_1$$

$$\underset{\sim}{M}_2 = \omega_2 B_1^2 + \omega_3 B_2$$

$$\underset{\sim}{M}_3 = \omega_4 (\text{tr } \underset{\sim}{B}_1{}^2) \underset{\sim}{B}_1 + \omega_5 B_5 + \omega_6 (\underset{\sim}{B}_1 B_2 + B_2 B_1)$$

etc.

B_1 is the usual deformation tensor, B_2, B_3, ... B_n are the Rivlin Ericksen tensors, and η_o is the viscosity of the solvent. It is apparent that all the ω will be proportional to the concentration N and that ω_1 will be proportional to τ_o; ω_1, and ω_2 to $\tau_o{}^2$; etc. The coefficients of M_n will be proportional to $N\tau_o{}^n$. In the free-draining molecule, which the model that was used implies, the relaxation time will be proportional to the intrinsic viscosity. It is, therefore, suggested that the tensors M_1, M_2, etc. can be expressed in terms of the concentration N and the intrinsic viscosity (η)

$$\underset{\sim}{M}_1 = (\eta_o + N[\eta]) \underset{\sim}{B}_1$$

$$\underset{\sim}{M}_2 = N[\eta]^2 (\alpha_2 \underset{\sim}{B}_1{}^2 + \alpha_3 \underset{\sim}{B}_2)$$

$$\underset{\sim}{M}_3 = N[\eta]^3 (\alpha_4 \{\text{tr } \underset{\sim}{B}_1{}^2\} \underset{\sim}{B}_1 + \alpha_5 B_3 + \alpha_6 \{B_1 B_2 + B_2 B_1\})$$

$$\underset{\sim}{M}_4 = N[\eta]^4 (\ . \ . \ . \ . \ \text{etc.})$$

At infinite dilution, $a_2 \ ... \ a_n$ should be independent of the molecular species.

CONCLUSIONS

There are several conclusions which can be drawn from this discussion. The first and most important one is that the memory functions which appear in the constitutive equation depend on a single time parameter. Thus, the relaxation time of the polymer molecule from which the intrinsic viscosity may be calculated is a unique parameter defining the hydrodynamic characteristics of a dilute solution. As a result, the dependence of the drag reduction on the Weissenberg (Ref. 12) number which can be derived from the second-order fluid and which has been verified experimentally may be the result of this dependence. It need not depend on the specific model of the second-order fluid. Indeed, neither the experimental facts nor the results of a study of the Kirkwood theory can be used to establish the second-order fluid. However, both indicate that at sufficient dilution, a single parameter exists which, together with the concentration, governs all the observed effects.

This theory cannot, however, explain the reversal of the drag reduction as the concentration increases. This reversal takes place at a much lower concentration than would be expected if it were due merely to an increase in viscosity. It has been plausibly suggested that this change in direction of the drag reduction may be due to interaction between the molecules. This theory is incapable in its present form of considering molecular interactions.

On the other hand, although an exact form of the Weissenberg conjecture (which establishes the value of ω_2/ω_3) has not been obtained, the ratio of ω_2/ω_3 is found to be independent of the molecular species.

In deriving the more specific results, we neglected the interaction potential. If this had not been done, the relaxation time would not have had the simple dependence on the friction factor. Although a relaxation time could be defined in this case, also, it would not lead to the simple dependence on the intrinsic viscosity. This automatically excludes consideration of stearic effects. It is possible that the observed difference between guar gum (Ref. 13) and polyox (Refs. 12, 14) may be due to the greater stearic hindrance which must exist in the bulky polysaccharide when compared to the much slimmer polyether.

It appears that the assumption that some authors have made that the Kirkwood-Riseman theory of polymer viscosity is applicable only to the linear approximation is not correct. Indeed, Kirkwood obtained quadratic terms and it yields terms of all degrees. It follows, therefore, that this theory is capable of describing non-Newtonian characteristics which are nonlinear – as well as those which are viscoelastic. So far, however, it has not been extended and cannot readily be extended to high concentrations. The theory assumes in its basic formulation that each polymer molecule is isolated and does not interact in any way with its neighbors. It would be interesting to extend this theory to the case of polymer-polymer interaction by starting out with a general diffusion equation in the space of the coordinates of all molecules. It should then be possible to develop solutions in ascending power series in the concentration.

If any practical applications of these additives are to be found in the development of the hardware, attention must be paid not only to the hydrodynamics but also to the physical chemistry of the problem which they present. Are there molecules other than those which have been tested which might be more promising? Can

they be chosen without extensive experimental work to determine
their suitability? Is there reasonable promise in a program of
organic synthesis of materials or is such a program not worth
the probable expense? Do polyelectrolytes offer advantages?
These questions must be answered either through a long and
tedious experimental investigation or through a study of the
basic molecular mechanism. The methods which we have outlined
provide a possible starting point for such a study.

ACKNOWLEDGMENTS

This work was sponsored by the Office of Naval Research
(Fluid Dynamics Branch) and Office of Advanced Research and
Technology, National Aeronautics and Space Administration (Fluid
Mechanics Branch).

REFERENCES

1.   Boggs, F. W. and J. Thompsen, "The Mechanism of Noise
      Reduction by Polymeric Additives (U)," Twenty-Fifth Symposium
      on Underwater Acoustics, Page 451, 1967

2.   Weissenberg, K., "Abnormal Substances and Abnormal
      Phenomena of Flow," Proceedings of the International
      Rheological Congress, Scheveningen (the Hague)
      Netherlands, 1948, North Holland Publishing Co.,
      Amsterdam, 1949

3.   Boggs, F. W. and J. Thompsen, "Flow Properties of
      Dilute Solutions of Polymers, Part III," United
      States Rubber Company Final Report, Contract Nos. Nonr
      3120(00) and N00014-66-C0322

4.   Boggs, F. W., Work to be published

5.   Rouse, P. E., "A Theory of the Linear Viscoelastic
      Properties of Dilute Solutions of Coiling Polymers,"
      J. Chem. Phys. 21:1272

6.   Zimm, B. H., "Dynamics of Polymer Molecules in Dilute
      Solutions: Viscoelasticity, Flow Birefringence and
      Dielectric Loss," J. Chem. Phys. 24:264 1956

7.   Kirkwood, J. G. and J. Riseman, "The Intrinsic
      Viscosities and Diffusion Constants of Flexible
      Macromolecules in Solution, "J. Chem. Phys. 16:565 1948

8.   Kirkwood, J. G. and P. L. Auer, "The Viscoelastic
     Properties of Solutions of Rod-Like Macromolecules,"
     J. Chem. Phys. 16:565 1948

9.   Kirkwood, J. G., "The General Theory of Irreversible
     Processes in Solutions of Macromolecules" J. Polymer
     Sci. 12:1 1954

10. Metzner, A. B., J. L. White, and M. M. Denn, "Behavior
     of Viscoelastic Materials in Short-Time Processes,"
     Chem. Eng. Progress 62, (12) 81 1966

11. Rivlin, R. S. and J. L. Ericksen, "Stress-Deformation
     Relations for Isotrophic Materials," J. Rat. Mech. Anal.
     4:373, 1955

12. Boggs, F. W. and J. Thompsen, "Flow Properties of Dilute
     Solutions of Polymers, Part I," United States Rubber
     Company Final Report, Contract Nos. Nonr 3120(00) and
     N00014-66-C0322

13. Hoyt, J. W. and A. C. Fabula, "The Effect of Additives on
     Fluid Friction," Paper presented at the Fifth Symposium
     on Naval Hydrodynamics at Bergen, Norway, Sept. 12, 1964

14. Shin, H., "Reduction of Drag and Turbulence by Dilute
     Polymer Solutions," Sc.D. thesis, MIT, Department of
     Chemical Engineering, May 1965

15. Fabula, A. G., personal communication

AUTHOR INDEX

SUBJECT INDEX

Aging effects on drag reduction, 132, 133, 301
Airships, 313
Aluminum dioleate, 214
Attachment line of swept wings, transition at, 85, 101

Boundary layer, see transition, turbulent, stability, etc.
Boundary layer thickness, effects of additives on, 262, 355

Carboxymethylcellulose, 132, 161
Centrimide, 305
Coating, compliant, to reduce turbulent skin friction, 409
Coating, drag-reducing additive material, 362, 376
Constitutive equation, 476
Critical wall shear stress, see wall shear stress, critical
Concentration effects on drag reduction, 112, 137, 166, 177, 256,
    267, 491
Correlations,
    for effects of roughness in turbulent shear flow, 139, 147, 165
    for onset of drag reduction, 123
    for wall shear stress in drag-reducing fluids, 132, 135, 225, 235
    274, 351, 362
Cylinders, rotating, flow on, 447

Degradation effects on drag reduction, 182, 215, 257, 266, 305, 337,
    363
Diameter effects on drag reduction, 112, 208, 265, 363
Diffusion, 132, 299, 332, 362
Discs, rotating, flow on, 107, 252
Disturbances,
    finite, 7, 86
    linear amplification of, 6
    roughness, 11, 15, 34
    scale of, 14
    with suction, 96
    three-dimensional, 13, 20, 23, 86
    transverse contamination, 8, 86
    turbulent spots, 10, 86, 100, 471
    two-dimensional, 15, 23
Dolphin, flow about a, 409
Drag reduction with additives
    aging effects, 132, 133, 301
    concentration effects, 113, 137, 166, 177, 256, 267, 491